EXPLORING THE ATMOSPHERE'S
FIRST MILE
(Project Great Plains)

VOLUME
II

SITE DESCRIPTION AND DATA TABULATION

EXPLORING THE ATMOSPHERE'S FIRST MILE

*Proceedings of the
Great Plains Turbulence Field Program
1 August to 8 September 1953
O'Neill, Nebraska*

VOLUME II
SITE DESCRIPTION AND DATA TABULATION

Edited by

HEINZ H. LETTAU AND BEN DAVIDSON

Published by the

Symposium Publications Division

PERGAMON PRESS . NEW YORK . LONDON . PARIS

on behalf of the

GEOPHYSICS RESEARCH DIRECTORATE
AIR FORCE CAMBRIDGE RESEARCH CENTER
AIR RESEARCH AND DEVELOPMENT COMMAND

PUBLISHED ON BEHALF OF THE

GEOPHYSICS RESEARCH DIRECTORATE

AIR FORCE CAMBRIDGE RESEARCH CENTER
AIR RESEARCH AND DEVELOPMENT COMMAND

by

PERGAMON PRESS

122 E. 55th Street, New York 22, N.Y.
4 & 5 Fitzroy Square, London, W.1
24 Rue des Ecoles, Paris V^e

First published 1957

Printed in Great Britain by The Campfield Press, St. Albans

iv

CONTENTS

VOLUME II

A. GENERAL INTRODUCTION

A.1

GENERAL DESCRIPTION OF SITE

By B. DAVIDSON*

Geophysics Research Directorate

A.1.1. General Information

THE focal area of the experiments during the Great Plains Turbulence Field Program was a section (square mile) of land located in the prairie country some five miles east-north-east of the town of O'Neill, Nebraska. Site geophysical information follows:

Latitude and longitude: 42° 28'N, 98° 32'W
Elevation (barometer): 1978 ft
Coriolis parameter: 0.9847 10^{-4} sec^{-1}
Gravity (best available estimate†): 980.227 cm/sec^{-2}
Mean solar time: CST minus 34 min

A.1.2. Topography of Section ($\frac{1}{2}$-Mile Radius)

The general disposition of the observing groups is shown in Fig. A.1.1. All observations recorded in this volume were made under southerly surface wind conditions. The area south of the observing line was completely devoid of trees to the end of the section line, a distance of approximately 1300 m. The only obstacles to wind flow in this region were the barbed wire fences separating quarter sections. For the section as a whole, the topography was relatively flat. The maximum height differences in the entire mile area is not more than 3 m.

Fig. A.1.2 shows the detailed topographical features of the mown grass area which is bounded by the observing line and the fences along the borders of the quarter section. The approximate location of the principal mast or instrument installation of each group along the observing line is indicated. The map is based on a survey made jointly by the county surveyor and GRD personnel. Heights relative to an arbitrary reference point of the observing line are shown in units of centimeters. The map shows the essential contour

---

* Mr. Davidson's present affiliation: College of Engineering, New York University.

†At this latitude and considering the "free air correction" for 1978 ft elevation above mean sea level, Lambert's equation for the variation of gravity (see Brunt: *Physical and Dynamical Meteorology*, 2nd ed., 1941, p. 28) yields $g = 980.21$ cm/sec^{-2}. During a gravimetric survey conducted by the Geology Department of the University of Wisconsin in 1954 (under sponsorship extended by the Geophysics Research Directorate under Contract AF 19(604)-585) $g = 980.231$ cm/sec^{-2} was measured at Atkinson, Nebraska, approximately 20 miles west of the O'Neill site. Elevation and latitude effects on g amount to -0.007 and $+0.003$ cm/sec^{-2} between Atkinson and the O'Neill site. Thus, the reduction of the observed gravity value to conditions at the field site yields the above listed value for O'Neill.

378   B. Davidson

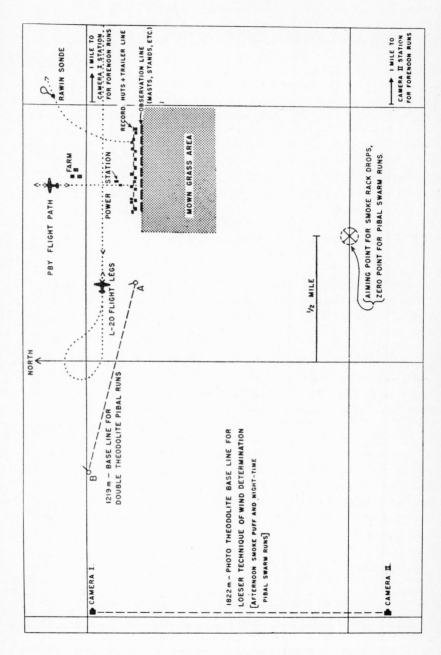

Fig. A.1.1. Array of surface and free air sampling methods at the field site.

features of the last 500 m of southerly wind fetches prior to being sampled at the observing line. A physical idea of the terrain may be gleaned from the photographs shown in Fig. A.1.3 and Fig. A.1.4.

On a much smaller scale, we summarize below the standard deviation of relative height difference values for the 2 m fetch immediately south of the indicated instrument installation. Values of relative height difference were read at 10 cm intervals along the 2 m path, making a total of 20 readings for each determination of the standard deviation S(cm) of elevation differences.

Group	Instrument	S(cm)
Johns Hopkins University	0.8 m-Anemometer	1.4
UCLA	0.5 m-Anemometer	0.9
University of Wisconsin	Lift Psychrometer	1.5
Iowa State College	1.0 m-Anemometer	1.7
MIT	2.0 m-Anemometer	1.8

A.1.3. Vegetation Characteristics of Section

(a) *Description*—An excerpt from a letter by A. Neil Daws, Holt County Extension Agent, O'Neill, Nebraska, follows:

"The site was strictly in the Short Grass Area with a scattering of mid-grasses and forbes. This is due to the gravelly characteristic of the soil and the limiting factor of moisture. The primary or dominant species of grass is Bouteloua gracillis (Blue grama). This species accounts for 75 per cent of the vegetation. There is also some 1 to 2 per cent Buchloe doctyleides (Buffalo grass), approximately 2 per cent Sporobolus asper

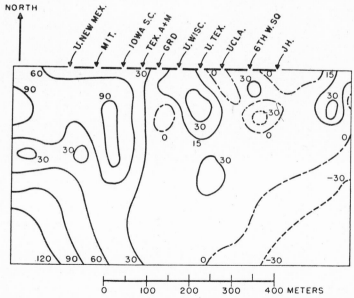

Fig. A.1.2. Arrangement of group sites along the observation line and topography (cm) of "Mown Grass Area" (approx. 800 m × 500 m).

(Tall Dropseed), a trace of Bouteloua curtipendula (Side-oat grama), a trace of Andro-
pogon scoparius (Little bluestem), and a trace of Eragrostis trichodes (Sand Lovegrass).
A total of approximately 2 to 3 per cent for the trace grasses. In addition to the Native
Grasses, there was an abundance of Annuals. There was approximately 8 to 10 per cent
Bromus tectorum (Downy brome). The area also has some native legumes, such as
Amorphia canescens (Prairie lead plant). The forbes present are: Aster multifolorus
(many flowered Aster), Plantage purshii (Purshs' plantain), Artimisia gnaphadodes
(Prairie sage), and Amorasia elatior (annual ragweed). The total percentage of forbes is
approximately 5 per cent."

It can be added the area also had some low-growing opuntias (prickly pears),
and that hard and dry cattle droppings covered approximately 0.1 per cent
of the section.

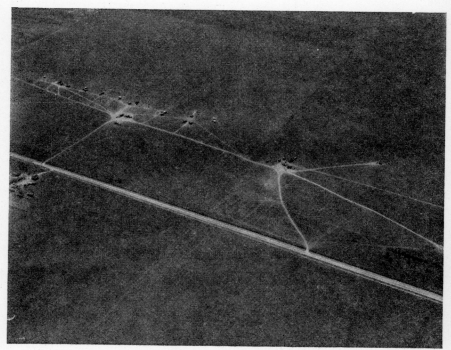

FIG. A.1.3. An aerial photograph of the field site at O'Neill, Nebraska.

(b) *Vegetation Density*—When viewed laterally, the vegetation presented
a uniform appearance to the eye. This, however, was not the case when the
grass was viewed directly from above. The density of the vegetation varied
considerably. Occasional thick clumps of grass were surrounded by relatively
thin patches with small (approximately 10 cm diameter) patches of bare
ground distributed randomly throughout the field. This inhomogeneity of
surface cover is important in interpreting some of the soil heat conductivity,
subsoil heat flux, and ground drag measurements (see Sec. 2.2, 2.4, and 3.2
in Volume I).

(c) Mowing Data and Natural Vegetation Changes—The mown grass area indicated in Fig. A.1.1 and Fig. A.1.2 was given a rough mowing in late July 1953, prior to the beginning of the field program. The mean height of the grass on 1 August 1953 was about 10 cm but scattered stalks were considerably higher than this. On 12 August the site was given a smooth mowing by gang mowers borrowed from the O'Neill golf course. The mean height of the grass then was about 6 cm with occasional stalks extending to 10 to 15 cm. The height of the grass in adjacent upwind areas was between 20 and 40 cm.

The sandy loam of the O'Neill area (see the description of subsoil characteristics at the field site in Sec. 2.2) has a quite narrow moisture range between field capacity and permanent wilting percentage. The relatively small amounts

Fig. A.1.4. A picture of the terrain at the test site, O'Neill, Nebraska.

of precipitation during August 1953 and the subsequent general decrease of soil moisture content during the time of the Great Plains Turbulence Field Program (see Sec. 2.2.3) and increase of soil moisture tension (see Sec. 2.3) appear to be responsible for the gradual wilting of the vegetation at the field site. During the first three general observation periods the grass looked fresh and green; during the last two general observation periods it was of yellowish color, and individual stalks showed a withered appearance. Growth of grass after the second mowing on 12 August 1953 was negligible, and the surface

of the site looked smoother towards the end of the program than at the
beginning. The change of surface color is important in interpreting the results
of the albedo measurements which are available only for the first week of
September 1953 (see Sec. 3.1.1).

A.1.4. Topography of the Region (200-Mile Radius)

The large-scale topography of the states surrounding the observation area
is mapped in Fig. A.1.5. The outlines of this map are the same as for the

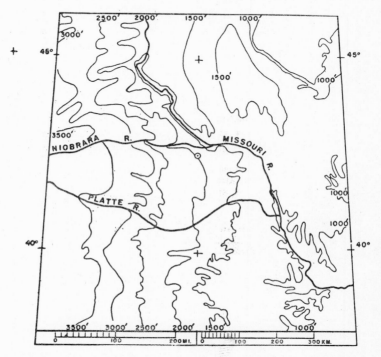

Fig. A.1.5. Ground topography (elevations above mean sea level in feet). Heavy lines
represent the location of major rivers and the small circle the location of the test site near
O'Neill, Nebraska.

local synoptic charts constructed for each general observation period. To the
south of O'Neill, the contours run almost due north-south. The mean large-
scale slope in the direction of the gradient is on the order of 2/1000. The
contours make a rather sharp bend to the north-west just north of O'Neill
and the gradient is oriented from the north-east to south-west, the mean
slope here being on the order of 3/1000.

On a scale too small to appear on this map, the primary obstruction to
general southerly flow is found in the regions of Nebraska which lie to the

west, south, and east of the observation site and are known as the Sand Hill and Loess Hill country. These regions are rolling hills usually not more than 100 ft high. In general the rolling hills become less and less pronounced as one approaches O'Neill from any direction so that the last 10 to 20 miles of fetch is almost free of any hilly obstructions. A line of trees along the Elkhorn river which runs about 5 miles south of the observing site is the most prominent unbroken obstruction to southerly wind flow within 10 miles of the site.

CLIMATOLOGY OF THE REGION

By P. DAVIS

Geophysics Research Directorate

THE general climatology for Nebraska is well described in *Climate and Man* (1941). The climate is typical for the interior of large continents in middle latitudes with considerable variation in monthly temperatures and rainfall from year to year. Summers are usually hot with most of the precipitation occurring in showers and thunderstorms, frequently nocturnal. Southerly flow is dominant during the summer months. Special summaries of kite observations of pressure, temperature, relative humidity, and winds at

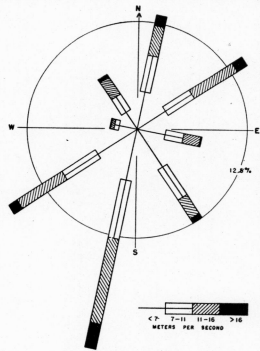

FIG. A.2.1. Distribution of sea-level geostrophic winds for 1 August to 15 September, O'Neill, Nebraska. Data derived from USWB three-hourly charts for 1942 to 1945, 1947 to 1948, and 1950 (2,572 observations).

Drexel, Nebraska, and other stations in Central United States are presented by Gregg (1919, 1922). Means (1954) discusses a low-level jet in southerly flow in the South Central United States and its relationship to summertime precipitation.

Prior to the field program, a synoptic-climatological study was made of data from US Weather Bureau three-hourly maps for the time period 1 August to 15 September during the seven years 1942 to 1945, 1947 to 1948, and 1950. Average values of the meteorological elements of interest were determined from the synoptic charts for an area surrounding the O'Neill site (including portions of Nebraska and South Dakota). The meteorological elements of interest for planning purposes included cloudiness, the frequency distribution of geostrophic wind speeds and directions, the diurnal steadiness of the pressure gradient, and the vertical variation of the geostrophic direction (advection).

The distribution of sea-level geostrophic wind speeds and directions for all sky conditions are presented in the wind rose in Fig. A.2.1. Observations with the sky equal to or less than 3/10 clouded occurred 58 per cent of the

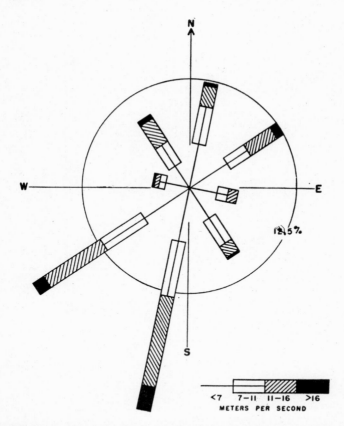

FIG. A.2.2. Distribution of sea-level geostrophic winds with skies equal to or less than 3/10 clouded for 1 August to 15 September, O'Neill, Nebraska. Data derived from USWB three-hourly charts for 1942 to 1945, 1947 to 1948, and 1950 (1,488 observations).

time. The wind rose for these clear or nearly clear hours is presented in
Fig. A.2.2. Winds from the south are dominant in both wind roses.

During the seven years the total number of 24-hr periods studied was 322.
Of the total, 122 occurred with sea-level geostrophic winds from the ESE
to SW for complete 24-hr periods. The maximum number (21) of periods
of southerly geostrophic flow occurred in 1942 and the minimum number
(13) occurred in 1945. Persistent geostrophic flow from NW to NE occurred
57 times. The maximum number (21) of 24-hr periods of northerly flow
occurred in 1943, 1944, and 1947, and the minimum number (five) occurred
in 1948. On the average the periods of persistent southerly flow occurred
more than twice as frequently as the periods of persistent northerly flow
between 1 August and 15 September.

Table A.2.1 presents an analysis of characteristics of the sea level geostrophic flow as a function of three classes of sky conditions during periods
of at least 24 consecutive hours of southerly flow beginning at 2100 or 2400

TABLE A.2.1

Number of Periods of at Least 24 *Consecutive Hours of Southerly Flow which began
at* 2100 *or* 2400 *Local Time for Three Groups of Sky Conditions and Three Geostrophic
Characteristics* (*North-eastern Nebraska and South-eastern South Dakota,* 1 *August
to* 15 *September*)

	Sky clear for 24 hr	Clear nights, cloud cover not exceeding 5/10 during day	Other sky conditions
Geostrophic wind (m/sec)			
Greater than 16	0	3	5
11 to 16	9	11	23
5 to 10	6	12	34
Less than 5	0	1	3
TOTALS (7 years)	15	27	65
Best year (1948)	6	4	—
Worst year (1945)	0	2	—
Trend of geostrophic wind speed (m/sec per 24 hr)			
12 to 8	0	2	3
7 to 4	4	5	16
−4 to −7	1	2	14
−8 to −12	0	0	1
Change in geostrophic wind direction, sea level to 850 mb			
Veering	1	9	7
Backing	0	2	6

local time. If, instead of the hours of 2100 or 2400, the actual starting time is used for any given period of southerly flow, the frequency of occurrence of the second cloud category of Table A.2.1 increases from 27 to a maximum possible total of 33 cases and for the third category from 65 to a maximum of 74 cases. The first (clear skies) and second (clear nights, scattered daytime clouds) cloud categories represent conditions usually associated with a pronounced diurnal variation of the low level thermal stratification.

The veering or backing of the geostrophic wind direction from sea level to 850 mb, noted in Table A.2.1, can be considered indicative only of changes equal to or greater than 22.5 deg, since all directions were read to the nearest of 16 compass points. A geostrophic direction which veers with height is often associated with warm air advection whereas backing is frequently associated with cold air advection.

Table A.2.2 presents a summary of the frequency of occurrence of precipitation and fog in the area of north-eastern Nebraska and south-eastern South Dakota surrounding O'Neill.

TABLE A.2.2

Number of Days with (A) Thunderstorms or Showers, (B) Stratiform Precipitation, (C) Lightning (no precipitation at observation points), and (D) Fog were Reported in North-eastern Nebraska and South-eastern South Dakota at Least Once During a 24-hr Period Beginning at 2100 Local Time (1 August to 15 September).
Total Days, 322 (seven years)

Year	A	B	C	D
1942	13	2	3	5
1943	9	0	9	2
1944	3	3	4	0
1945	5	3	3	0
1947	12	0	1	0
1948	11	2	1	4
1950	15	0	1	4
TOTALS	68	10	22	15

REFERENCES

United States Department of Agriculture, *Climate and Man*, Yearbook of Agriculture, US Govt. Printing Office, Washington, D.C., 1941.

GREGG, W. R.; "Free-air Data at Broken Arrow, Drexel, Ellendale, and Royal Center Aerological Stations, July, August, and September, 1918", *Monthly Weather Review Suppl.*, No. 14, Washington D.C., 1919.

GREGG, W. R.; "An Aerological Survey of the United States: Part I: Results of Observations by Means of Kites", *Monthly Weather Review Suppl.*, No. 20, Washington D.C., 1922.

MEANS, L. L.; "A Study of the Mean Southerly Wind-Maximum in Low Levels Associated with a Period of Summer Precipitation in the Middle West", *Bull. Am. Meteorol. Soc.* **35**, 166-170, 1954.

B

SUMMARY OF CLIMATOLOGICAL CONDITIONS IN NORTH-EASTERN NEBRASKA DURING THE LATE SUMMER OF 1953

By P. Davis and P. Giorgio

Geophysics Research Directorate

TABLE A.3.1 lists the climatological data for August 1953 for those US Weather Bureau (USWB) cooperative observing stations immediately surrounding O'Neill, Nebraska. This data was taken from the USWB publication *Climatological Data for the United States*. From the same source daily maximum and minimum temperatures and precipitation totals are presented in Table A.3.2 for the USWB cooperative weather observing station at O'Neill, Nebraska, for the period 1 August through 10 September 1953. The detailed standard meteorological observations, taken at the observation site, are listed in Table 1.3 for the general observation periods.

The departures from normal indicate that the August 1953 temperatures were slightly above normal and that precipitation was significantly below normal in north-eastern Nebraska.

Table A.3.3 lists daily totals of insolation on a horizontal surface as

TABLE A.3.1

Climatological Data for Six Stations in Nebraska for August 1953

Station	Butte	Chambers	Ewing	Newport	Niobrara	O'Neill
Temperature (°F) data						
Average maximum	87.4	86.6	88.5	87.1	89.8	86.6
Average minimum	62.6	58.6	62.4	60.9	62.7	61.8
Departure from normal	1.4	−0.1	2.7	1.2	1.3	−1.0
Highest temperature	98	95	98	102	98	96
Date	13	28;30	30	13	29;30	30
Lowest temperature	50	46	47	49	51	48
Date	8	8	8	8	8	8
Number of days ≥ 90°F	13	12	15	12	16	13
Precipitation (inches) data						
Total	2.11	1.26	1.85	1.27	2.51	1.05
Departure from normal	−0.49	−1.20	−1.02	−1.45	−0.21	−1.46
Amount on day with greatest precipitation	0.99	0.42	1.15	0.92	0.78	0.70
Date	3	11	11	15	5	15
Number of days ≥ 0.01	7	7	3	6	7	5

recorded by the GRD Eppley pyrheliometer; for the specifications of this observation see Sec. 3.1.1 of Volume I.

TABLE A.3.2

Daily Maximum and Minimum Temperature (°F) and Precipitation (10⁻² inches) from the Records of the USWB Cooperative Station, O'Neill, Nebraska, 1 August through 10 September 1953

August	1	2	3	4	5	6	7	8	9	10	
Maximum	92	90	81	81	88	85	76	80	90	92	
Minimum	75	69	68	62	62	60	52	48	59	63	
Precipitation	T[1]	T[1]	1	1	—	—	—	—	—	24	
August	11	12	13	14	15	16	17	18	19	20	
Maximum	76	88	95	85	77	75	79	80	82	83	
Minimum	59	50	64	62	55	58	62	56	56	57	
Precipitation	9	—	—	—	70	—	—	—	—	—	
August	21	22	23	24	25	26	27	28	29	30	31
Maximum	84	86	86	90	95	95	94	95	94	96	94
Minimum	55	56	58	64	69	70	68	70	74	66	70
Precipitation	—	—	—	—	—	—	—	—	—	—	—
September	1	2	3	4	5	6	7	8	9	10	
Maximum	94	94	72	71	81	77	83	88	90	93	
Minimum	71	69	51	43	41	47	48	53	54	65	
Precipitation	—	2	24	—	—	—	—	—	19	—	

[1] Traces.

TABLE A.3.3

Recorded Daily Totals of Insolation (ly/day) on a Horizontal Surface, O'Neill, Nebraska, 5 August through 8 September 1953

Date (August)	5	6	7	8	9	10	11	12	13
Insolation	614	504	669	668	634	425	422	688	678
Date (August)	14	15	16	17	18	19	20	21	22
Insolation	657	215	468	431	643	624	599	615	600
Date (August)	23	24	25	26	27	28	29	30	31
Insolation	494	604	619	606	590	M[1]	406	577	592
Date (September)	1	2	3	4	5	6	7	8	
Insolation	497	M[1]	M[1]	521	591	591	570	282[2]	

[1] Missing data.   [2] Recorded total for first half of the day.

A.4

SCHEDULING OF OBSERVATIONS—REMARKS ON DATA PRESENTATION AND TABULAR SUMMARY OF AVAILABLE DATA

By H. H. Lettau

Geophysics Research Directorate

A.4.1. Criteria of General Observation Periods

FROM a very basic scientific point of view the ideal observation period should be characterized by a large diurnal variation of the heat budget terms at the earth/air interface. This automatically selects a clear day or a combination of a partially cloudy afternoon and clear night as a criterion for selection. Although non-steady conditions and the effect of horizontal advection are extremely important problems, it was felt that the primary objective of the program, given the present status of atmospheric turbulence research, would best be realized by restricting observation days to those characterized by approximately zero advection (that is, little or no vertical shear of the geostrophic wind) and steady pressure gradient conditions. The last requirement may, in some ways, be at variance with an additional desired condition, namely, a large range of Richardson numbers. For this reason and other obvious reasons, it seemed desirable to select observation days with the additional criterion that the mean geostrophic wind speed during the day vary from one to the next observation period. Moreover, the presence of many groups at the proposed field site and the necessity of assuring an unobstructed fetch for each group demanded that the general observation periods be characterized by a relatively constant wind direction. In view of the climatological facts (see Sec. A.2) this wind direction should be between SE and SW.

With the above criteria in mind the synoptic-climatological data contained in Tables A.2.1 and A.2.2 had been prepared. For the seven years studied in Sec. A.2, there were 42 cases which did not seriously depart from the proposed criteria. Moreover, the indications were that roughly as many satisfactory days occur with geostrophic speeds between 11 and 16 m/sec as occur with geostrophic speeds of 5 to 11 m/sec. An average of approximately one suitable day per week in the period 1 August to 15 September is likely to be found.

A meeting was held at the Geophysics Research Directorate on 30 January 1953 to plan the program, and all branches of the Armed Forces, universities, and institutions known to be engaged in research in the field of atmospheric boundary layer turbulence and diffusion were invited. The objectives of the experimental procedures and programs were agreed upon.

On the basis of the above discussed synoptic-climatological study, and considering the possibility of equipment failures, etc., it was decided that a general observation period should be initiated whenever the forecast satisfied or nearly satisfied the criteria, regardless of the time of beginning of suitable and steady weather conditions. The termination date of 15 September was determined by university commitments of participants.

A.4.2. Selection of General Observation Days

The primary duty of the field coordinators (B. Davidson and H. H. Lettau) at O'Neill was to designate certain days as general observation periods. This selection was done on the basis of forecasts of meteorological conditions for the next 24 to 36 hr, and on the basis of the meteorological criteria discussed above and agreed upon at the preliminary conference. From the end of July through 8 September 1953 the facsimile charts of the US Weather Bureau were received daily at O'Neill. In cases of promising weather development additional forecast information was provided by the Kansas City office of the US Weather Bureau. During regular briefings the weather situation was discussed with the participants of the program. The call for the beginning of a general observation period was normally made 6 hr before the actual start of activity on the site.

It should be emphasized that the synoptic-climatological study made by P. Davis (see Sec. A.2) prior to the field project had shown that one could expect approximately one day per week which meets the established criteria. However, there was also a relatively large variability in the number of suitable days from year to year. Fortunately, 1953 proved to be a more or less normal year inasmuch as the weather conditions confirmed the above expectancy. The Great Plains Turbulence Field Program was in operation for approximately six weeks and seven general observation periods (average duration 25 hr) were realized. Some of these periods were not ideal. The shortest one lasted only for 10 hr (fourth general observation period). A significant vertical shear of the geostrophic motion was nearly always present. On the whole, the expectancies of the program were fulfilled. No favorable weather situation occurred which was not recognized early enough in order to initiate a general observation period. The termination of activity was in most cases determined by weather conditions changing to unfavorable, and only once (seventh and last period) by fatigue and strain on the personnel.

A.4.3. Remarks on Data Presentation

According to the established program the participating agencies were responsible for securing observational data bi-hourly, that is, for the even hours of average local time (CST plus 35 min) once a general observation period was initiated. Additional data for the odd hours, or activity during days outside the general observation periods were optional. In the following presentation of observational results only the bi-hourly data obtained during the seven general observation periods are presented. It was impossible to publish all the results. A certain amount of raw data is preserved on punch cards at the Atmospheric Analysis Laboratory of the Geophysics Research Directorate. These cards contain, for example, the fast-response data collected by the Massachusetts Institute of Technology, and the photo-theodolite data of smoke-puff and pibal swarm positions. The data can be made available on request.

The amount of information obtained during the program is unusually large, in direct proportion to the over-all effort devoted to the instrumentation. The order of magnitude of the number of mean profile measurements in the atmospheric surface layer is 10^3 per element, that of the total of upper air measurements is 10^4, while that of turbulence structure data ranges up to 10^5 and 10^6. Table A.4.1 can serve as a guide for checking the availability of data published in this volume.

TABLE A.4.1

Summary of Measurements and Available Data Presented in Tables 1.1.a through 7.4 in Volume II

Code: "A" indicates that the instrument was active and tabulated data are complete or nearly complete; "a" the instrument was active during less than half of the period; "O" the instrument was on the site but inactive, or no data are available due to failure or other reasons; "—" the instrument was not on the site

Table No.	Instrument, or Type of Data	Authority	General Observation Period No. 1	2	3	4	5	6	7
1.1.a, b	Geostrophic winds	GRD	A	A	A	A	A	A	A
1.2	Standard wind vane	MIT	A	A	A	A	A	A	A
1.3	Standard synoptic data	4th W. Gr.	A	A	A	A	A	A	A
2.1.a	Soil thermistors	U. Tex.	A	A	A	A	A	A	A
2.1.a	Soil thermocouples	JHU	A	A	A	A	A	A	A
2.1.a	Soil thermocouples	UCLA	A	A	A	A	A	A	A
2.1.b	Soil temperature integrators	U. Wisc.	A	A	A	A	A	A	A
2.2.a	Soil thermal conductivity	U. Tex.	a	a	A	A	a	A	A
2.2.b	Soil moisture	JHU	a	a	a	a	a	a	a
2.2.b	Soil density	JHU	a	O	O	O	O	a	a
2.2.c	Soil heat capacity	U. Wisc.	A	a	a	O	a	a	a
2.3	Soil moisture tension	JHU	A	A	A	A	A	O	A
2.4	Soil heat flux, from soil temp. integrators	U. Wisc.	A	A	A	A	A	A	A
2.4	Soil heat flux, from Gier & Dunkle flow meter	U. Tex.	O	A	A	A	A	A	A
2.4	Soil heat flux, from Gier & Dunkle flow meter	UCLA	A	A	A	A	A	A	A
2.4	Soil heat flux, from Albrecht flow meter	U. Tex.	a	a	A	A	a	A	A
2.4	Soil heat flux, from numerical integration	JHU	A	A	A	A	A	A	A

Table No.	Instrument, or Type of Data	Authority	General Observation Period No.						
			1	2	3	4	5	6	7
3.1	Eppley pyrheliometer	GRD	A	A	A	A	A	A	A
3.1	Eppley pyrheliometer	JHU	O	O	O	O	O	A	A
3.1	Gier & Dunkle radiometer	JHU	A	A	A	A	A	A	A
3.1	Gier & Dunkle radiometer	U. Tex.	O	A	A	A	A	A	A
3.1	Suomi net radiometer	U. Wisc.	A	A	A	A	A	A	A
3.2	Boundary shear stress recorder	UCLA	a	a	A	a	a	A	A
3.2	Sheppard type drag plate	JHU	A	A	A	A	A	A	A
3.3	Low-level smoke-puff data	JHU	A	A	A	A	A	A	A
3.4	Micro-barogram data	GRD	A	A	A	O	A	A	a
3.5	Taylor dew gauge	GRD	A	O	A	O	O	O	A
3.5	Duvdevani dew blocks	GRD	A	O	A	O	A	O	A
4.1.a	60-min mean wind profile data:								
4.1.a	Standard 3-cup anemometers	MIT	A	A	A	A	A	A	A
4.1.a	Modified Sheppard type anemometers	UCLA	O	O	O	A	A	A	A
4.1.a	Ping-pong ball anemometers	ISC	O	O	A	A	A	A	A
4.1.a	Modified SCS anemometers	JHU	A	A	A	A	A	A	A
4.1.b	15-min mean wind speed profile data:								
4.1.b	Standard 3-cup anemometers	MIT	A	A	A	A	A	A	A
4.1.b	Modified Sheppard type anemometers	UCLA	A	A	A	A	A	A	A
4.1.b	Ping-pong ball anemometers	ISC	A	A	A	A	A	A	A
4.1.b	Semi-cylindrical anemometers	JHU	O	O	O	A	O	O	A
4.2	Mean air temp., from aspirated thermocouples	MIT	A	A	A	A	A	A	A
4.2	Mean air temp., from aspirated thermocouples	UCLA	A	A	A	A	A	A	A
4.2	Mean air temp., from shielded thermocouples	JHU	A	A	A	A	A	A	A
4.2	Mean air temp., from shielded thermistors	U. Tex.	O	O	A	A	A	A	A
4.3.a	Moisture profile data from dew point apparatus	JHU	A	A	A	A	A	A	a
4.3.b	Double psychrometer lift apparatus	U. Wisc.	A	A	A	A	A	A	A
4.4	Ozone recorders	U. New Mex.	A	A	A	A	A	O	A
5.1	Temp. fluctuation data, from thermocouples	MIT	O	A	A	O	a	A	A
5.1	Temp. fluctuation data, from thermistors	ISC	O	A	A	A	A	A	A
5.2.a	Wind fluctuation data, from bivanes	MIT	O	A	A	O	a	A	A
5.2.b	Wind fluctuation data, from rotating pressure tube	Tex. A & M	O	a	a	A	A	A	A
5.2.c	Sonic anemometer*	U. Wisc.	a	a	a	a	a	a	a
5.3	PBY-6A data	WHOI	—	—	—	a	a	—	—
6.1.a	Loeser technique smoke-puff data	GRD	—	A	a	A	A	A	A

* The analysis of sonic anemometer data is at the present time not completed. A sample of results is presented in Table 5.2.4.1 in Volume I.

Table No.	Instrument, or Type of Data	Authority	General Observation Period No.						
			1	2	3	4	5	6	7
6.1.b	Loeser technique pibal swarm data	GRD	A	A	A	O	A	A	A
6.2	Rawinsonde GMD-1A data	6th W. Sq.	A	A	A	A	A	A	A
6.3	Double theodolite pibal data	4th W. Gr.	A	A	A	A	A	A	A
6.4	Radiosonde temp. and humidity data	6th W. Sq.	A	A	A	A	A	A	A
6.5	Aerograph L-20 temp. and humidity data	GRD	—	O	A	A	A	A	A
7.1	Representative wind components	GRD	A	A	A	A	A	A	A
7.2.a, b	Representative temp. and humidity data	GRD	A	A	A	A	A	A	A
7.3.a	Surface heat budget summary, after Suomi	U. Wisc	A	A	A	A	A	O	A
7.3.a	Surface heat budget summary, after Halstead	JHU	A	A	A	A	A	A	O
7.3.a	Surface heat budget summary, after Lettau	GRD	A	A	A	A	A	A	A
7.3.b	Representative surface layer data	GRD	A	A	A	A	A	A	A
7.4	Richardson numbers 0.8 to 8.0 meters	GRD	A	A	A	A	A	A	A

It was not feasible to include in the tables for the general observation days published in Volume II all results of measurements made at O'Neill. Certain information was collected too sporadically, or at times outside the general observation periods. Some data are the results of computations or interpolations. These results are included in the various sections of Volume I. Table A.4.2 can serve as a guide for locating this additional information.

TABLE A.4.2

Summary of Measurements and Available Data Obtained at O'Neill and Presented in Tables in Volume I

Article	Type of data and days for which data are presented		Table No.
1.1	850 mb geostrophic winds estimated by NYU personnel	All gen. obs days	1.1.1
2.1.2	Soil temperature differences at three sites	9 Aug.	2.1.2.1
2.2.2	Soil heat capacities (electric calorimeter)	5, 6, 7, 12 Aug. and 5 Sept.	2.2.2.1
2.2.2	Soil density and heat capacity	9, 12, 13 Aug. and 5, 6 Sept.	2.2.2.2
2.2.3	Estimated soil heat capacity	Means for all gen. obs. days	2.2.3.2
2.4.1	Soil heat flux at 2.5 cm	22, 25 Aug.	2.4.1.1
3.1.1	Incoming and reflected short-wave radiation, albedo	4, 5, 6, 7 Sept.	3.1.1.1

Article	Type of data and days for which data are presented		Table No.
3.1.1	Unshaded and shaded Eppley data	31 Aug., 7 Sept.	3.1.1.2
3.3	Summary of low-level smoke-puff data	Mean of all gen. obs. days	3.3.1
3.5	Summary of dew duration recordings	5 Aug. through 8 Sept.	3.5.1
4.1	Anemometer comparison (all groups)	4 Sept.	4.1.0.1
4.1.3	UCLA anemometer comparison	Means of all gen. obs. days	4.1.3.1
4.1.5	MIT anemometer comparison	18, 20 Aug., 9 Sept.	4.1.5.1
4.2	Fourier analysis of temperature variations 0.1 to 16 m	31 Aug., 7 Sept.	4.2.0.1
	Thermometer comparison (all groups)	31 Aug., 7 Sept.	4.2.0.2
	Fourier analysis of temperature variations 100 to 2000 m	31 Aug., 7 Sept.	4.2.0.3
4.4	Vertical flux of ozone	8, 23, 24 Aug.	4.4.1
5.1.3	RMS values of refractive index and temperature	13,19,22,31 Aug., 5 Sept.	5.1.3.1
5.2.2	Frequency of 1-sec average wind directions	31 Aug., 1 Sept.	5.2.2.1
5.2.2	Frequency of 1-sec average wind directions	7, 8 Sept.	5.2.2.2
5.2	RMS vertical velocity comparison (U. of Wisc., MIT, Tex. A & M, WHOI)	22, 30, 31 Aug.	5.2.0.1
5.2.4	Power spectral density of vertical motion	31 Aug.	5.2.4.1
5.3	RMS vertical velocity comparison (PBY-WHOI, and U. of Wisc.)	25 Aug.	5.3.1
5.3	Shearing stress comparison (PBY-WHOI, and JHU)	22, 24, 25 Aug.	5.3.2
6.1	Average duration of evaluated smoke-puff drift	Mean of six gen. obs. days	6.1.1
7.3	Height integrated 2-hr temp. differences	"Day means"	7.3.2
	Height integrated 2-hr temp. differences	"Night means"	7.3.3
	Height integrated 2-hr moist. differences	"Day means"	7.3.4
	Height integrated 2-hr moist. differences	"Night means"	7.3.5
	Heat equivalent of dew formation	8/9, 18/19 Aug.	7.3.6
7.4	Local Richardson numbers from MIT 60-min and 15-min data	7/8 Sept.	7.4.2
	Distribution of classes of convective stability	All gen. obs. days	7.4.4
	Class averages of wind speed	All gen. obs. days	7.4.5
	Roughness parameters	All gen. obs. days	7.4.7
7.5	Various dimensionless parameters	Means of all gen. obs. days	7.5.1 to 7.5.14
7.6	Class averages of vertical motion from smoke puffs	Mean of six gen. obs. days	7.6.1
7.6	Occurrence of predominant vertical gusts	Mean of six gen. obs. days	7.6.2

FIRST GENERAL OBSERVATION PERIOD

1805 CST 8 August through 2105 CST 9 August 1953

Solar Data for the Field Site near O'Neill, Nebraska

	Sun's elevation angle at apparent noon	Sunrise CST	Apparent noon CST	Sunset CST
8 August	63° 36′	0534	1240	1946
9 August	63° 18′	0535	1240	1945

Summary of Synoptic Conditions

The personnel and equipment participating in the Great Plains Turbulence Field Program were ready and prepared to take observations by 1 August 1953. However, atmospheric conditions from 1 August through 7 August were generally unfavorable for the requirements of the field trials. This whole period was characterized by very changeable conditions. There was a series of frontal passages with consequent variable wind directions, cloudiness and precipitation. On the 7th a ridge of high pressure, oriented north-south, extended through Western Nebraska. The winds were northerly at 10 to 20 m.p.h. The skies were clear in the western section and in the eastern section they were clear at night and broken during the day. The winds shifted to the south during the afternoon of the 8th and the first general observation period was begun at 1805 CST.

During the first general observation period North Central Nebraska was under the influence of a polar continental air mass which had moved into the area on the 7th and had been modified considerably. The circulation was dominated by a low-pressure area centered at Glasgow, Montana, and a high-pressure cell centered at St. Cloud, Minn., with a ridge from South Central Manitoba to Western Arkansas. At 0630 CST of the 8th a warm front oriented north-south was situated in Western Nebraska and moved eastward slowly followed by an overtaking cold front. This frontal system was rather weak and shallow, disappearing aloft below 800 mb and remained west of O'Neill for the entire period. The winds in the local area were southerly at 5 to 15 m.p.h. veering to northerly at Valentine, Nebraska, during the afternoon of the 9th.

The skies were generally clear with some daytime broken alto-stratus and alto-cumulus clouds. The only precipitation within 500 miles of the test site consisted of intense thunderstorm activity during the very beginning of the period to the west in association with a pre-frontal squall line ahead of a cold front just east of the Rocky Mountains. The first general observation was ended at 2105 CST on the 9th.

1.1.a. Mean Geopotential H (dynamic m above 601 = geopotential of test site). West and South components of the geostrophic wind u_g, v_g (m/sec) at indicated pressure (mb) levels. Values are estimated for the O'Neill site from local synoptic charts.

mb	H	8 Aug. 2100		9 Aug. 0900		9 Aug. 2100	
		u_g	v_g	u_g	v_g	u_g	v_g
750	2025	4.0	0.9	9.4	4.8	6.9	2.1
800	1472	4.4	0	7.9	3.7	5.0	0.8
850	948	3.1	3.9	8.2	7.4	3.7	3.4
900	456	1.8	2.9	9.3	12.3	4.2	8.5
950	—21	5.3	7.9	10.3	13.2	2.7	6.4

1.1.b. Direction (deg from North) and speed (m/sec) of the 950 mb geostrophic wind. Values are estimated for the O'Neill site from local synoptic charts.

8 August		9 August 1953							
1830	2130	0030	0330	0630	0930	1230	1530	1830	2130
212	214	208	208	209	218	216	212	209	203
4.9	9.5	12.5	13.3	12.5	16.7	16.7	11.8	9.5	6.9

1.2. Direction (deg from North) of the mean surface wind from standard vane recordings at 1-min intervals (Mass. Inst. Tech., 16 m level). Hourly and 15-min averages centered at indicated CST.

	8 August			9 August 1953										
	1835[1]	2035	2235	0035	0235	0435[2]	0635	0835	1035	1235	1435	1635	1835	2035
60-min mean:	103	130	151	158	174	173	173	178	180	180	181	177	157	157
15-min mean:	97	132	153	162	175	174	173	179	178	180	180	177	159	160

[1] Data missing from 1827-1833.   [2] Period 0405-0500 CST.

1.3. Standard shelter temperature (°F), relative humidity (%); station pressure (inches) and air density (mg cm^{-3}); amount (tenths) and types of clouds.

Month	Day	CST	Temp.	RH	Pressure	Density	Clouds	Remarks
Aug.	8	1830	76	50	28.050	1.10	8 Cs	Clouds high and thin, some stratus to NW
		2030	61	83	.055	1.14	4 Cs	
	9	0030	59	86	.025	1.14	1 Ac	
		0230	61	81	.010	1.13	1 Ac	Strong gust about 0138C to 15 mph
		0430	59	89	.005	1.14	2 Ac	Lightning visible to E. Cloud layer below 20°
		0630	61	84	27.970	1.13	4 AcCs	Gusts to 20 mph
		0830	70	64	.925	1.11	5 AcCs	Gusts to 26 mph
		1030	77	54	.905	1.09	9 AcCs	Gusts to 29 mph
		1230	84	45	.860	1.08	9 AcCs	Cloud layer more dense. Sun intermittent
		1430	87	43	.855	1.07	7 AcCs	Winds gusty
		1630	90	40	.835	1.06	1 Cs	Thin veil over entire sky
		1830	85	49	.810	1.07	1 Cs	Winds steady
		2030	79	57	.830	1.09	1 Cs	Cloud bank to SW and W possibly part of cold front

2.1.a. Soil temperature (°C) from thermistors (University of Texas) and soil thermocouples (University of California and Johns Hopkins University). Values are readings at indicated CST.

Inst. Set	Depth (cm)	8 August 1835	2035	2235	9 August 1953 0035	0235	0435	0635	0835	1035	1235	1435	1635	1835	2035
UT	0.5	27.18	22.33	20.21	18.74	18.09	17.56	17.90	23.01	31.07	35.55	36.18	33.84	29.32	25.53
UCLA	1.3	28.22	23.44	21.17	19.56	19.00	18.44	17.94	20.89	26.67	31.67	34.28	33.61	29.39	25.44
UT	1.5	27.74	23.46	21.23	19.71	18.89	18.31	18.31	21.91	28.17	32.00	33.61	32.48	29.13	26.01
UT	2.5	28.04	24.28	21.94	20.49	19.55	18.93	18.68	21.46	26.67	30.41	32.29	31.82	29.10	26.29
JH	2.5	26.65	24.05	22.19	20.92	20.06	19.48	19.12	20.10	22.82	25.50	27.29	27.90	26.87	24.95
UT	3.5	28.30	24.79	22.47	21.05	20.05	19.38	19.04	21.19	25.79	29.21	31.21	31.18	29.14	26.61
UT	4.5	28.33	25.16	22.89	21.45	20.41	19.71	19.27	21.01	25.02	28.33	30.43	30.74	29.04	26.71
JH	5.0	26.70	24.64	22.90	21.69	20.77	20.16	19.74	20.10	21.98	24.22	26.01	27.00	26.56	25.16
UT	5.5	28.48	25.59	23.46	22.03	20.98	20.25	19.77	21.08	24.56	27.54	29.71	30.25	28.94	26.92
UCLA	10.0	26.00	24.44	23.17	21.78	20.83	20.28	19.44	19.72	21.11	23.33	25.00	26.11	26.11	25.00
JH	10.0	26.13	25.08	23.74	22.76	21.86	21.19	20.70	20.54	21.40	22.90	24.38	25.50	25.80	25.24
JH	20.0	24.12	24.26	23.90	23.38	22.84	22.34	21.94	21.53	21.44	21.84	22.50	23.20	23.78	24.05
UCLA	25.0	22.78	23.06	23.06	22.78	22.50	21.94	21.56	21.11	20.72	21.17	21.67	22.22	22.78	23.06
JH	40.0	22.02	22.30	22.50	22.57	22.56	22.48	22.36	22.14	21.99	21.88	21.84	21.87	22.04	22.23
JH	80.0	21.17	21.18	21.15	21.10	21.08	21.08	21.08	21.05	21.01	21.00	21.01	20.96	20.98	20.97

2.1.b Change of soil temperature ($°C\ hr^{-1}$) averaged over indicated layers from soil temperature integrators (University of Wisconsin). Values are differences between readings at the end and beginning of 1-hr intervals centered at indicated CST.

Depth (cm)	8 August 1835	2035	2235	9 August 1953 0035	0235	0435	0635	0835	1035	1235	1435	1635	1835
0–5	−5.34	−1.73	−0.78	−0.59	−0.29	−0.22	0.14	9.27[1]	1.57	1.18	0.68	−0.75	−3.78
5–15	−0.57	−0.83	−0.61	−0.50	−0.38	−0.29	−0.13	0.31	0.89	0.87	0.80	0.25	−0.33
15–50	0.15	0.05	−0.06	−0.10	−0.13	−0.13	−0.15	−0.10	0.00	0.10	0.16	0.19	0.15

[1] Doubtful value.

2.2.a. Soil thermal conductivity ($mcal\ cm^{-1}\ sec^{-1}\ deg^{-1}$) computed from soil thermistor response to defined heating pulses (University of Texas, Albrecht heat flux meter No. 2). Values are derived from 60-sec trials beginning at indicated CST.

Depth (cm)	9 August 1953 0440	0640	0840	1040	1240
0.5	0.74	0.73	0.77	0.77	0.66
1.5	0.98	1.01	1.06	1.01	1.04
2.5	1.30	1.18	1.18	1.16	1.21
3.5	1.56	1.45	1.38	1.53	1.45
4.5	1.63	1.67	1.53	1.62	1.58
5.5	1.82	1.82	1.92	1.95	1.81

2.2.b. Soil moisture (% wet weight) and density ($g\ cm^{-3}$) from soil samples at the Johns Hopkins University site. Indicated CST refers to the approximate time of soil sample extraction.

Depth (cm)	Soil Moisture 7 August 1300	8 August 1300	Soil Density 6 August 1300
4	12.2	11.1	—
10	8.9	9.4	1.76
20	—	6.7	1.85
25	6.9	—	—
40	4.0	4.4	1.78
60	2.0	—	—
80	—	1.7	—
90	2.5	—	—

2.2.c. Soil heat capacity (cal cm^{-3} deg^{-1}) from soil samples at the University of Wisconsin site (calorimetric determination). Indicated CST refers to the approximate time of soil sample extraction (0-10 cm layer).

8 August	9 August 1953																		
1900	2000	0000	0100	0200	0300	0400	0500	0700	0900	1000	1100	1200	1300	1500	1600	1700	1800	1900	2000
0.29	0.27	0.37	0.44	0.41	0.40	0.41	0.38	0.29	0.39	0.42	0.36	0.26	0.39	0.43	0.29	0.34	0.35	0.34	0.38

2.3. Soil moisture tension (mb) from tensiometers (Johns Hopkins University). Values are readings at indicated CST.

Depth (cm)	8 August 1835	2035	2235	9 August 1953 0035	0235	0435	0635	0835	1035	1235	1435	1635	1835
5	623	578	367	156	65	31	38	90	—	368	468	557	643
10	613	586	468	380	341	319	310	368	—	544	595	647	662
20	634	612	449	184	13	13	13	14	—	258	423	559	626
40	440	475	398	200	13	10	10	12	—	103	205	337	447

2.4. Vertical flux of heat (mcal cm^{-2} min^{-1}) from soil temperature integrators (University of Wisconsin), Albrecht heat flux meter No. 2 (University of Texas), Gier and Dunkle heat flow meters (University of California) and numerical integration of soil temperature profile changes (Johns Hopkins University). UW and JH values are 60-min averages, UCLA values are 15-min averages and UT values are approximately 2-min averages. All averages are centered at indicated CST.

Inst. Set	Depth (cm)	8 August 1835	2035	2235	9 August 1953 0035	0235	0435	0653	0835	1035	1235	1435	1635	1835
UW	0.0	−153	−86	−71	−70	−62	−57	−41	266	96	108	105	40	−93
UT	0.0[1]	—	—	—	—	—	−55	−66	112	215	320	—	—	—
JH	0.0[1]	—	−62	−67	−68	−55	−57	−23	37	100	112	110	28	−23
UCLA	1.3[2]	−3	−58	−45	−49	−40	−36	−14	68	141	173	180	111	19
UT	2.0	—	—	—	—	—	−42	−24	30	98	107	—	—	—
UW	5.0	5	−35	−51	−52	−53	−51	−25	12	—	73	85	62	57
UCLA	10.0	24	−3	−20	−30	−31	−31	−21	−6	24	52	74	61	29
UW	15.0	38	12	−16	−24	−32	−34	−38	−26	0	24	40	48	38

[1] Values are extrapolated to surface.   [2] Average of two heat flow meters at the same depth.

3.1. Summary of data on radiation (mcal cm^{-2} min^{-1}). Short-wave radiation from Eppley pyrheliometer (GRD); net radiation from Gier and Dunkle radiometer (Johns Hopkins University) and the Suomi net radiometer (University of Wisconsin). Values are hourly averages centered at indicated CST.

	Inst. Set	8 August 1835	2035	2235	9 August 1953 0035	0235	0435	0635	0835	1035	1235	1435	1635	1835	2035
(Short-Wave)	GRD[1]	287[1]	0	0	0	0	0	203	780	1050	1140	1180	770	207	0
	GRD[2]	270	0	0	0	0	0	200	760	1220[3]	1440[3]	1180[3]	770	200	0
(Net)	JH	40	−90	−80	−80	−80	−70	20	470	710	830	800	460	20	−70
	UW	−36[4]	−101	−100	−103	−106	−85	68	520	712	774	753	391	−19	−99[5]

[1] 30-min average 1810-1840.   [4] 30-min average 1835-1905.
[2] 10-min average centered at indicated CST.   [5] 40-min average 2005-2045.
[3] Subject to error because of clouds.

3.2. Boundary shear-stress (dynes cm^{-2}) from drag recorder (University of California) and Sheppard-type drag plate (Johns Hopkins University); direction of boundary shear stress (deg from North) from drag recorder (University of California). Values are 10-min means centered at indicated CST.

Inst. Set	8 August			9 August 1953					
	1835	2035	2235	0035	0235	0435	0635	0835	1035[1]
UCLA	—	—	0.40	—	—	—	—	—	—
JH	—	0.01	0.11	0.3	0.8	0.9	2.5	4.3	4.5
UCLA	—	—	160	—	—	—	—	—	—

[1] No data after 1035 due to strong winds.

3.3. Characteristics of low-level smoke-puff drift (Johns Hopkins University); direction of drift (deg from North); time t_{25} (sec) required to cross 25 m circle; lateral width S (deg) at 25 m and time t_D (sec) required to reach threshold of visibility. Values are ensemble averages for 10 smoke puffs fired at approximately 1-min intervals beginning at indicated CST.

	8 August			9 August 1953										
	1800	2000	2200	0000	0200	0400	0600	0800	1000	1200	1400	1600	1800	2000
dd	107	126	151	162	174	170	172	180	179	173	178	172	156	155
t_{25}	9.6	17.3	8.4	7.7	5.1	7.0	5.1	3.7	3.8	2.8	3.4	4.5	5.8	5.9
S	15.6	14.2	14.0	13.5	15.2	14.0	14.6	12.6	13.7	13.7	12.7	14.8	14.6	13.2
t_D	43	101	—	—	—	—	26	18	15	13	10	12	24	30

3.4. Characteristics of surface pressure variations from micro-barograms (GRD, Paulin-type aneroid system); trend (WBAN Synoptic Code number); qualitative index of micro-variations ("a" = calm to "d" = very unruly); trace ratio (trace length relative to trend length); trend ratio (trend length relative to chart length); period (min), amplitude (10^{-2} mb) and number of perceptible waves. Values refer to 2-hr intervals centered at indicated CST.

	8 August			9 August 1953									
	1935	2135	2335	0135	0335	0535	0735	0935	1135	1335	1535	1735	1935
Trend	3	0	7	6	7	7	7	7	7	7	7	6	3
Index	a	a	a	a-b	a	b	c	c-d	d	d	c	b-a	a
Trace ratio	1.1	1.2	1.4	1.6	1.5	1.9	1.8	1.8	1.6	2.1	1.6	1.2	1.1
Trend ratio	1.3	1.2	1.25	1.0	1.2	1.1	1.0	1.2	1.3	1.2	1.2	1.1	1.1
Period	15	20	40	35	15	25[1]	20	45	40	10	20	35	25
Ampl.	4	5	12	10	6	25	11	10	9	6	6	4	2.5
Number	4	2	2	1	6	1	2	1	2	7	2	2	2
Period	—	10	—	15	—	20	45	15	20	20	10	15	—
Ampl.	—	3	—	8	—	10	7.5	6.5	7	5	4	3	—
Number	—	4	—	3	—	2	1	3	4.5	1	2	3	—
Period	—	—	—	10	—	40	10	—	5	—	5	—	—
Ampl.	—	—	—	4	—	9	5	—	4	—	3	—	—
Number	—	—	—	3	—	1	4	—	5	—	6	—	—

[1] Pressure surge.

3.5. Dew deposition data (GRD); Taylor dew gauge trace characteristics and Duvdevani dew block scale numbers. Values are readings at indicated CST.

Inst. Set	Height (cm)	8 August 2035	2135	2235	2335	9 August 1953 0035	0135	0235	0335	0435	0535	0635[3]
Gauge	7	#[1]	#	#	#	#	#	#	#	#	#	#[2]
Block	100	Tr.	Tr.	O	O	O	O	O	O	O	O	—
Block	50	Tr.	2a	1	1	1	1	Tr.	Tr.	Tr.	O	—
Block	8	1	2b	3a	3b	4a	5b	5b	5b	5b	5b	—

[1] Beginning of trace 2010 CST.
[2] End of trace 0645 CST.
[3] No dew deposit during evening of 9 August at or before 2035 CST.

4.1.a. Hourly mean wind speed (cm sec⁻¹) from standard three-cup anemometers (Mass. Inst. Tech.), and modified SCS cup anemometers (Johns Hopkins University); centered at indicated CST.

Inst. Set	Height (m)	8 August 1835	2035	2235	9 August 1953 0035	0235	0435	0635	0835	1035	1235	1435	1635	1835	2035
MIT	16.0	548	483	518	535	709	691[2]	928	1176	1208	1157	1083	882	774	701
MIT	8.0	497	350	403	423	604	584[2]	829	1056	1088	1047	981	796	681	584
JH	6.4	442	292	385	413	603	555	791	1051	1105	999	950	804	647	613
MIT	4.0	431	213	315	342	524	512[2]	743	950	985	947	892	711	598	500
JH	3.2	399	197	312	348	533	489	718	955	1017	910	867	729	578	551
MIT	2.0	394	155[1]	274	297	458	448[2]	656	840	872	837	794	634	539	442
JH	1.6	346	150	261	298	468	429	634	850	901	806	770	649	508	481
JH	0.8	294	112	217	249	393	358	535	729	774	691	660	555	436	409
JH	0.4	245	88	179	207	322	296	446	603	653	572	549	462	360	334

[1] Questionable due to light winds.   [2] Mean for period 0405 to 0500 CST.

4.1.b. 15-min mean wind speed (cm sec⁻¹) from standard three-cup anemometers (Mass. Inst. Tech.), modified Sheppard-type anemometers (University of California), and ping-pong ball anemometers (Iowa State College); centered at indicated CST. ISC data are 10-min means centered at indicated CST.

Inst. Set	Height (m)	8 August 1835	2035	2235	9 August 1953 0035	0235	0435	0635	0835	1035	1235	1435	1635	1835	2035
MIT	16.0	520	497	490	551	736	686	919	1193	1237	1183	1074	834	787	726
MIT	8.0	480	348	382	439	632	584	811	1068	1115	1068	976	760	689	608
UCLA	8.0	457[1]	364	386	436	624	597	860	1154	1242[1]	1146	—	862	704	650
ISC	7.0	435	325	340	415	605	552	812	1100	1054	1034	906	729	676	607
UCLA	4.15	400[1]	261	314	363	538	518	740	1026	1113[1]	1026	936	774	631	566
MIT	4.0	415	209	301	365	551	510	726	963	1010	970	885	672	605	524
ISC	4.0	366	237	300	361	552	508	709	1018	971	948	838	675	622	549
MIT	2.0	382	155	257	311	480	446	638	855	889	861	791	601	540	466
UCLA	2.0	356[1]	174	250	298	467	442	662	884	970[1]	887	794	670	552	487
UCLA	1.0	306[1]	124	201	248	394	368	558	748	818[1]	744	678	570	464	406
ISC	1.0	264	208	200	263	400	361	565	775	734	728	631	512	465	403
UCLA	0.5	258[1]	100	166	204	324	306	468	628	684[1]	633	566	476	387	337

[1] 10-min mean centered at tabulated time.

4.2. Mean air temperature (°C) from aspirated thermocouples (Mass. Inst. Tech., 15-min means; University of California, average of six readings taken every 3 min), and shielded thermocouples (Johns Hopkins University, average of 20 readings at each level during a 5-min interval); centered at indicated CST.

Inst. Set	Height (m)	8 August 1835	2035	2235	9 August 1953 0035	0235	0435	0635	0835	1035	1235	1435	1635	1835	2035
MIT	16.0	23.60	20.42	17.50	16.03	16.79	15.90	17.06	21.37	25.17	27.41	29.51	31.46	29.86	26.36
MIT	8.0	23.66	18.88	17.05	15.73	16.67	15.78	17.10	21.69	25.57	27.83	29.89	31.67	29.85	26.13
UCLA[1]	8.0	23.33[2]	16.56	16.39	14.94	16.11	15.06	16.17	20.83	24.72	28.06	29.44	30.78	29.22	25.50
JH	6.4	22.98	17.81	16.53	15.21	16.19	15.35	16.55	21.33	24.94	27.64	29.32	30.94	29.53	25.81
MIT	4.0	23.70	17.30	16.70	15.52	16.55	15.70	17.09	21.77	25.76	28.08	29.95	31.55	29.73	25.93
JH	3.2	23.00[2]	16.84	16.15	14.99	16.04	15.27	16.62	21.76	25.31	28.12	29.69	31.15	29.43	25.57
MIT	2.0	23.60	16.40	16.40	15.30	16.40	15.60	17.10	22.00	26.10	28.40	30.30	31.70	29.60	25.70
UCLA	2.0	23.33[2]	16.00	15.78	14.44	15.61	14.86	16.22	21.44	24.89	27.83	30.06	31.11	28.89	25.06
JH	1.6	22.98	16.24	15.93	14.70	15.90	15.11	16.65	22.04	25.83	28.44	30.09	31.33	29.41	25.35
UCLA	1.0	23.89[2]	15.33	15.33	14.17	15.61	14.58	16.28	21.56	24.89	28.39	30.28	31.39	29.00	24.67
JH	0.8	22.98	15.76	15.65	14.50	15.72	14.99	16.70	22.22	26.16	29.07	30.49	31.55	29.22	25.13
UCLA	0.5	23.89[2]	15.06	15.44	13.72	15.39	14.58	16.56	21.83	24.83	29.17	30.83	31.72	29.11	24.72
JH	0.4	22.98	15.41	15.41	14.34	15.53	14.92	16.72	22.46	26.74	29.52	30.85	31.70	29.10	24.95
JH	0.2	22.96	14.95	15.17	14.13	15.33	14.79	16.72	22.78	27.23	30.12	31.35	31.84	29.00	24.67
JH	0.1	23.16	14.75	14.99	14.03	15.22	14.70	16.78	22.96	27.72	30.67	31.67	31.96	28.90	24.46

[1] No UCLA data for 4.0 m level due to open circuit.   [2] Average of three readings.

4.3.a. Mean water vapor pressure (mb) from dew-point apparatus (Johns Hopkins University). Simultaneous air sampling at given intake levels. Values are 5-min averages centered at indicated CST.

Height (m)	8 August 1835	2035	2235	9 August 1953 0035	0235	0435	0635	0835	1035	1235	1435	1635	1835	2035
6.4	14.73	14.44	14.25	14.02	14.40	14.70	14.84	15.38	—	16.43	16.81	17.72	19.14	18.29
3.2	14.90	14.34	13.98	13.96	14.86	14.67	15.04	15.69	—	17.42	17.24	17.92	18.63	18.35
1.6	15.11	14.26	14.16	13.59	14.53	14.65	15.12	15.90	—	17.39	17.88	18.13	18.85	18.47
0.8	15.30	14.20	14.14	13.53	14.68	14.61	15.01	15.93	—	17.29	18.36	18.41	19.08	18.55
0.4	15.50	14.08	14.12	13.44	14.71	14.80	15.00	16.12	—	17.56	18.61	18.71	19.21	18.66
0.2	15.69	14.01	14.02	13.52	14.71	14.84	15.38	16.19	—	17.81	19.02	19.02	19.37	18.82
0.1	15.82	14.61	14.08	13.60	14.68	14.56	16.91	16.45	—	18.07	19.73	19.40	19.57	18.88

4.3.b. Mean vertical difference (between 82 and 39 cm) of dry-bulb temperature (10^{-3}°C) and water vapor pressure (10^{-3} mb) from double psychrometer lift-apparatus (University of Wisconsin). Values are hourly means (based on one sample every 10 min); centered at indicated CST.

	8 August 1835	2035	2235	9 August 1953 0035	0235	0435	0635	0835	1035	1235	1435	1635	1835	2035
10^{-3} °C	71	449	254	241	197	149	165	−224	−518	−531	−414	−299	63	207
10^{-3} mb	−141	268	96	130	132	67	—	−237	−553	−551	−346[1]	−514	−155	167

[1] Doubtful due to scarcity of measurements at this hour.

4.4. Mean ozone concentration (10^{-8} g O_3/g air) from automatic ozone recorders (University of New Mexico). Values are 60-min means estimated from traces on chart recorders centered at indicated CST.

Height (m)	8 August 1830	2030	2230	9 August 1953 0030	0230	0430	0630	0830	1030	1230	1430	1630	1830
12.5	4.9	4.1	3.9	3.8	4.1	3.8	4.0	—	—	6.5	6.9	7.5	7.5
6.25	4.5	3.4	3.5	3.4	3.8	3.4	3.8	4.6	5.5	5.9	6.3	6.9	7.2
1.6	4.6	2.8	3.4	3.3	3.9	3.6	3.8	4.6	5.5	5.9	6.2	6.9	7.0
0.4	4.6	2.4	3.2	3.1	3.7	3.4	3.8	4.8	5.9	6.3	6.8	7.5	7.4

6.1.b. Loeser technique of night-time wind profile measurements (GRD). Median values of West and South components u, v (m/sec) of drift; number N of balloons of a pibal swarm which cross the indicated levels. Basic data are overlapping 24-sec mean displacements toward the East and North of each of the N balloons at 12-sec intervals during a 4-min period centered at indicated CST.

Height (m)	8 August 2035 u	v	N	2235 u	v	N	9 August 1953 0035 u	v	N	0235 u	v	N	0435 u	v	N
1800	—	—	—	2.0	3.4	1	—	—	—	—	—	—	—	—	—
1600	—	—	—	1.2	1.6	2	—	—	—	—	—	—	—	—	—
1400	7.0	2.5	2	2.7	1.0	4	—	—	—	—	—	—	5.7	4.1	1
1200	9.8	5.6	3	9.2	3.6	5	—	—	—	—	—	—	6.9	4.7	2
1000	7.5	7.1	4	9.6	6.4	7	—	—	—	—	—	—	9.0	6.4	3
800	3.4	7.0	7	5.9	9.4	7	—	—	—	6.4	12.1	1	9.0	9.2	3
700	1.7	8.0	8	3.6	8.9	7	4.8	9.5	2	5.5	12.1	1	6.0	11.9	4
600	0.2	8.2	7	2.2	10.0	7	3.7	11.9	4	5.5	12.5	3	5.3	13.8	4
500	−2.3	8.3	6	−1.5	11.6	6	1.7	13.7	5	5.0	15.4	4	5.0	15.3	2
400	−3.1	8.3	5	−3.0	12.4	6	−1.0	14.3	6	2.4	16.4	3	3.5	16.3	3
300	−4.6	8.8	5	−4.1	14.3	5	−2.7	15.6	5	1.1	17.7	4	1.8	17.7	4
200	−5.4	9.4	5	−3.6	13.8	4	−3.5	16.5	5	−0.3	18.5	5	1.2	19.1	4
100	−6.9	8.6	2	3.1	11.5	1	−2.6	13.2	3	−0.8	13.8	4	0.2	14.2	1

6.2. Rawinsonde (GMD-1A) wind speed (m/sec) and direction (deg from North) from 2-min mean drift at 60-sec intervals, at indicated height (m), for first 7 min of ascent started at indicated CST.

8 August 1835 m	m/sec	deg	2035 m	m/sec	deg	2235 m	m/sec	deg	9 August 1953 0035 m	m/sec	deg	0235 m	m/sec	deg
2182	2.8	316	2315	2.2	350	1326	7.5	275	2017	6.3	250	2314	5.9	260
1888	3.6	280	1995	1.0	308	1120	4.6	264	1748	4.0	252	2035	5.6	285
1609	3.9	253	1677	5.8	228	919	9.6	198	1476	1.3	223	1731	4.4	269
1342	3.9	254	1368	8.8	242	715	11.3	207	1193	2.9	214	1392	4.8	231
1107	4.5	225	1061	10.1	223	530	10.5	187	906	6.8	212	1050	9.8	209
687	6.5	158	720	9.4	186	345	12.6	167	615	11.0	192	705	15.0	199
316	6.6	127	360	10.8	153	167	11.7	160	327	14.7	170	357	17.3	185

9 August 1953 0435 m	m/sec	deg	0635 m	m/sec	deg	0835 m	m/sec	deg	1035 m	m/sec	deg	1244 m	m/sec	deg
1877	5.8	209	1928	6.8	211	2210	10.2	227	2025	7.4	207	2243	10.3	233
1600	4.5	228	1680	7.7	203	1952	8.4	202	1785	11.9	184	1960	11.4	214
1325	5.3	229	1401	6.6	199	1651	6.4	196	1518	14.9	180	1681	14.3	207
1073	9.0	226	1122	8.7	203	1360	8.5	182	1238	15.6	192	1357	14.7	206
809	12.9	213	841	14.7	207	1051	14.8	191	940	17.5	196	1033	12.2	198
554	14.8	196	562	18.1	201	741	20.3	199	619	16.4	189	696	11.9	181
287	15.7	184	283	18.5	188	431	20.4	191	305	15.0	179	346	5.9	176

C

9 August 1953

1435			1635			1835			2035		
m	m/sec	deg	m	m/sec	deg	m	m/sec	deg	m	m/sec	deg
2228	10.4	277	2240	10.8	266	—	—	—	1925	9.5	277
2015	10.0	275	1980	11.5	264	1771	10.9	244	1650	8.6	262
1801	10.5	252	1678	11.3	243	1510	9.4	237	1372	8.6	240
1521	11.4	230	1369	11.3	222	1249	9.5	222	1099	12.2	218
1224	10.6	215	1053	11.9	198	986	10.1	203	820	15.4	203
886	10.2	198	740	14.4	197	688	14.2	198	600	14.6	196
455	11.3	185	400	11.0	183	364	13.1	168	380	16.4	170

6.3. Double theodolite pibal wind speed (m/sec) and direction (deg from North) from 1-min mean drift at 30-sec intervals, at indicated height (m), for first 7 min of ascent started at indicated CST.

8 August   9 August 1953

2030			2130			2330			0130			0330			0530		
m	m/sec	deg	m	m/sec	deg	m	m/sec	deg	m	m/sec	deg	m	m/sec	deg	m	m/sec	deg
659	8.2	178	626	10.6	178	440	14.1	182	731	9.8	205	814	10.1	231	1606	5.9	218
614	15.0	212	593	12.0	170	398	15.5	178	664	16.8	196	781	7.4	245	1484	5.7	217
552	8.7	166	525	11.0	167	368	12.6	175	601	11.6	200	747	12.0	210	1344	5.9	221
520	8.0	163	494	10.1	167	336	14.1	169	566	14.2	195	651	15.2	202	1228	6.0	228
482	8.8	159	431	12.3	166	298	15.3	170	503	17.7	192	596	12.5	206	1134	7.6	231
430	10.7	154	388	10.8	162	268	15.6	161	452	16.7	192	540	13.9	200	1026	9.5	225
372	9.8	152	365	12.2	159	230	12.5	159	404	18.3	188	484	14.3	197	909	12.0	222
334	9.4	149	319	13.5	158	208	15.2	156	352	16.3	184	430	16.2	189	796	14.3	213
287	11.0	146	270	13.4	156	175	19.2	155	312	14.6	181	358	15.6	185	665	15.5	201
238	11.4	144	238	13.3	154	144	18.2	155	267	16.8	175	316	14.3	183	556	17.2	197
190	11.6	142	186	13.1	155	100	15.0	154	217	17.3	171	274	17.3	178	464	17.0	196
140	11.1	140	155	13.7	154	78	10.5	152	177	18.4	170	213	18.0	176	393	17.9	192
102	9.8	139	94	12.9	150	56	12.3	151	110	17.5	170	142	15.2	176	277	20.8	188
47	7.6	136	61	9.7	149	34	9.4	150	48	11.7	171	84	10.2	174	154	17.4	185

9 August 1953

0830			1030			1230			1430			1530			1730		
m	m/sec	deg	m	m/sec	deg	m	m/sec	deg	m	m/sec	deg	m	m/sec	deg	m	m/sec	deg
820	11.4	198	1205	19.0	192	875	15.9	182	1030	13.2	200	854	16.4	192	954	10.8	196
764	15.3	201	1138	17.0	196	764	15.3	184	982	14.1	199	770	15.6	190	892	11.5	194
712	17.6	201	1092	16.2	202	726	12.4	186	894	13.4	200	712	12.8	190	804	10.8	191
656	16.6	204	1060	16.1	205	667	16.0	184	820	12.8	197	657	13.6	186	745	10.2	187
604	18.3	203	1014	17.0	204	613	13.2	183	763	12.6	191	597	13.7	185	664	12.6	183
538	19.5	200	949	19.4	202	607	12.5	179	686	11.7	186	542	14.1	184	576	10.9	183
475	18.4	196	872	17.4	196	580	16.2	177	597	11.0	182	477	13.9	182	512	9.8	184
415	21.4	190	784	15.5	186	544	14.6	177	531	10.4	183	416	13.8	177	444	11.0	182
334	19.8	190	707	15.5	183	541	16.1	178	470	11.4	183	356	15.2	172	374	10.6	176
286	14.5	188	568	14.8	182	437	17.9	179	416	12.0	181	298	15.0	168	300	10.5	173
225	15.1	183	438	14.1	178	362	14.4	179	361	11.3	181	238	13.4	132	232	10.1	172
162	15.2	179	326	14.3	183	248	13.4	176	306	10.9	179	184	13.7	158	168	10.1	168
114	15.7	178	220	14.3	186	174	12.2	173	210	11.1	171	118	13.3	155	114	10.1	166
65	14.8	181	96	13.6	182	67	13.3	176	88	11.2	168	56	10.1	153	68	10.8	164

6.4. Radiosonde pressure (mb), temperature (°C), and relative humidity (%) at significant levels of ascent started at indicated CST. (M = "motorboating", i.e., a humidity value below the minimum value that the radiosonde can measure at that temperature.)

	8 August		9 August 1953											
	1835	2035	2235	0035	0235	0435	0635	0835	1035	1244	1435	1635	1835	2035
mb	950	949	950	949	948	947	946	946	945	944	943	942	941	942
°C	23.8	16.2	16.6	15.0	16.0	15.3	17.0	23.0	27.1	29.0	31.0	32.5	29.5	25.0
%	54	83	78	86	82	87	66	52	47	46	40	40	50	61
mb	811	934	933	932	924	908	902	903	860	829	822	790	814	925
°C	15.0	20.9	19.5	18.5	18.8	19.1	21.4	19.1	19.2	15.5	19.3	17.6	20.3	27.1
%	52	—	73	83	74	77	51	54	65	72	65	57	60	52
mb	791	829	894	882	894	876	816	890	845	766	751	748	733	844
°C	17.1	16.7	18.5	19.0	19.7	18.5	20.6	22.1	20.9	15.7	17.9	17.0	14.7	24.8
%	20	M	63	57	53	58	50	51	63	52	42	38	M	51
mb	736	772	870	857	862	848	748	839	774	739	693	660	—	722
°C	13.0	15.9	18.5	18.4	18.0	20.0	13.9	22.0	17.6	13.6	13.5	8.5	—	13.5
%	M	M	52	65	63	70	61	49	52	43	46	45	—	53
mb	700	747	835	832	824	—	736	735	755	630	540	—	—	680
°C	11.4	14.6	16.5	18.8	18.6	—	13.9	15.1	17.6	4.0	−4.7	—	—	10.2
%	22	M	M	52	47	—	34	56	50	57	78	—	—	40
mb	627	604	790	822	776	788	698	657	702	—	—	—	—	634
°C	5.4	2.2	16.7	18.6	14.8	15.3	10.0	8.8	13.5	—	—	—	—	4.7
%	M	M	20	27	44	63	61	28	51	—	—	—	—	38
mb	585	—	720	810	746	760	682	591	605	—	—	—	—	—
°C	0.9	—	11.6	17.6	11.7	12.9	8.5	1.4	3.5	—	—	—	—	—
%	M	—	M	20	57	73	20	40	58	—	—	—	—	—
mb	—	—	640	778	721	720	599	—	—	—	—	—	—	—
°C	—	—	4.2	15.5	10.6	10	2.3	—	—	—	—	—	—	—
%	—	—	M	18	22	55	22	—	—	—	—	—	—	—
mb	—	—	—	662	710	693	—	—	—	—	—	—	—	—
°C	—	—	—	5.7	10.1	8.9	—	—	—	—	—	—	—	—
%	—	—	—	M	21	—	—	—	—	—	—	—	—	—
mb	—	—	—	583	688	588	—	—	—	—	—	—	—	—
°C	—	—	—	−2.1	8.6	−1.5	—	—	—	—	—	—	—	—
%	—	—	—	M	M	—	—	—	—	—	—	—	—	—
mb	—	—	—	—	545	544	—	—	—	—	—	—	—	—
°C	—	—	—	—	−5.1	−4.7	—	—	—	—	—	—	—	—
%	—	—	—	—	M	M	—	—	—	—	—	—	—	—

7.1. Representative values of West and South components of the wind u, v (m/sec) at standard heights. Values are estimated from the combination of pibal swarm, rawinsonde and double theodolite pibal data at or near the indicated CST.

Height (m)	8 August 1835[1]	2035	2235	9 August 1953 0035	0235	0435	0635	0835	1035	1235	1435	1635	1835[1]	2035[1]
u 2000	2.1	1.0	2.4	4.2	5.7	4.1	3.1	3.0	1.3	7.0	10.8	11.2	10.4	9.8
1750	3.4	2.3	1.4	2.7	4.5	3.7	2.9	1.9	−0.1	6.6	10.0	10.1	9.5	8.1
1500	4.5	5.6	2.0	1.0	3.2	4.3	2.8	0.9	−0.5	6.4	8.8	8.7	8.6	7.3
1250	5.1	9.3	8.5	1.6	3.7	5.9	2.9	0.1	2.4	5.9	7.1	7.2	7.2	8.4
1000	2.2	7.0	8.0	3.8	5.6	8.3	5.5	3.4	6.3	3.0	4.5	5.4	5.9	6.5
800	−0.1	3.6	6.0	5.0	5.9	8.3	7.8	6.2	3.8	1.1	3.0	3.7	4.8	5.6
700	−2.3	1.3	4.0	4.8	5.7	6.1	7.6	6.8	2.6	0.4	2.1	2.8	4.2	4.7
600	−4.6	−0.9	2.0	3.8	5.3	5.2	6.7	6.8	1.8	−0.2	1.4	2.0	3.6	4.0
500	−5.2	−2.6	−0.8	1.9	4.7	4.8	5.4	5.6	1.0	−0.5	0.7	1.2	2.5	2.5
400	−5.5	−3.6	−2.6	−0.5	2.5	3.3	4.3	3.5	0.4	−0.7	0.2	0.1	0.1	−0.5
300	−5.5	−5.1	−4.3	−2.6	0.8	1.7	3.1	2.2	0.0	−1.0	−0.2	−1.3	−7.0	−5.5
200	−5.4	−6.1	−4.2	−4.0	−0.7	0.8	2.0	1.3	−0.4	−1.1	−0.6	−1.8	−11.6	−10.3
100	−5.3	−6.6	−3.6	−3.1	−1.0	0.0	0.9	0.8	−0.8	−1.0	−1.0	−1.9	−12.7	−11.2
v 2000	−0.1	5.9	4.6	2.8	0.1	5.0	6.2	7.4	8.4	9.9	1.2	0.7	3.4	−1.8
1750	0.2	4.6	3.1	1.4	0.4	3.5	6.0	6.8	12.1	11.5	4.5	4.3	4.3	0.4
1500	0.6	1.9	1.8	0.5	1.7	3.3	5.8	6.7	14.5	12.6	7.4	7.1	4.3	2.8
1250	1.7	5.4	2.6	2.0	4.3	4.2	5.5	9.9	15.8	13.0	9.0	9.3	7.0	5.6
1000	4.3	7.4	6.7	5.1	8.4	6.8	9.0	14.3	16.7	13.4	10.8	11.0	9.1	13.5
800	5.4	8.1	8.8	8.0	11.6	9.6	12.4	17.5	17.0	13.5	11.8	11.9	11.0	14.4
700	5.6	8.5	9.3	8.4	13.0	12.4	14.1	18.5	16.7	13.5	12.0	12.1	13.1	13.9
600	5.6	8.8	10.0	11.6	14.1	14.0	15.9	19.7	16.3	13.4	12.1	12.2	16.5	13.2
500	5.5	8.9	11.1	13.5	15.4	15.2	16.3	20.5	15.9	13.3	12.2	12.2	17.0	12.8
400	5.0	9.0	12.4	14.6	16.7	16.3	18.9	20.8	15.4	13.0	12.3	12.1	14.4	12.2
300	3.7	9.1	14.5	15.4	17.8	17.9	20.0	20.7	15.0	12.6	12.3	11.9	10.5	14.5
200	2.6	9.0	13.6	16.5	18.5	19.0	18.6	20.3	14.7	12.3	11.9	11.4	8.9	23.6[2]
100	2.3	8.4	11.4	14.0	15.0	15.0	17.0	20.0	14.3	12.0	11.0	10.9	8.5	26.2[2]

[1] Rawinsonde data only.   [2] Data affected by cold front approach.

7.2.a. Air temperature (°C) at standard heights. Values are interpolated from radiosonde data at or near the indicated CST.

Height (m)	8 August 1835	2035	2235	9 August 1953 0035	0235	0435	0635	0835	1035	1235	1435	1635	1835	2035
2000	15.1	15.0	14.0	13.8	13.3	12.5	14.6	16.6	17.6	15.1	18.0	17.1	16.7	16.7
1750	16.3	16.0	15.8	15.4	15.6	14.3	16.8	18.1	17.7	15.7	18.4	17.4	18.1	18.8
1500	16.1	16.3	16.6	16.9	17.1	16.3	19.0	19.6	18.8	15.6	18.8	18.6	19.5	20.9
1250	15.9	16.6	16.5	18.6	18.6	18.1	20.7	21.1	19.9	15.5	19.3	21.0	21.0	2.3
1000	17.4	17.4	17.2	18.6	18.2	20.0	20.9	22.0	20.6	17.7	21.6	23.3	22.7	24.9
800	18.7	18.2	18.3	18.6	18.0	19.0	21.1	22.1	19.9	20.0	23.5	25.1	24.0	25.4
600	20.0	19.0	15.5	18.9	19.3	18.7	21.3	22.2	21.6	22.2	25.4	27.0	25.4	26.0
400	21.2	19.8	19.2	18.9	19.3	19.0	20.8	19.5	23.5	24.5	27.2	28.8	26.1	26.6
200	22.5	20.6	20.4	18.6	18.5	17.3	18.9	21.2	25.2	26.7	29.1	30.6	28.1	27.0
100	23.1	19.8	20.0	17.3	17.2	16.3	17.9	22.1	26.2	27.9	30.1	31.6	28.8	26.0

7.2.b. Mixing ratio (g water vapor/kg air) at standard heights. Values are interpolated from radiosonde data at or near the indicated CST.

Height (m)	8 August 1835	2035	2235	9 August 1953 0035	0235	0435	0635	0835	1035	1235	1435	1635	1835	2035
2000	—	—	—	—	8.7	8.6	8.3	8.7	8.5	7.1	7.5	6.8	—	8.8
1750	—	—	—	2.6	6.1	8.8	8.7	9.0	8.7	8.1	8.9	8.4	—	9.8
1500	4.7	—	—	2.9	6.9	9.5	9.2	9.3	9.7	8.8	10.2	9.5	—	10.8
1250	7.0	—	—	5.4	7.8	10.9	9.5	9.6	10.8	9.5	11.5	10.0	11.4	11.8
1000	7.8	—	8.5	9.1	8.8	12.3	9.3	9.8	11.5	10.2	11.7	10.5	12.0	12.7

Height (m)	8 August 1835	2035	2235	9 August 1953 0035	0235	0435	0635	0835	1035	1235	1435	1635	1835	2035
800	8.4	—	9.0	9.3	9.3	10.1	9.2	9.7	10.7	10.7	11.9	10.9	12.4	12.8
600	9.0	—	9.6	9.4	8.5	10.0	9.1	9.6	10.9	11.2	12.0	12.4	12.9	13.0
400	9.6	—	9.9	10.8	9.8	11.9	9.0	8.5	11.0	11.7	12.2	12.8	13.4	13.1
200	10.2	—	10.0	12.2	11.8	11.2	8.8	9.1	11.2	12.2	12.3	13.2	13.8	13.2
100	10.5	—	10.0	11.7	10.9	10.7	8.7	9.4	11.2	12.4	12.4	13.4	14.1	13.2

7.3.a. Summary of heat budget constituents (mcal cm^{-2} min^{-1}) of the earth-air interface according to the theoretical models by Suomi, Halstead, and Lettau. Net radiation flux R, heat transfer to the soil S, sensible heat transfer to the air Q, and latent heat transfer to the air (heat equivalent of evaporation) E. Values are hourly means centered at indicated CST.

	8 August 1835	2035	2235	9 August 1953 0035	0235	0435	0635	0835	1035	1235	1435	1635	1835
Suomi													
R_0	36	101	101	103	106	85	−68	−521	−712	−774	−753	−391	19
S_0	−153	−86	−71	−70	−62	−57	−41	266	90	108	105	40	−93
Q_0	−68	−8	−18	−17	−21	−16	—	116	226	257	273	92	−24
E_0	185	−7	−12	−16	−23	−12	—	139	396	419	375	259	98
Halstead													
R_0	—	90	80	80	80	70	−20	−470	−710	−830	−800	−460	−20
S_0	—	−62	−67	−68	−55	−57	−23	37	100	112	110	28	−23
Q_0	—	−73	−70	−57	−60	−33	13	218	442	377	277	97	—
E_0	—	−30	0	10[1]	30	−18	75	295	305[1]	413	630	393	177
Lettau													
R_0	6	97	92	94	96	79	−49	−500	−711	−796	−772	−419	3
S_0	−153	−74	−69	−69	−58	−57	−39	144	121	152	107	34	−58
Q_0	−9	−11	−27	−28	−51	−31	−31	141	344	339	255	110	−29
E_0	57	−23	−14	−30	−10	2	37	145	307	244	266	248	78

[1] Interpolated value.

7.3.b. Representative logarithmic height derivatives of wind speed (zV', mm sec^{-1}, from UCLA and JH data), potential temperature ($z\theta'$, 10^{-3} °C, from JH and UW data), and water vapor pressure (ze', 10^{-3} mb, from JH and UW data); representative values of Karman number k (from zV' and UCLA, JH, and MIT stress data), interpolated ground drag τ_0 (dynes cm^{-2}, from zV' and representative k values), and ratio of heat and momentum diffusivities N_Q; representative ground-flux ratio F_0 and inverse Bowen ratio B. Values refer to indicated CST and are employed in the computation of the heat budget constituents Q_0 and E_0 (Lettau model; see Table 7.3.a).

	8 August 1835	2035	2235	9 August 1953 0035	0235	0435	0635	0835	1035	1235	1435	1635	1835
zV'	702	405	551	636	1017	918	1309	1728	1799	1625	1568	1324	1031
$z\theta'$	52	563	337	277	252	164	90	−273	−620	−683	−505	−305	147
ze'	−216	230	75	132	27	−5	75[1]	−223	−459	−409	−458	−518	−216
k	0.38	0.30	0.36	0.36	0.37	0.37	0.38	0.38	0.38	0.38	0.39	0.38	0.37
τ_0	0.80	0.17	0.46	0.62	1.65	1.34	2.83	4.87	5.22	4.22	3.96	2.76	1.61
N_Q	1.07	0.32	0.66	0.70	0.86	0.88	1.07	1.26	1.33	1.33	1.40	1.20	0.90
F_0	−17[2]	0.66	0.57	0.65	0.65	0.64	−3.1[2]	3.21	2.27	2.52	3.61	4.20	−1.66
B	−7[2]	0.66	0.36	0.77	0.17	−0.05	1.4[2]	1.31	1.18	0.95	1.45	2.71	−2.35

[1] Questionable value; −75 used for computation of E_0.   [2] Value disregarded for evaluation of N_Q.

7.4. Richardson number (Ri; units of 10^{-3}) from Mass. Inst. Tech. and Johns Hopkins University data on simultaneous temperature and wind velocity differences, centered at indicated CST and mean height z_m (meters). (Ri') = average height derivative of Richardson number (10^{-3} m^{-1}).

Inst. Set	Height (m)	8 August 1835	2035	2235	9 August 1953 0035	0235	0435	0635	0835	1035	1235	1435	1635	1835	2035
MIT	8.0	−21	150	84	74	42	36	−9	−20	−26	−31	−30	−13	34	65
MIT	4.0	2	124	75	67	31	25	−2	−11	−13	−15	−16	−4	31	50
JH	3.2	8	120	64	64	28	28	−3	−26	−29	−29	−32	−20	13	42
JH	1.6	0	114	43	39	13	13	−1	−6	−10	−14	−13	−9	8	17
JH	0.8	0	82	30	17	7	4	−1	−2	−5	−7	−6	−4	5	7
(Ri')		−1	34	17	15	7	6	−1	−4	−5	−5	−6	−3	5	10

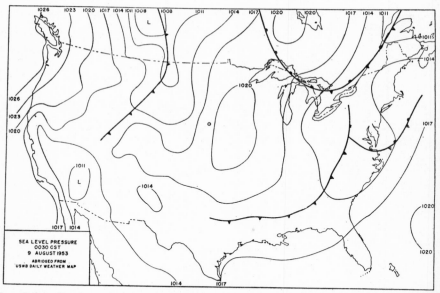

Fig. B.1.1. Continental scale synoptic chart. Sea level pressure distribution for the first general observation period.

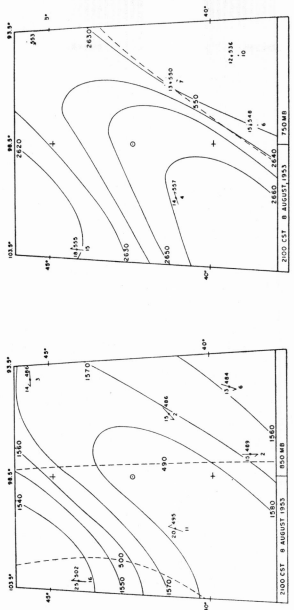

Fig. B.1.2.a. Local synoptic charts. Topographies of the 850 and 750 mb surfaces at 2100 CST, 8 August 1953.

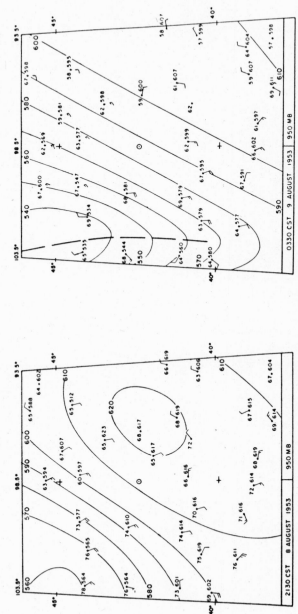

FIG. B.1.3.a. Local synoptic charts. Topography of the 950 mb surface at 2130 CST, 8 August, and 0330 CST, 9 August 1953.

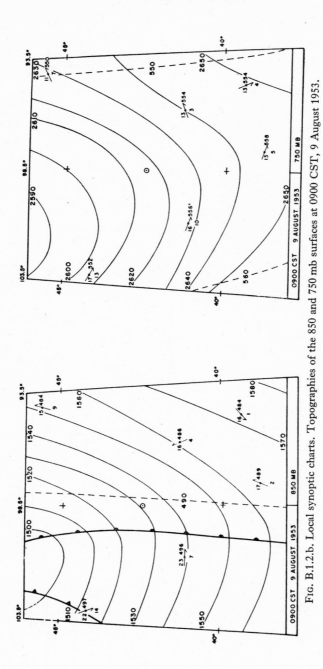

FIG. B.1.2.b. Local synoptic charts. Topographies of the 850 and 750 mb surfaces at 0900 CST, 9 August 1953.

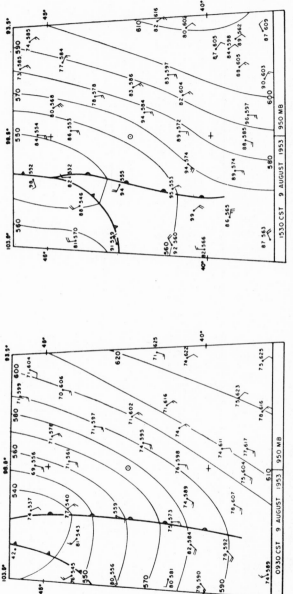

FIG. B.1.3.b. Local synoptic charts. Topography of the 950 mb surface at 0930 and 1530 CST, 9 August 1953.

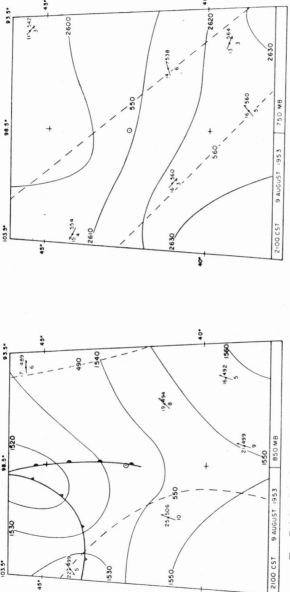

FIG. B.1.2.c. Local synoptic charts. Topographies of the 850 and 750 mb surfaces at 2100 CST, 9 August 1953.

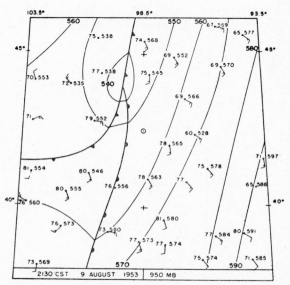

Fig. B.1.3.c. Local synoptic chart. Topography of the 950 mb surfaces at 2130 CST, 9 August 1953.

SECOND GENERAL OBSERVATION PERIOD

0405 CST 13 August through 0305 CST 14 August 1953

Solar Data for the Field Site near O'Neill, Nebraska

	Sun's elevation angle at apparent noon	Sunrise CST	Apparent noon CST	Sunset CST
13 August	62° 07′	0539	1239	1939
14 August	61° 48′	0540	1239	1938

Summary of Synoptic Conditions

On 10 August a cold type occlusion moved through the area from the north-west accompanied by scattered thunderstorms and a wind shift from south to north, passing Norfolk, Nebraska, and Sioux Falls, South Dakota, on the night of the 10th. The skies were generally clear, becoming overcast in the vicinity of the front.

On the 11th the frontal system moved out of the area to the east. A high-pressure cell, centered over Montana, moved rapidly southeastward and dominated the entire western part of the United States by 12 August. Winds were northerly backing to westerly at 5 to 10 mph with the southeastward displacement of the high center. The skies were overcast during the day and clear at night.

On the 12th, the high cell was dissipating while a weak trough developed in the Great Plains area oriented through Western Nebraska. A cold front approached from the north-northwest. The winds were westerly on the 12th, backing to southerly on the 13th at 10 to 15 mph. There were no clouds in the area. The second general observation period was begun on 13 August at 0405 CST. The cold front accompanied by clear skies passed through the area during the early morning of the 14th. The resulting wind shift to the northwest forced the termination of the second observation period at 0305 CST. Several hours after the frontal passage there were thunderstorms in the area. A ridge of high pressure to the northwest oriented northwest-southeast moved east-southeastward and then stalled northeast of Nebraska on the 15th. The winds were generally northerly shifting to easterly. On the 14th there were scattered clouds, becoming broken to overcast on the 15th.

1.1.a. Mean geopotential H (dynamic m above 610 = geopotential of test site), West and South components of the geostrophic wind u_g, v_g (m/sec) at indicated pressure (mb) levels. Values are estimated for the O'Neill site from local synoptic charts.

		13 Aug. 0900		13 Aug. 2100	
mb	H	u_g	v_g	u_g	v_g
750	2028	13.1	2.3	13.7	−3.7
800	1477	13.8	3.4	10.4	−3.8
850	952	12.4	4.8	12.7	−3.9
900	454	14.3	5.8	12.6	−4.3
950	−20	13.6	4.4	9.0	−3.1

1.1.b. Direction (deg from North) and speed (m/sec) of the 950 mb geostrophic wind. Values are estimated for the O'Neill site from local synoptic charts.

| | 13 August | | | | | | | 14 August 1953 | |
	0330	0630	0930	1230	1530	1830	2130	0030	0330
deg.	239	243	252	251	253	259	289	015	041
m/sec	14.3	14.3	14.3	14.3	12.5	11.8	9.5	9.1	8.0

1.2. Direction (deg from North) of the mean surface wind from standard vane recordings at 1-min intervals (Mass. Inst. Tech., 16 m level). Hourly and 15-min averages centered at indicated CST.

| | 13 August | | | | | | | | | | 14 August | |
	0435	0635[1]	0835	1035	1235	1435	1635	1835	2035	2235	0035	0235[2]
60-min mean:	196	197	212	209	209	213	204	181	174	180	262	329
15-min mean:	197	197	213	208	209	213	200	178	170	180	297	340

[1] Period 0605-0704 CST.

[2] Values may not be representative since personnel were working on tower from 0231-0251 CST.

1.3. Standard shelter temperature (°F) and relative humidity (%); station pressure (inches) and air density (mg cm^{-3}); amount (tenths) and types of clouds.

Month	Day	CST	Temp.	RH	Pressure	Density	Clouds	Remarks
Aug.	13	0430	69	60	27.991	1.11	0 Sc	Ac on horizon. Light of sunrise just visible
		0630	66	68	.987	1.11	0 Sc	Sc disappearing. Winds shifting to SSW
		0830	75	63	.974	1.11	0 —	
		1030	84	46	.956	1.08	0 —	
		1230	90	44	.924	1.07	0 —	Winds gusty
		1430	95	36	.913	1.06	0 —	Gustiness increasing
		1630	95	34	.899	1.06	0 —	Warm gusty winds
		1830	87	49	.885	1.07	1 Ci	
		2030	75	60	.898	1.10	1 Ci	
		2230	69	69	.903	1.11	1 Ci	Weak front passage. Wind direction shifted from S to WNW to SW to WNW at 0003 then SW at 0019 CST
	14	0030	Missing					
		0230	69	64	28.001	1.12	0 —	Wind direction NNW, steady

2.1.a. Soil temperature (°C) from thermistors (University of Texas) and soil thermocouples (University of California and Johns Hopkins University). Values are readings at indicated CST.

Inst. Set	Depth (cm)	13 August 0435	0635	0835	1035	1235	1435	1635	1835	2035	2235	14 August 0035	0235
UT	0.5	19.16	18.66	24.26	33.32	40.15	40.93	36.78	30.79	25.31	22.64	21.20	20.55
UCLA	1.3	19.17	18.61	21.11	26.72	29.72	37.67	32.89	24.22	24.11	21.72	20.17	19.78
UT	1.5	19.59	18.89	22.93	30.07	35.64	37.23	35.00	30.65	26.18	23.58	22.03	21.18
UT	2.5	20.06	19.28	22.35	28.41	33.65	35.65	34.25	30.63	26.67	24.25	22.71	21.69
JH	2.5	20.42	19.80	20.80	24.12	27.92	29.80	29.69	28.32	25.59	23.84	22.52	21.73
UT	3.5	20.42	19.59	21.95	27.23	32.07	33.99	33.49	30.61	27.07	24.69	23.11	22.01
UT	4.5	20.73	19.79	21.74	26.40	31.04	33.48	33.02	30.45	27.25	24.96	23.43	22.27
JH	5.0	20.94	20.36	20.68	22.90	26.04	28.28	28.76	28.01	25.96	24.38	23.16	22.31
UT	5.5	21.13	20.27	21.72	25.62	29.82	32.54	32.43	30.42	27.59	25.40	23.91	22.78
UCLA	10.0	21.22	20.28	20.44	21.83	21.28	23.44	23.61	22.06	26.11	24.72	23.61	22.61
JH	10.0	21.77	21.25	21.04	22.00	24.01	26.04	27.11	27.20	26.18	25.01	23.98	23.20
JH	20.0	22.45	22.12	21.72	21.65	22.10	23.03	24.00	24.69	24.77	24.53	24.12	23.70
UCLA	25.0	22.50	21.67	21.39	21.11	18.06	18.33	18.06	17.78	23.61	23.61	23.61	23.22
JH	40.0	22.16	22.12	21.95	21.83	21.75	21.74	21.90	22.14	22.37	22.59	22.72	22.80
JH	80.0	20.71	20.70	20.72	20.70	20.70	20.69	20.70	20.72	20.73	20.74	20.74	20.75

Note—UCLA reference thermoelement ice bath renewed between 1840 and 2030 CST on 13 August.

2.1.b. Change of soil temperature ($°C\ hr^{-1}$) averaged over indicated layers from soil temperature integrators (University of Wisconsin). Values are differences between readings at the end and beginning of 1-hr intervals centered at indicated CST.

Depth (cm)	13 August 0435	0635	0835	1035	1235	1435	1635	1835	2035	2235	14 August 0035	0235
0–5	−0.53	0.18	3.84	2.42	1.53	0.02	−0.81	−1.82	−5.06	−1.92	−0.20	−0.52
5–15	−0.27	−0.21	0.33	0.98	1.21	0.78	0.17	−0.38	−0.63	−0.60	−0.44	−0.32
15–50	−0.10	−0.12	−0.10	−0.01	0.15	0.21	0.22	0.18	0.06	−0.01	−0.07	−0.09

2.2.a. Soil thermal conductivity ($mcal\ cm^{-1}\ sec^{-1}\ deg^{-1}$) computed from soil thermistor response to defined heating pulses (University of Texas, Albrecht heat flux meter No. 2). Values are derived from 60-sec trials beginning at indicated CST.

Depth (cm)	13 August 1953 0440	0640	0840	1040	1240
0.5	0.80	0.84	0.75	0.65	0.62
1.5	1.00	0.98	0.99	1.00	1.01
2.5	1.22	1.10	1.06	1.10	1.04
3.5	1.40	1.39	1.31	1.13	1.21
4.5	1.56	1.58	1.61	1.75	1.74
5.5	1.84	1.80	1.73	1.70	1.63

2.2.b. Soil moisture (% wet weight) from soil samples at the Johns Hopkins University site. Approximate time of soil sample extraction is midday.

Depth (cm)	13 August	14 August
4	7.8	6.4
10	6.2	5.6
20	6.2	6.0
40	4.0	3.9

2.2.c. Soil heat capacity (cal cm^{-3} deg^{-1}) from soil samples at the University of Wisconsin site (calorimetric determination). Indicated CST refers to the approximate time of soil sample extraction (0-10 cm layer).

	13 August		14 August 1953
	1600	2300	0100
	0.29	0.34	0.32

2.3. Soil moisture tension (mb) from tensiometers (Johns Hopkins University). Values are readings at indicated CST.

Depth (cm)	13 August 0435	0635	0835	1035	1235	1435	1635	1835	2035	2235	14 August 1953 0035
5	497	450	434	571	642	679	700	730	751	722	673
10	489	457	482	587	673	710	735	749	767	747	709
20	576	516	476	529	623	669	700	721	750	744	727
40	400	254	182	199	279	425	532	609	646	648	597

2.4. Vertical flux of heat (mcal cm^{-2} min^{-1}) from soil temperature integrators (University of Wisconsin), Albrecht heat flux meter No. 2 (University of Texas-Al), Gier and Dunkle heat flow meters (University of California; University of Texas-GD), and numerical integration of soil temperature profile changes (Johns Hopkins University). UW and JH values are 60-min averages, UCLA values are 15-min averages and UT values are approximately 2-min averages. All averages are centered at indicated CST.

Inst. Set	Depth (cm)	13 August 0435	0635	0835	1035	1235	1435	1635	1835	2035	2235	14 August 1953 0035	0235
UW	0.0	−57	−37	106	126	152	98	42	−29	−170	−95	−40	−55
UT-Al	0.0[1]	−36	−35	125	293	387	—	—	—	—	—	—	—
JH	0.0[1]	−43	−30	57	130	173	117	60	−30	−55	−47	−47	—
UCLA	0.2[2]	—	—	—	—	—	299	145	−36	−74	−76	−73	−44
UT-GD	0.2[2]	−32	−22	71	122	282	208	103	−10	—	—	−49	−33
UCLA	1.3	−29	−21	33	82	133	124	83	11	−25	−29	−32	−14
UT-Al	2.0	−31	−24	36	104	122	—	—	—	—	—	—	—
UW	5.0	−41	−42	−7	54	107	98	66	25	−20	−38	−43	−40
UCLA	10.0	−20	−24	2	38	79	84	70	38	−3	−24	−24	−20
UW	15.0	−26	−30	−26	−2	38	54	56	46	16	−4	−18	−22

[1] Values are extrapolated to surface.
[2] Approximate depth; the upper plates of the heat flow meters were "just covered with soil".

3.1. Summary of data on radiation (mcal cm^{-2} min^{-1}). Short-wave radiation from Eppley pyrheliometer (GRD); net radiation from two Gier and Dunkle radiometers (Johns Hopkins University and University of Texas) and the Suomi net radiometer (University of Wisconsin); total radiation from the Gier and Dunkle radiometer (University of Texas). Values are hourly averages centered at indicated CST.

Inst. Set	13 August 0435	0635	0835	1035	1235	1435	1635	1835	2035	2235	14 August 0035	0235
(Short-Wave) GRD	0	50	593	1107	1363	1277	913	487	0	0	0	0
GRD[1]	0	140	730	1200	1380	1210	790	200	0	0	0	0
(Net) JH	−80	0	440	800	950	820	430	0	−60	−80	−60	−70
UT	−102	−22	481	928	1054	864	420	−21	—	—	−107	−116
UW	−110	20	456	807	925	747	336	−44	−99	−94	−66	−63
(Total) UT	481	564	1294	1879	2106	1902	1334	668	—	—	493	500

[1] 10-min average centered at indicated CST.

3.2. Boundary shear-stress (dynes cm^{-2}) from drag recorder (University of California) and Sheppard-type drag plate (Johns Hopkins University); direction of boundary shear-stress (deg from North) from drag recorder (University of California). Values are 10-min means centered at indicated CST.

Inst. Set	13 August 1953 0435	0635	0835	1035	1235	1435	1635	1835	2035	2235[1]
UCLA	—	—	—	—	—	—	—	0.65	0.49	0.66
JH	2.0	1.8	2.3	—	2.7	4.2	2.7	0.2	0.1	0.4
UCLA	—	—	—	—	—	—	—	177	176	176

[1] No data after 2235.

3.3. Characteristics of low-level smoke-puff drift (Johns Hopkins University); direction of drift (deg from North); time t_{25} (sec) required to cross 25 m circle; lateral width S (deg) at 25 m and time t_D (sec) required to reach threshold of visibility. Values are ensemble averages for 10 smoke puffs fired at approximately 1-min intervals beginning at indicated CST.

	13 August 0400	0600	0800	1000	1200	1400	1600	1800	2000	2200	14 August 0000	0200
dd	201	198	216	209	204	215	221	190	186	185	194	125
t_{25}	5.2	5.4	4.7	4.3	4.6	3.7	4.2	7.6	9.8	7.9	9.7	8.2
S	14.9	15.5	13.5	10.4	12.0	10.4	12.7	13.4	9.6	13.2	16.3	17.4
t_D	—	33	20	12	15	16	18	25	—	—	—	—

3.4. Characteristics of surface pressure variations from micro-barograms (GRD, Paulin-type aneroid system); trend (WBAN Synoptic Code number); qualitative index of micro-variations ("a" = calm to "d" = very unruly); trace ratio (trace length relative to trend length); trend ratio (trend length relative to chart length); period (min), amplitude (10^{-2} mb), and number of perceptible waves. Values refer to 2-hr intervals centered at indicated CST.

	13 August 0535	0735	0935	1135	1335	1535	1735	1935	2135	2335	14 Aug. 0135
Trend	7	8	7	7	7	7	6	2	1	2	3
Index	b	b-d	c	c-b	c	c-b	a	a	a	a	a
Trace ratio	1.2	1.8	1.4	1.4	1.4	1.4	1.2	1.05	1.05	1.9	1.4
Trend ratio	1.0	1.0	1.1	1.0	1.2	1.1	1.1	1.2	1.1	1.7	1.7

D

| | 13 August | | | | | | | | | | 14 Aug. 1953 |
	0535	0735	0935	1135	1335	1535	1735	1935	2135	2335	0135
Period	50	25	25	45	10	30	20	25	55	10	10
Ampl.	5	8	6	4	3	5	2.5	3	4	24	10
Number	1	2	2	1	3	2	3	2	1	3	4
Period	—	20	40	5	5	5	—	—	—	—	20
Ampl.	—	4	5	3	2.5	3	—	—	—	—	3
Number	—	1	1	5	5	3	—	—	—	—	2

4.1.a. Hourly mean wind speed (cm/sec) from standard three-cup anemometers (Mass. Inst. Tech.), and modified SCS cup anemometers (Johns Hopkins University); centered at indicated CST.

| Inst. Set | Height (m) | 13 August | | | | | | | | | | 14 August 1953 | |
		0435	0635	0835	1035	1235	1435	1635	1835	2035	2235	0035	0235
MIT	16.0	867	784	943	808	889	1036	851	542	656	682	448	613[1]
MIT	8.0	746	687	851	742	813	942	770	448	481	505	316	492[1]
JH	6.4	754	681	823	759	782	906	769	427	413	460	318	407
MIT	4.0	667	627	785	684	752	867	704	375	370	399	234	381[1]
JH	3.2	672	609	754	—	723	828	700	364	314	364	243	330
MIT	2.0	585	558	701	614	679	775	632	333	301	332	202	324[1]
JH	1.6	592	541	674	628	651	742	628	314	247	300	193	278
JH	0.8	512	473	592	549	574	655	549	270	203	251	162	251
JH	0.4	433	401	502	471	491	559	466	229	166	213	136	217

[1] Values may not be representative since personnel were working on tower from 0231 to 0251 CST.

4.1.b. 15-min mean wind speed (cm/sec) from standard three-cup anemometers (Mass. Inst. Tech.), modified Sheppard-type anemometers (University of California), and ping-pong ball anemometers (Iowa State College); centered at indicated CST.

| Inst. Set | Height (m) | 13 August | | | | | | | | | | 14 August 1953 | |
		0435	0635	0835	1035	1235	1435	1635	1835	2035	2235	0035	0235
MIT	16.0	851	787	956	794	899	1081	841	557	669	696	402	595
MIT	8.0	730	693	861	730	821	980	764	463	493	530	267	507
UCLA	8.0	762	700	878	758	828	938	826	480	508	534	—	491[3]
ISC	7.0	—	—	818	719	767	928	740	443	460	482	257	457
UCLA	4.15	676	626	805	695	736	850	744	409	388	424	—	376[3]
MIT	4.0	655	628	797	679	763	892	696	398	385	405	179[4]	385
ISC	4.0	—	554	754	541[1]	703	824	674	389	377	400	190	381
MIT	2.0	578	561	713	605	686	797	632	351	321	341	155[4]	321
UCLA	2.0	580	548	708	630	664	755	657	346	309	344	—	294[3]
UCLA	1.0	502	480	622	554	578	660	575	299	254	291	242[1]	242
ISC	1.0	469[2]	436	594	527	563	672	535	295	258	281	118	286
UCLA	0.5	426	406	530	475	498	578	492	254	211	244	—	201[3]

[1] Doubtful value   [3] Centered at 0135 CST.
[2] Centered at 0514 CST.   [4] 10-min mean centered at tabulated time.

4.2. Mean air temperature (°C) from aspirated thermocouples (Mass. Inst. Tech., 15-min means; University of California, average of six readings taken every 3 min), and shielded thermocouples (Johns Hopkins University, average of 20 readings at each level during a 5-min interval); centered at indicated CST.

Inst.	Height	13 August										14 August 1953	
Set	(m)	0435	0635	0835	1035	1235	1435	1635	1835	2035	2235	0035	0235
MIT	16.0	20.94	19.53	24.37	28.00	31.47	33.99	34.50	31.93	27.10	23.86	22.30	21.57[2]
MIT	8.0	20.75	19.50	24.65[1]	28.15[1]	31.55	34.03	34.37	31.61	25.58	22.52	20.48	21.33[2]
UCLA	8.0	20.17	18.89	23.89	27.00	28.28	30.44	30.00	25.56	24.83	21.94	20.33	20.89[3]
JH	6.4	20.27	19.26	24.29	27.70	31.49	33.79	34.04	30.80	24.40	21.79	20.45	20.73
MIT	4.0	20.55	19.31	24.53	28.29	31.64	34.08	34.27	31.25	24.64	21.75	19.19	21.03[2]
UCLA	4.0	20.00	18.94	24.06	27.50	28.83	30.83	30.00	25.50	23.89	21.39	19.33	21.00[3]
JH	3.2	20.01	19.22	24.44	28.09	31.95	31.14	34.12	30.63	23.55	21.13	19.15	20.52
MIT	2.0	20.40	19.30	24.80	28.80	32.20	34.50	34.50	31.10	24.20	21.40	18.80	21.00[2]
UCLA	2.0	19.83	18.72	24.39	28.28	29.72	31.11	30.06	25.17	23.33	21.11	18.72	21.00[3]
JH	1.6	19.85	19.18	24.81	28.61	32.60	34.52	34.28	20.34	23.01	20.59	18.69	20.31
UCLA	1.0	19.56	18.61	24.22	28.39	29.44	31.56	30.33	25.06	22.94	20.44	18.00	20.17[2]
JH	0.8	19.65	19.16	24.98	28.96	33.09	34.91	34.44	30.12	22.52	20.17	18.32	20.11
UCLA	0.5	19.39	18.50	24.56	29.00	30.28	32.28	30.56	24.67	22.50	20.11	17.50	20.00[2]
JH	0.4	19.39	19.08	25.19	29.31	33.51	35.25	34.57	29.95	22.17	19.89	17.96	19.86
JH	0.2	19.19	19.04	25.59	29.87	34.16	35.69	34.65	29.75	21.92	19.54	17.24	19.64
JH	0.1	18.95	19.02	25.79	30.32	34.60	35.97	34.77	29.51	21.59	19.26	16.95	19.34

[1] Temperature questionable due to inadequate ventilation.   [2] Values may not be representative.
[3] Average of five readings.

Note—UCLA reference thermocouple ice bath renewed between 1840 and 2030 CST on 13 August.

4.3.a. Mean water vapor pressure (mb) from dew-point apparatus (Johns Hopkins University). Simultaneous air sampling at given intake levels. Values are 5-min averages centered at indicated CST.

Height	13 August										14 August 1953	
(m)	0435	0635	0835	1035	1235	1435	1635	1835	2035	2235	0035	0235
6.4	13.90	14.32	15.00	16.63	18.65	16.96	16.78	18.96	16.65	15.51	14.27	17.44
3.2	13.95	14.34	14.99	16.58	18.88	17.34	17.13	18.96	16.89	15.62	14.42	17.68
1.6	13.98	14.52	15.56	17.23	18.63	17.68	17.67	19.48	17.08	15.72	15.20	17.67
0.8	13.99	14.50	15.53	17.50	19.09	18.26	17.88	20.01	17.14	15.84	15.40	17.74
0.4	14.11	14.44	15.73	18.41	19.50	18.85	18.39	20.12	17.26	15.99	15.09	17.78
0.2	13.99	14.30	16.15	18.50	19.97	19.36	18.66	20.70	17.31	16.05	15.13	17.78
0.1	13.99	14.27	16.45	19.38	20.36	19.61	19.22	20.71	17.46	16.13	15.22	17.98

4.3.b. Mean vertical difference (between 82 and 39 cm) of dry-bulb temperature (10^{-3} °C) and water vapor pressure (10^{-3} mb) from double psychrometer lift-apparatus (University of Wisconsin). Values are hourly means (based on one sample every 10 min) centered at indicated CST.

	13 August										14 August 1953	
	0435	0635	0835	1035	1235	1435	1635	1835	2035	2235	0035	0235
10^{-3} °C	38	63	−305	−516	−579	−366	−128	178	331	—	308	357
10^{-3} mb	−105	−49	−282	−618	−716	−467	−309	−240[1]	−173	—	−46	213

[1] Interpolated value.

4.4. Mean ozone concentration (10^{-8} g O_3/g air) from automatic ozone recorders (University of New Mexico). Values are 60-min means estimated from traces on chart recorders centered at indicated CST.

Height (m)	13 August										14 August 1953	
	0430	0630	0830	1030	1230	1430	1630	1830	2030	2230	0030	0230
12.5	5.6	5.1	5.3	5.9	6.5	7.1	7.0	5.3	5.5	4.8	4.8	4.6
6.25	5.4	4.8	5.0	5.7	6.4	6.9	—	—	—	4.6	4.3	4.5
1.6	4.4	4.1	4.0	4.6	5.0	5.6	5.7	5.1	4.0	3.6	3.9	4.3
0.4	5.0	4.6	5.0	5.7	6.2	6.7	6.5	5.6	4.3	4.0	3.8	4.1

5.1. Standard deviation of temperature fluctuations (10^{-2} °C) from fast-response thermocouples (Mass. Inst. Tech., one sample per sec during 11-min periods) and bead thermistors (Iowa State College, 10 samples per sec during 10-min periods). Periods are centered at indicated CST.

Inst. Set	Height (m)	13 August										14 August 1953	
		0435	0635	0835	1035	1235	1435	1635	1835	2035	2235	0035	0235
MIT	12.0	13	9	16	22	—	—	6	28	18	17	—	—
ISC	8.0	—	17	—	—	—	54	—	56	58	53	—	42
MIT	6.0	19	11	20	42	—	—	7	27	23	19	—	—
ISC	4.0	—	17	38	72	78	57	—	44	48	42	39[1]	37
MIT	3.0	22	12	26	45	—	24	11	38	28	23	—	—
ISC	2.0	—	17	41	74	89	58	—	46	50	42	38[1]	35
MIT	1.5	17	10	21	29	—	17	9	38	26	18	—	—
ISC	1.0	—	17	45	85	87	63	—	45	48	41	34[1]	34
ISC	0.5	—	17	46	79	88	62	—	44	51	37	29[1]	35
ISC	0.25	—	19	45	86	94	68	—	42	55	36	34[1]	34

[1] Duration of test 5 min.

5.2.a. Statistics of fluctuation quantities from 1-sec samplings of fast-response probes (Mass. Inst. Tech.). Total air speed V (cm sec^{-1}); standard deviation of horizontal (parallel and perpendicular to 10-min mean wind) and vertical eddy components $S(u)$, $S(v)$, and $S(w)$ (cm sec^{-1}); gustiness ratios $G(x)$, $G(y)$, and $G(z)$; mean cross products of eddy components $\overline{uv}$, $\overline{vw}$, and $\overline{wu}$ (cm^2 sec^{-2}); horizontal Reynolds' stress (parallel to 10-min mean wind) τ (dynes cm^{-2}); linear correlation coefficients between eddy components and air temperature $(u;v)$, $(v;w)$, $(u;w)$, $(u;T)$, $(v;T)$, and $(w;T)$; mean cross product of vertical eddy component and air temperature multiplied by density and specific heat of air Q (mcal cm^{-2} min^{-1}). Values are 10-min means or totals centered at indicated CST.

Date	CST	Height (m)	V	$S(u)$	$S(v)$	$S(w)$	$G(x)$	$G(y)$	$G(z)$	$\overline{uv}$	$\overline{vw}$	$\overline{uw}$	τ	$(u;v)$	$(v;w)$	$(u;w)$	$(u;T)$	$(v;T)$	$(w;T)$	Q
1953 13 Aug.	0435	12.0	790	101	60	46	.13	.08	.06	600	−320	−1150	1.3	0.10	−0.12	−0.25	0.23	0.13	0.00	0
		6.0	694	96	48	43	.14	.07	.07	20	−170	−1300	1.5	0.00	−0.08	−0.31	0.55	0.11	−0.24	−30
		3.0	628	103	51	44	.16	.08	.07	150	−110	−950	1.1	0.03	−0.05	−0.21	0.49	0.09	−0.10	−18
		1.5	522	104	52	35	.20	.10	.07	−120	100	−1070	1.2	−0.02	0.05	−0.29	0.57	0.00	−0.17	−18
	0635	12.0	735	113	63	39	.15	.09	.05	−1320	−120	−1040	1.2	−0.19	−0.05	−0.24	0.49	0	−0.28	−18
		6.0	655	95	55	39	.15	.08	.06	−120	−70	−1510	1.7	−0.03	−0.03	−0.41	0.57	0	−0.23	−18
		3.0	600	103	46	39	.17	.08	.07	80	−30	−1020	1.1	0.02	−0.02	−0.25	0.57	0	−0.21	−18
		1.5	515	91	50	33	.18	.10	.06	170	60	−760	0.9	0.04	0.04	−0.24	0.55	0	0	0
	0835	12.0	893	179	132	57	.20	.15	.06	5810	−690	−3580	4.0	0.25	−0.09	−0.35	0.07	0	0	0
		6.0	828	158	110	52	.19	.13	.06	4100	−40	−2650	2.9	0.24	−0.01	−0.32	−0.28	0	0.29	48
		3.0	755	162	105	52	.21	.14	.07	2220	−300	−2350	2.6	0.13	−0.05	−0.28	−0.28	0.04	0.15	30
		1.5	665	152	105	40	.23	.16	.06	780	300	−1980	2.2	0.05	0.07	−0.33	−0.16	0.23	0	0
	1035	12.0	757	114	137	49	.15	.18	.06	−1530	−580	−2330	2.5	−0.10	−0.09	−0.42	−0.32	−0.10	0.19	30
		6.0	702	106	133	39	.15	.19	.06	−1560	−300	−1080	1.2	−0.11	−0.06	−0.26	−0.40	−0.13	0.31	78
		3.0	647	116	102	40	.18	.16	.06	−750	−170	−1150	1.3	−0.06	−0.04	−0.25	−0.54	−0.13	0.11	30
		1.5	536	106	101	34	.20	.19	.06	−1350	10	−1160	1.3	−0.13	0.00	−0.32	−0.33	−0.07	0.10	18

Date	CST	Height (m)	V	$S(u)$	$S(v)$	$S(w)$	$G(x)$	$G(y)$	$G(z)$	$\overline{uv}$	$\overline{vw}$	$\overline{uw}$	τ	$(u;v)$	$(v;w)$	$(u;w)$	$(u;T)$	$(v;T)$	$(w;T)$	Q
	1435[1]	3.0	853	159	113	50	.19	.13	.06	1240	230	−2050	2.2	0.07	0.05	−0.26	−0.52	0.04	0.17	30
		1.5	744	144	118	47	.19	.16	.06	430	−80	−1680	1.8	0.03	−0.01	−0.25	−0.49	0.05	0.13	18
	1635	12.0	803	142	76	43	.18	.09	.05	1010	−280	−2360	2.5	0.09	−0.09	−0.39	0.00	0.00	0.00	0
		6.0	721	141	95	41	.20	.13	.06	60	−220	−2490	2.7	0.01	−0.06	−0.43	−0.51	−0.30	0.35	18
		3.0	661	146	65	42	.22	.10	.06	260	−330	−2210	2.4	0.03	−0.12	−0.36	−0.62	−0.14	0.22	18
		1.5	571	131	76	31	.23	.13	.05	−320	60	−1350	1.4	−0.03	0.03	−0.33	−0.17	0.29	0.00	0
	1835	12.0	513	54	39	22	.11	.08	.04	260	0	−380	0.4	0.12	0.00	−0.32	0.40	0.37	−0.16	−18
		6.0	434	57	51	20	.13	.12	.05	300	−30	−480	0.5	0.10	−0.03	−0.42	0.52	0.22	−0.19	−18
		3.0	384	60	31	17	.16	.08	.04	350	−40	−460	0.5	0.19	−0.08	−0.45	0.57	0.26	−0.31	−30
		1.5	313	56	27	15	.18	.09	.05	0	20	−360	0.4	0.00	0.05	−0.42	0.47	0.10	−0.18	−18
	2035	12.0	590	42	37	17	.07	.06	.03	−90	0	−180	0.2	−0.06	0.00	−0.25	0.13	0.15	0.00	0
		6.0	446	47	29	17	.11	.07	.04	−320	30	−270	0.3	−0.23	0.06	−0.33	0.46	−0.15	−0.26	−18
		3.0	354	44	23	15	.12	.06	.04	−230	10	−240	0.3	−0.23	0.03	−0.36	0.49	−0.16	−0.24	−18
		1.5	288	42	22	13	.15	.08	.05	−80	20	−240	0.3	−0.04	0.07	−0.44	0.46	0.00	−0.30	−18
	2235	12.0	624	40	28	17	.06	.04	.03	−90	−50	−120	0.1	−0.08	−0.11	−0.17	0.00	0.42	0.00	0
		6.0	466	48	44	20	.10	.09	.04	−340	−10	−230	0.3	−0.16	−0.01	−0.23	0.11	0.12	−0.26	−18
		3.0	377	48	30	18	.13	.08	.05	−160	−10	−200	0.2	−0.11	−0.02	−0.23	0.36	0.00	−0.24	−18
		1.5	308	43	22	16	.14	.07	.05	−110	30	−240	0.3	−0.11	0.09	−0.34	0.39	0.00	0.00	0

[1] Data at 12 and 6 m level missing.

5.2.b. Standard deviation, $S(u)$, $S(w)$, of eddy components (in the direction of the estimated mean wind, u, and the vertical; cm/sec) and gustiness ratios $G(x)$, $G(z)$, from rotating pressure tube anemometer (Texas A & M College); one sample per sec during 5-min periods centered at indicated CST.

Date (1953)	CST	Height (m)	u	$S(u)$	$S(w)$	$G(x)$	$G(z)$
13 August	1232	1.2	420	81	18	.19	.043
	1632	1.2	439	70	22	.16	.050

6.1.a. Loeser technique of daytime wind profile measurements (GRD). Mean height Z (m); duration t (sec) of evaluated drift; mean West, South, and upward components u, v, w (m/sec) of drift of individual smoke puffs. Values are t-sec averages centered at indicated $CST+t/2$ seconds.

13 August, 1953

CST	Z	t	u	v	w	CST	Z	t	u	v	w	CST	Z	t	u	v	w
0630	1320	72	7.6	1.8	0.2							0640	1447	48	7.5	1.6	0.4
	1049	66	12.3	−0.1	0.4								1217	66	9.4	0.8	0.1
	853	48	16.0	1.1	0.8								868	54	15.6	0.8	0.0
	692	36	20.5	4.3	0.2								729	42	19.6	3.2	0.2
	544	36	23.0	7.6	0.5								597	42	22.3	6.5	0.0
	436	42	21.8	8.9	0.6								506	48	23.3	9.5	0.1
	213	36	12.9	12.1	0.2								431	42	22.2	8.6	0.6
	136	36	7.8	12.2	0.2													
0830	1450	84	6.7	5.4	0.3	0835	1467	66	7.0	5.7	−0.3	0840	1499	18	8.0	6.2	−0.3
	1176	90	5.8	3.6	0.2		1289	96	6.0	4.5	0.7		1274	78	6.9	4.8	0.1
	978	84	5.4	1.0	−0.2		1099	96	5.9	3.4	0.0		1091	84	6.8	4.0	0.1
	816	78	6.4	−1.0	0.1		948	90	5.1	0.7	0.4		851	78	5.5	−0.3	0.2
	688	78	11.5	0.8	0.2		799	78	6.1	−0.7	0.3		727	78	7.8	0.0	0.4
	573	78	15.0	3.7	0.1		671	78	9.4	0.4	0.0		599	72	12.6	3.0	−0.4
	478	66	18.4	7.1	0.7		595	78	14.2	3.5	0.4		497	60	15.2	4.8	−0.2
	370	66	16.9	10.8	0.0		503	60	16.4	5.8	−0.5		402	60	17.5	6.8	−0.5
	271	30	9.6	9.7	0.2		421	48	18.9	8.0	0.0		336	60	16.2	10.2	0.0
	247	54	8.6	9.7	0.1		355	54	15.8	9.8	−0.4		275	60	11.6	8.9	0.2
	146	36	8.7	9.5	−0.4		297	42	13.3	10.7	−0.5		246	42	10.2	8.5	1.5
	128	24	8.6	9.4	0.0		266	42	12.5	9.9	−0.4		207	42	11.2	9.0	1.1
1030	1637	42	8.6	5.6	0.4	1035	1603	42	8.1	5.7	0.6	1040	1569	54	8.1	5.5	0.1
	1473	78	7.8	4.9	0.2		1360	102	6.7	4.9	0.3		1357	120	6.4	4.4	0.3
	1338	120	6.2	4.8	0.4		1197	114	5.8	4.2	0.5		1185	120	5.5	4.0	0.3
	1205	120	5.7	4.5	0.3		1024	114	4.4	3.6	0.3		1033	120	4.1	3.5	0.2
	1091	120	5.1	3.7	0.3		908	108	3.7	3.5	0.2		920	120	3.2	3.6	0.2
	992	120	4.1	3.3	0.1		796	108	2.6	2.4	0.2		812	120	2.1	2.6	0.2
	904	120	3.3	2.8	0.2		685	102	2.3	1.2	0.3		708	120	1.7	1.6	0.2
	836	120	2.6	2.0	0.1		598	102	5.0	1.4	0.4		636	120	3.5	1.3	0.5
	707	114	3.4	0.6	0.0		518	102	7.1	2.0	0.4		568	120	5.4	1.6	0.4
	657	114	4.8	1.1	−0.1		441	102	8.3	5.3	0.2		502	120	7.6	3.0	0.3
	620	114	5.4	1.1	−0.1		364	96	7.3	5.4	−0.1							
							298	84	5.7	5.4	−0.4							
1230	1453	114	4.6	0.1	0.2	1235	1424	108	4.8	0.4	0.5	1240	1446	114	4.7	0.4	0.4
	1222	108	5.4	1.0	0.4		1202	102	5.4	1.7	0.6		1192	108	5.9	1.9	0.3
	1028	102	5.6	4.5	0.1		853	96	7.4	7.6	0.4		989	102	6.6	6.8	0.0
	904	102	5.9	8.0	0.5		734	90	7.4	6.9	0.3		817	102	7.7	7.2	0.0
	768	96	5.7	7.4	0.6		594	90	8.2	8.6	0.0		636	96	8.0	8.2	−0.3
	638	96	5.6	7.1	0.3		505	90	7.8	9.0	0.1		594	96	8.1	7.4	1.3
	506	96	6.2	7.0	−0.5		451	72	7.6	7.2	1.3		491	78	7.8	8.1	1.4
	452	90	5.6	7.0	−0.3		359	72	6.3	6.4	1.7		375	78	9.1	6.7	1.1
	364	90	5.2	7.7	−0.6								294	60	7.3	5.0	1.1
	328	90	4.8	8.4	0.0													
	270	90	5.6	8.1	0.5													

13 August 1953

CST	Z	t	u	v	w	CST	Z	t	u	v	w	CST	Z	t	u	v	w
1430	1424	78	5.7	2.5	0.2	1435	1444	102	6.9	2.7	0.2	1440	1423	108	5.7	2.9	0.0
	1091	96	6.9	4.2	−1.4		1190	96	6.9	4.6	−0.6		1123	96	6.0	3.5	−0.9
	878	90	9.7	6.2	−1.5		1033	90	7.4	6.4	−0.5		938	96	7.2	4.0	−0.6
	770	90	9.4	6.3	−0.6		925	90	7.5	6.9	0.2		809	96	7.1	5.8	−0.2
	610	84	9.3	6.9	−1.0		780	84	7.7	6.9	−0.5		677	90	7.7	6.5	0.0
	489	84	8.8	7.7	−1.3		699	84	9.5	7.7	0.0		544	90	8.2	6.9	−0.3
	409	78	8.3	8.1	−1.2		611	84	8.1	8.4	−0.2		421	78	7.4	6.1	−0.2
							557	84	7.7	7.0	−0.2		362	84	7.6	6.3	−0.3
1830	1508	108	7.2	1.9	0.5	1835	1411	120	6.5	2.5	0.2	1840	1336	120	4.8	3.3	0.1
	1153	96	4.5	5.0	0.2		1198	120	5.2	5.2	0.1		1123	120	5.3	8.2	0.2
	990	96	5.3	7.9	0.3		913	120	5.2	9.8	0.2		955	120	5.7	9.8	0.2
	862	96	5.1	9.9	0.3		802	120	5.6	10.2	0.2		807	120	5.3	10.9	0.5
	755	90	5.3	9.9	0.5		671	114	5.5	11.2	0.2		674	120	5.2	11.4	0.5
	665	90	5.0	10.7	0.4		589	114	4.9	11.6	0.2		566	120	4.9	12.0	0.3
	592	90	4.6	11.3	0.4		518	114	4.9	11.7	0.3		383	120	4.4	13.2	0.3
	525	84	4.6	11.7	0.4		433	108	4.6	12.4	0.3		318	120	3.8	13.0	0.2
	483	84	4.6	12.1	0.3		395	108	4.7	12.6	0.4		247	66	2.8	12.2	0.4
	440	84	4.5	11.9	0.3		345	108	4.6	13.0	0.2		209	60	2.0	11.2	0.3
	390	78	4.4	12.0	0.0		304	108	4.3	13.4	0.2		184	60	1.7	10.9	0.5

6.1.b. Loeser technique of night-time wind profile measurements (GRD). Median values of West and South components u, v (m/sec) of drift; number N of balloons of a pibal swarm which cross the indicated levels. Basic data are overlapping 24-sec mean displacements toward the East and North of each of the N balloons at 12-sec intervals during a 4-min period centered at indicated CST.

Height (m)	13 August 2035			2235			14 August 1953 0035		
	u	v	N	u	v	N	u	v	N
1800	—	—	—	—	—	—	19.5	2.7	1
1600	—	—	—	9.4	0.9	2	14.5	5.7	1
1400	5.8	4.0	2	10.1	2.5	2	16.0	2.8	1
1200	6.8	5.6	2	11.0	6.4	2	17.5	5.7	2
1000	8.4	8.5	2	11.0	9.9	4	16.7	9.9	2
800	8.0	12.8	4	9.6	12.0	6	—	—	—
700	6.6	14.0	5	9.3	12.6	6	15.2	10.8	1
600	7.0	15.0	4	8.9	13.3	7	13.7	7.5	2
500	7.4	15.2	6	9.8	15.8	7	12.7	4.3	3
400	7.0	15.4	7	9.4	16.0	6	11.4	5.0	4
300	7.1	15.5	5	9.9	16.8	5	10.7	3.1	5
200	5.8	14.3	5	8.8	15.7	4	10.4	0.5	5
100	2.8	11.0	4	4.5	12.3	4	8.0	−0.8	4

6.2. Rawinsonde (GMD-1A) wind speed (m/sec) and direction (deg from North) from 1-min mean drift at 30-sec intervals, at indicated height (m), for first 7 min of ascent started at indicated CST.

13 August 1953

0435			0649			0835			1110		
m	m/sec	deg	m	m/sec	deg	m	m/sec	deg	m	m/sec	deg
2168	9.2	246	2415	9.2	229	2068	9.0	224	1812	9.6	246
1860	6.7	257	2070	8.4	228	1826	8.8	222	1567	8.2	242
1708	8.6	265	1900	9.7	239	1694	8.9	226	1456	8.1	245
1555	11.4	264	1730	11.5	242	1535	9.1	224	1330	7.4	243
1385	13.7	263	1562	8.2	242	1367	7.7	225	1204	6.5	240
1210	15.8	262	1394	6.5	253	1217	7.5	233	1080	6.4	234
1033	18.4	261	1226	7.8	266	1058	7.5	238	954	5.2	226
862	21.9	253	1059	11.9	269	902	7.5	249	815	4.5	215
711	24.1	244	883	16.7	266	745	10.3	254	651	5.9	220
565	25.8	237	708	22.1	256	542	10.1	257	487	7.6	227
418	26.4	231	534	24.9	249	438	14.2	249	324	6.6	220
270	20.4	222	361	25.2	240	283	18.7	235	201	6.7	214
140	14.3	209	182	16.9	221	142	15.0	220	102	7.3	209

13 August 1953

1235			1435			1635			1835		
m	m/sec	deg	m	m/sec	deg	m	m/sec	deg	m	m/sec	deg
2100	8.7	255	2360	7.9	288	1995	7.8	268	2267	8.2	286
1845	5.6	261	2074	6.2	290	1736	8.1	244	1919	8.4	278
1701	6.1	254	1932	4.1	293	1594	7.6	237	1753	9.0	274
1556	5.6	256	1787	3.9	276	1451	9.2	238	1586	8.4	265
1410	5.5	254	1631	6.3	250	1309	9.3	243	1416	8.4	246
1265	6.0	249	1465	8.0	241	1167	9.7	242	1243	8.6	238
1118	6.7	239	1300	9.1	239	1023	9.5	238	1071	9.2	221
960	7.8	227	1133	9.7	237	873	9.4	234	897	11.2	211
800	8.2	219	968	11.1	227	722	9.8	223	741	11.3	208
640	8.9	218	775	12.0	222	567	9.9	214	582	12.2	202
480	9.6	219	583	11.5	219	413	8.9	211	424	12.8	200
320	9.4	214	391	11.7	219	261	7.9	209	269	11.4	197
160	10.5	211	196	11.6	217	128	9.4	202	130	8.8	192

13 August   14 August 1953

2035			2235			0035			0235		
m	m/sec	deg	m	m/sec	deg	m	m/sec	deg	m	m/sec	deg
2218	6.0	272	1804	6.2	262	2424	6.5	268	2147	16.4	268
1899	6.9	259	1523	7.4	264	2083	11.4	306	1852	21.2	265
1739	7.3	260	1383	9.6	257	1912	12.6	276	1708	18.9	265
1579	7.9	245	1241	12.0	248	1741	14.3	271	1553	14.7	268
1421	8.7	233	1106	11.9	241	1564	15.7	265	1401	12.6	275
1262	8.8	227	981	12.8	225	1385	16.4	259	1247	11.4	280
1101	9.9	221	856	17.2	218	1209	17.3	248	1092	10.1	285
949	11.4	219	732	17.8	216	1030	20.3	242	935	9.1	292
801	13.7	214	606	17.9	212	857	23.8	238	767	9.3	297
653	14.9	208	483	21.1	209	684	20.7	232	618	8.1	302
524	17.1	204	360	22.3	207	511	15.2	236	459	7.3	336
357	19.5	202	239	20.0	206	342	13.7	244	301	11.0	359
183	16.4	196	119	15.0	201	161	9.9	251	149	11.4	004

6.3. Double theodolite pibal wind speed (m/sec) and direction (deg from North) from 1-min mean drift at 30-sec intervals, at indicated height (m), for first 7 min of ascent started at indicated CST.

13 August 1953

0430			0830			1030			1230			1430		
m	m/sec	deg	m	m/sec	deg	m	m/sec	deg	m	m/sec	deg	m	m/sec	deg
792	23.5	252	990	8.0	249	1038	4.5	219	941	6.5	229	720	10.2	231
722	17.0	256	936	6.0	258	1000	4.2	212	882	9.0	221	646	8.4	226
688	16.2	253	838	6.0	264	906	3.9	204	818	8.9	216	600	8.7	223
632	29.5	235	792	5.1	281	842	3.9	208	750	8.1	213	531	10.4	222
571	33.1	236	719	7.5	282	748	5.4	216	678	7.9	212	464	8.3	218
537	24.3	243	680	14.1	254	674	4.6	218	610	8.2	217	389	10.6	224
486	22.9	238	558	16.4	251	596	7.3	220	546	8.6	221	304	11.2	226
410	23.6	236	502	12.7	254	520	9.4	217	482	7.0	218	249	10.4	222
372	23.7	231	435	17.4	247	460	8.9	216	420	9.5	215	224	12.2	222
301	24.0	225	368	19.6	239	398	10.2	215	358	9.3	211	203	9.4	223
250	19.9	218	292	17.9	230	332	10.0	226	297	8.8	220	188	8.4	224
184	17.8	210	241	15.5	225	276	9.2	213	237	9.3	180	166	10.7	227
124	15.5	204	161	13.3	219	193	8.3	216	150	9.3	204	115	12.1	226
73	11.5	199	65	10.8	216	83	8.2	217	62	8.8	207	55	12.2	221

13 August

1630			2030			2230			14 August 1953 0030		
m	m/sec	deg	m	m/sec	deg	m	m/sec	deg	m	m/sec	deg
1128	7.8	244	899	12.6	221		—		840	5.5	266
1060	9.9	240	830	12.0	221		—		860	2.7	290
977	9.9	236	782	14.6	214		—		852	6.1	252
906	9.3	232	718	16.4	209	675	7.0	227	778	8.9	244
821	10.3	220	660	16.6	205	626	16.2	212	714	9.1	235
730	9.6	215	602	16.7	203	554	18.1	211	657	8.3	220
658	8.5	216	540	18.2	202	503	17.7	210	628	12.0	226
590	10.1	213	469	18.1	203	444	18.7	210	549	16.3	228
506	10.4	214	410	16.2	203	392	18.2	209	450	15.5	222
411	9.0	217	353	17.4	202	334	19.0	208	383	13.0	230
306	8.5	215	288	17.4	202	274	21.4	208	293	12.0	253
232	8.4	208	240	16.0	201	202	21.2	209	169	10.2	263
134	8.6	206	172	14.6	196	133	16.2	204	127	6.7	267
76	8.7	208	84	11.0	188	74	11.7	193	34	4.2	268

6.4. Radiosonde pressure (mb), temperature (°C), and relative humidity (%) at significant levels of ascent started at indicated CST. (M = "motorboating", i.e., a humidity value below the minimum value that the radiosonde can measure at that temperature.)

	13 August									14 August 1953	
	0435	0649	0835	1110	1235	1435	1635	1835	2035	2235	0035	0235
mb	948	947	947	946	946	946	944	944	944	944	946	947
°C	20.0	20.2	25.5	30.3	32.5	35.2	35.5	31.0	23.0	20.0	19.0	20.0
%	63	65	48	45	42	34	33	47	69	74	59	78

	13 August										14 August 1953	
	0435	0649	0835	1110	1235	1435	1635	1835	2035	2235	0035	0235
mb	900	930	916	896	887	850	861	930	922	941	919	912
°C	21.8	19.6	23.6	24.2	26.5	25.5	26.9	31.4	29.6	25.1	24.8	20.0
%	53	60	44	47	35	39	39	39	32	60	40	75
mb	887	902	906	886	856	787	803	898	888	925	885	894
°C	23.5	23.3	26.3	26.6	24.6	20.2	21.6	29.4	26.9	29.1	23.5	23.6
%	47	41	42	33	27	42	38	36	28	26	33	65
mb	877	886	862	838	838	741	751	772	811	883	871	883
°C	23.3	24.6	26.7	23.7	24.6	16.1	17.4	18.9	22.0	27.0	23.8	22.6
%	42	37	28	30	23	25	23	55	40	23	35	55
mb	838	856	826	749	678	670	700	716	727	828	764	868
°C	22.4	24.6	23.6	15.6	9.4	9.4	12.2	13.6	12.5	22.9	17.3	22.9
%	43	33	27	25	20	22	22	42	57	37	42	52
mb	782	826	700	684	646	636	655	693	703	654	687	782
°C	17.5	22.8	10.4	9.4	6.7	6.1	7.2	10.2	11.5	7.0	9.4	16.3
%	47	32	50	20	M	M	23	53	35	—	48	59
mb	703	792	684	635	—	—	610	641	652	626	664	735
°C	8.9	19.6	10.2	6.2	—	—	2.8	5.5	5.9	2.9	7.5	14.5
%	65	30	17	M	—	—	M	23	52	28	28	57
mb	654	743	611	—	—	—	572	591	641	—	647	706
°C	3.7	14.6	3.6	—	—	—	0.8	2.2	5.0	—	5.2	11.7
%	73	41	M	—	—	—	M	M	34	—	28	52
mb	648	674	—	—	—	—	542	—	621	—	—	662
°C	5.2	6.5	—	—	—	—	−2.2	—	3.4	—	—	7.9
%	23	58	—	—	—	—	M	—	24	—	—	33
mb	604	651	—	—	—	—	—	—	570	—	—	638
°C	−0.4	5.3	—	—	—	—	—	—	−1.5	—	—	5.2
%	M	22	—	—	—	—	—	—	M	—	—	37
mb	582	590	—	—	—	—	—	—	528	—	—	—
°C	−1.4	0.3	—	—	—	—	—	—	−4.0	—	—	—
%	M	M	—	—	—	—	—	—	M	—	—	—

7.1. Representative values of West and South components of the wind u, v, (m/sec) at standard heights. Values are estimated from the combination of smoke puff or pibal swarm, rawinsonde and double theodolite pibal data at or near the indicated CST.

	Height (m)	13 August										14 August 1953	
		0435	0635	0835	1035	1235	1435	1635	1835	2035	2235	0035	0235[1]
u	2000	3.9	8.2	6.8	8.5	7.5	5.1	6.8	8.3	5.4	5.7	17.0	20.0
	1750	7.6	7.7	6.5	8.1	6.3	5.5	7.2	8.0	6.0	7.1	17.0	18.3
	1500	11.7	7.4	6.3	7.5	5.4	6.2	7.8	7.2	6.3	9.1	17.0	14.9
	1250	15.3	8.7	6.1	6.0	5.4	7.1	8.3	6.2	6.5	11.0	17.0	11.7
	1000	19.2	13.4	5.9	4.0	6.3	7.7	8.4	5.4	7.8	10.5	17.0	9.5

	(m)	0435	0635	0835	1035	1235	1435	1635	1835	2035	2235	14 August 1953 0035	0235[1]
	800	21.6	17.5	6.8	2.7	6.5	8.0	7.2	5.4	8.2	10.0	16.3	8.1
	700	22.2	20.5	9.2	2.9	6.6	8.0	6.5	5.2	7.5	9.5	15.4	7.1
	600	22.5	22.5	13.0	4.6	6.7	7.9	5.8	5.1	7.3	9.3	14.0	5.8
	500	22.4	22.8	15.9	6.6	6.6	7.7	5.2	4.7	7.1	9.7	12.8	4.0
	400	19.9	20.3	17.3	6.7	6.4	7.5	4.8	4.4	6.8	9.7	12.1	2.2
	300	15.7	16.6	13.8	5.5	5.6	7.2	4.3	3.8	6.8	9.6	11.3	0.9
	200	9.8	11.9	10.7	4.5	4.9	7.1	3.8	2.5	5.7	8.8	10.2	0.3
	100	5.9	6.9	7.2	3.9	4.7	6.9	3.5	1.0	2.7	4.8	8.0	1.0
v	2000	2.0	4.9	6.9	5.2	0.9	0.6	1.2	−1.6	0.7	−0.9	−0.6	1.6
	1750	1.1	3.6	6.4	4.9	1.0	1.5	2.3	−0.4	2.6	0.3	0.7	1.2
	1500	0.8	2.0	5.9	4.4	1.2	2.6	3.7	1.9	3.5	1.7	2.8	0.1
	1250	1.1	1.0	5.3	3.9	1.9	3.9	4.6	4.6	5.6	5.0	5.3	−1.6
	1000	2.8	0.6	2.2	3.5	5.3	5.7	5.5	8.6	8.3	9.2	10.0	−3.0
	800	7.1	2.0	0.1	3.1	7.0	7.0	6.4	10.1	12.7	12.8	11.9	−4.0
	700	9.8	4.2	1.2	3.0	7.3	7.4	6.9	10.7	14.0	13.7	11.4	−4.4
	600	14.0	6.8	3.0	3.3	7.6	7.6	7.4	11.4	15.0	14.9	9.9	−4.8
	500	16.5	8.9	5.1	3.9	7.9	7.7	7.9	12.0	15.9	16.1	7.9	−5.6
	400	16.2	9.9	8.3	4.8	7.7	7.9	8.1	12.5	16.6	17.4	6.0	−8.1
	300	15.4	11.2	10.6	5.5	8.0	8.2	8.2	12.6	16.8	17.4	4.0	−10.8
	200	14.0	11.7	11.5	6.0	8.7	8.8	8.1	10.9	15.7	16.1	2.0	−12.0
	100	11.9	11.1	11.1	6.3	8.9	9.1	8.2	8.3	12.1	13.0	0.1	−11.0

[1] Rawinsonde data only.

7.2.a. Air temperature (°C) at standard heights. Values are interpolated from radiosonde data at or near the indicated CST.

Height (m)	13 August 0435	0635	0835	1035	1235	1435	1635	1835	2035	2235	14 August 1953 0035	0235
2000	15.4	15.9	17.4	16.4	17.5	17.5	17.8	17.2	15.8	17.0	16.8	15.3
1750	17.2	18.2	20.4	18.4	19.5	19.4	19.6	19.4	18.3	18.9	18.2	16.2
1500	19.1	20.4	22.4	20.4	21.4	21.4	21.4	21.4	20.8	20.7	19.6	17.8
1250	21.1	22.6	23.5	22.5	23.4	23.4	23.5	23.3	22.8	22.5	21.0	19.6
1000	22.6	24.1	25.5	24.3	24.6	25.3	25.7	25.3	24.4	24.4	22.4	21.4
800	23.1	24.6	26.6	25.5	25.4	27.2	27.5	26.9	25.6	25.8	23.5	22.8
600	23.5	24.5	26.5	26.4	26.9	29.2	29.5	28.5	26.8	27.2	24.5	22.9
400	21.5	22.6	26.0	25.5	28.8	31.2	31.5	29.9	28.4	28.2	24.7	21.0
200	20.8	20.0	24.3	27.9	30.6	33.2	33.5	31.2	28.3	28.6	23.1	20.0
100	20.4	19.8	24.9	29.1	31.6	34.2	34.5	31.2	25.7	26.0	21.1	20.0

7.2.b. Mixing ratio (g water vapor/kg air) at standard heights. Values are interpolated from radiosonde data at or near the indicated CST.

Height (m)	13 August 0435	0635	0835	1035	1235	1435	1635	1835	2035	2235	14 August 1953 0035	0235
2000	7.3	5.6	5.9	4.1	3.9	5.4	4.6	8.8	7.6	—	7.0	8.5
1750	7.5	5.3	5.9	4.8	4.4	7.3	7.3	9.9	8.0	—	7.0	8.8
1500	8.0	5.6	6.0	5.6	4.8	8.5	10.1	10.1	8.3	—	7.1	9.3
1250	8.5	6.8	6.0	6.3	5.2	9.1	10.3	10.2	8.2	6.0	7.2	9.8
1000	8.7	7.5	6.8	7.1	5.8	9.7	10.2	10.4	7.9	6.2	7.4	10.3
800	8.3	8.0	7.7	7.8	7.1	10.4	10.3	10.5	7.6	6.3	7.6	10.7
600	10.1	8.4	9.0	8.5	9.2	11.2	11.1	10.7	7.3	6.5	6.9	11.5
400	9.8	8.6	10.2	10.8	11.0	12.0	11.9	10.8	8.4	6.9	8.1	12.9
200	9.8	9.3	9.7	12.1	12.9	12.8	12.7	11.0	10.1	8.0	8.8	12.4
100	9.9	9.8	10.3	12.7	13.8	13.2	13.1	12.6	11.6	11.4	8.8	12.5

7.3.a. Summary of heat budget constituents (mcal cm^{-2} min^{-1}) of the earth-air interface according to the theoretical models by Suomi, Halstead, and Lettau. Net radiation flux R, heat transfer to the soil S, sensible heat transfer to the air Q and latent heat transfer to the air (heat equivalent of evaporation) E. Values are hourly means centered at indicated CST.

	13 August 0435	0635	0835	1035	1235	1435	1635	1835	2035	2235	14 August 1953 0035	0235
Suomi												
R_0	110	−20	−456	−807	−925	−747	−336	44	99	94	66	63
S_0	−57	−37	106	126	152	98	42	−29	−170	−95	−40	−55
Q_0	—	34	142	235	260	215	61	−17	—	—	−34	−4
E_0	—	91	208	446	513	434	233	2	—	—	8	−4
Halstead												
R_0	80	0	−440	−800	−950	−820	−430	0	60	80	60	—
S_0	−43	−30	57	130	173	117	60	−30	−55	−47	−47	—
Q_0	−128	−32	170	262	353	247	70	−65	−110	−93	−87	—
E_0	68	0	303	540	520	570	520	227	78	50	58	—
Lettau												
R_0	99	−6	−455	−825	−955	−791	−381	25	83	88	71	74
S_0	−45	−32	87	133	220	156	75	−27	−105	−72	−49	−47
Q_0	−38	−16	113	267	422	224	55	−20	−30	−37	0	−30
E_0	44	2	109	331	326	313	180	72	31	36	0	−17

7.3.b. Representative logarithmic height derivatives of wind speed (zV', mm sec^{-1}, from UCLA and JH data), potential temperature ($z\theta'$, 10^{-3} °C, from JH and UW data), and water vapor pressure (ze', 10^{-3} mb, from JH and UW data); representative values of Karman number k (from zV' and UCLA, JH, and MIT stress data), interpolated ground drag τ_0 (dynes cm^{-2}, from zV' and representative k values), and ratio of heat and momentum diffusivities N_Q; representative ground-flux ratio F_0 and inverse Bowen ratio B. Values refer to indicated CST and are employed in the computation of the heat budget constituents Q_0 and E_0 (Lettau model; see Table 7.3.a).

	13 August										14 August 1953	
	0435	0635	0835	1035	1235	1435	1635	1835	2035	2235	0035	0235
zV'	1107	1008	1243	1112	1130	1248	1154	612	584	631	462	480
$z\theta'$	179	76	−312	−551	−659	−464	−169	246	490	446	440	381
ze'	−109	−6	−236	−778	−741	−677	−431	−360	−169	−169	6	102
k	0.37	0.37	0.38	0.39	0.40	0.40	0.38	0.36	0.35	0.36	0.20	0.37
τ_0	1.92	1.61	2.50	2.07	2.18	2.53	2.11	0.53	0.46	0.58	0.10	0.35
N_Q	0.86	0.88	1.26	1.79	2.32	1.66	1.20	0.64	0.54	0.62	0.00	0.76
F_0	1.2[1]	−2.2[1]	4.07[1]	4.69	4.00	4.68	6.9[1]	−0.1[1]	−0.40	0.27	1.7[1]	0.67
B	−1.0[1]	−0.1[1]	1.2[1]	2.24	1.77	2.31	4.0[1]	−2.3[1]	−0.55	−0.61	0.0[1]	0.44

[1] Value disregarded for evaluation of N_Q.

7.4. Richardson number (Ri; units of 10^{-3}) from Mass. Inst. Tech. and Johns Hopkins University data on simultaneous temperature and wind velocity differences, centered at indicated CST and mean height z_m (meters). (Ri') = average height derivative of Richardson number (10^{-3} m^{-1}).

Inst. Set	Height (m)	13 August										14 August 1953	
		0435	0635	0835	1035	1235	1435	1635	1835	2035	2235	0035	0235
MIT	8.0	50	52	−7	−47	−17[1]	7[1]	56[1]	111	123	103	215	42
MIT	4.0	31	30	−6	−55	−58	−25	−6	74	92	76	320	30
JH	3.2	26	10	−31	−72	−88	−36	−14	68	76	70	172	42
JH	1.6	11	3	−14	—	−36	−18	−9	43	63	56	96	51
JH	0.8	7	2	−10	−10	−12	−8	−4	20	48	35	138	46
(Ri')		7	6	−4	−12	−20	−10	−3	18	23	19	54	12

[1] Questionable values; not considered in computation of (Ri').

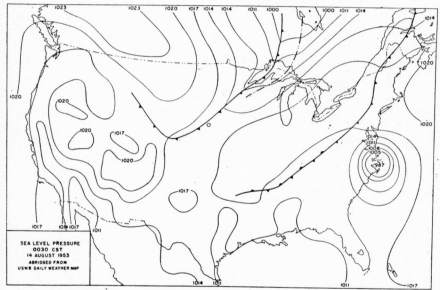

FIG. B.2.1. Continental scale synoptic chart. Sea level pressure distribution for the second general observation period.

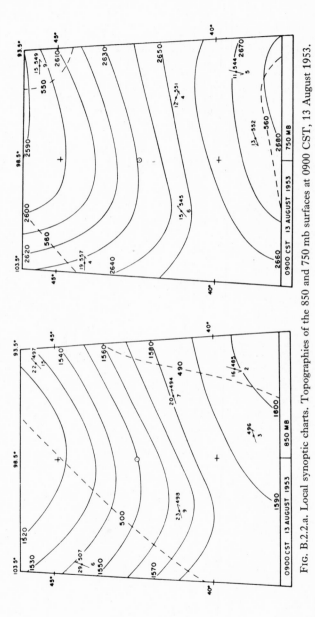

FIG. B.2.2.a. Local synoptic charts. Topographies of the 850 and 750 mb surfaces at 0900 CST, 13 August 1953.

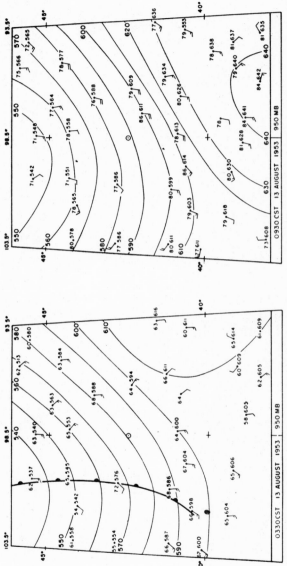

Fig. B.2.3.a. Local synoptic charts. Topography of the 950 mb surface at 0330 and 0930 CST, 13 August 1953.

E

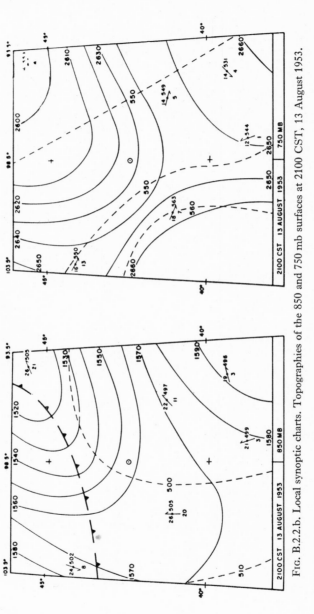

FIG. B.2.2.b. Local synoptic charts. Topographies of the 850 and 750 mb surfaces at 2100 CST, 13 August 1953.

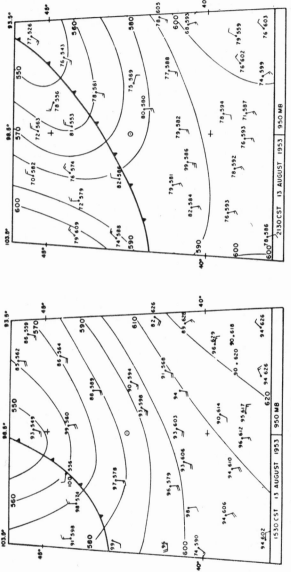

Fig. B.2.3.b. Local synoptic charts. Topography of the 950 mb surface at 1530 and 2130 CST, 13 August 1953.

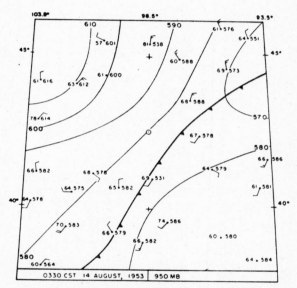

Fig. B.2.3.c. Local synoptic chart. Topography of the 950 mb surface at 0330 CST, 14 August 1953.

THIRD GENERAL OBSERVATION PERIOD

1805 CST 18 August through 2105 CST 19 August 1953

Solar Data for the Field Site near O'Neill, Nebraska

	Sun's elevation angle at apparent noon	Sunrise CST	Apparent noon CST	Sunset CST
18 August	60° 32′	0544	1238	1932
19 August	60° 13′	0545	1238	1930

Summary of Synoptic Conditions

On the 16th and 17th the winds were easterly, shifting to southeasterly on the 18th at 5 to 15 mph as a pressure ridge developed over Eastern Nebraska. The nights were clear; the days on the 16th and 17th had broken to overcast skies becoming scattered during the day of the 18th and scattered to broken on the evening of the 18th. On the 18th there was a stationary front and a trough of low pressure from Northern Saskatchewan to New Mexico and eastward to the Georgia coast. To the west and east of this trough were two high-pressure cells; a weak one centered over Londer, Wyoming, and a very extensive one centered over Western Ontario. The wind shift and clearing skies provided moderately favorable conditions for the third general observation period to start at 1805 CST on the 18th and to continue for 27 hr.

To the west and south there were showers and thunderstorms associated with the stationary front and an unconfirmed tornado in Western Minnesota at 1830 CST of the 18th. There were no other indications of extreme instability in this area. The stationary front started to move eastward slowly on the 19th and by 1230 CST was located in Western Nebraska with consequent shower activity in that area.

1.1.a. Mean geopotential H (dynamic m above 601 = geopotential of test site), West and South components of the geostrophic wind u_g v_g (m/sec) at indicated pressure (mb) levels. Values are estimated for the O'Neill site from local synoptic charts.

mb	H	18 Aug. 2100 u_g	v_g	19 Aug. 0900 u_g	v_g	19 Aug. 2100 u_g	v_g
750	2042	−1.6	−3.4	2.0	8.7	−2.3	0.8
800	1504	−2.5	−0.9	2.7	11.5	0.8	1.7
850	990	−0.8	2.9	3.2	12.9	0.9	1.9
900	497	−1.1	4.6	3.4	12.8	0.6	4.4
950	30	0	6.3	2.1	10.9	0.9	8.3

1.1.b. Direction (deg from North) and speed (m/sec) of the 950 mb geostrophic wind. Values are estimated for the O'Neill site from local synoptic charts.

18 August		19 August 1953							
1830	2130	0030	0330	0630	0930	1230	1530	1830	2130
193	180	198	216	202	191	193	189	183	186
9.1	6.3	5.1	5.4	10.5	11.1	12.5	11.1	9.1	8.3

1.2. Direction (deg from North) of the mean surface wind from standard vane recordings at 1-min intervals (Mass. Inst. Tech., 16-m level). Hourly and 15-min averages centered at indicated CST.

	18 August			19 August 1953										
	1835	2035	2235	0035	0235	0435	0635	0835	1035	1235	1435	1635	1835	2035
60-min mean:	144	144	142	150	173	178[1]	187	188	186	165	167	145	141	132
15-min mean:	142	143	142	154	173	182	191	196	185	171	166	148	140	131

[1] Data missing from 0411 to 0417 CST.

1.3. Standard shelter temperature (°F); relative humidity (%); station pressure (inches) and air density (mg cm^{-3}); amount (tenths) and types of clouds.

Month	Day	CST	Temp.	RH	Pressure	Density	Clouds	Remarks
Aug.	18	1830	70	64	28.113	1.12	7 AsCi	As increasing from NW and W
		2030	60	78	.131	1.14	8 AsCs	
		2230	63	70	.126	1.14	4 AsCi	Clouds to W seem to be thicker
	19	0030	58	84	.075	1.14	2 Ci	Stars toward horizon not visible
		0230	55	89	.130	1.15	1 Ci	Clear overhead
		0430	55	83	.140	1.15	4 Ac	Dew on grass. Some clouds visible to E and N
		0630	58	77	.140	1.15	9 AcCi	Clouds all quadrants
		0830	70	55	.160	1.12	9 AcCs	Light shadows, thin cloud cover over sun
		1030	76	52	.160	1.11	7 AcCs	Ac, As covering sun
		1230	79	47	.150	1.10	7 Cs	Wind gusty. Clouds variable in thickness
		1430	81	45	.120	1.09	7 CuCs	
		1630	81	39	.095	1.09	4 CuCs	Wind very gusty. Cu increasing
		1830	75	45	.080	1.11	4 AcCi	Few Cu dissipating. Haze in all directions
		2030	61	80	.090	1.14	3 Ci	Clouds dissipating. As S and SW

2.1.a. Soil temperature (°C) from thermistors (University of Texas) and soil thermocouples (University of California and Johns Hopkins University). Values are readings at indicated CST.

Inst. Set	Depth (cm)	18 August			19 August 1953										
		1835	2035	2235	0035	0235	0435	0635	0835	1035	1235	1435	1635	1835	2035
UT	0.5	24.57	20.92	18.88	17.74	16.35	15.67	15.69	21.44	29.13	34.46	35.12	31.22	25.47	21.28
UCLA	1.3	23.11	20.83	16.72	15.50	14.22	13.44	13.17	17.67	28.39	34.17	36.50	31.78	24.78	20.33
UT	1.5	25.08	21.68	19.64	18.44	17.16	16.34	16.16	20.34	26.73	31.64	32.78	30.40	25.93	22.28
UT	2.5	25.50	22.34	20.25	19.08	17.80	16.97	16.59	19.78	25.40	30.16	31.57	30.06	26.16	22.92
JH	2.5	24.76	22.32	20.71	19.54	18.60	17.88	17.42	18.65	21.96	25.30	27.03	26.82	24.78	22.55
UT	3.5	25.72	22.83	20.74	19.59	18.37	17.53	17.03	19.38	24.33	28.88	30.30	29.68	26.42	23.37
UT	4.5	25.84	23.15	21.11	19.95	18.72	17.83	17.26	19.11	23.67	27.90	29.77	29.30	26.42	23.63
JH	5.0	24.91	22.90	21.40	20.32	19.39	18.65	18.08	18.53	20.94	23.70	25.75	26.27	24.92	23.12
UT	5.5	26.02	23.60	21.52	20.25	19.11	18.34	17.72	18.94	22.79	26.74	28.58	28.69	26.28	23.77
UCLA	10.0	23.78	21.94	20.39	18.89	18.06	16.94	16.00	14.72	20.00	22.78	25.44	25.56	24.72	23.33

Inst. Set	Depth (cm)	18 August 1835	2035	2235	19 August 1953 0035	0235	0435	0635	0835	1035	1235	1435	1635	1835	2035
JH	10.0	24.79	23.56	22.32	21.30	20.49	19.78	19.16	18.98	20.15	21.98	23.98	25.08	24.82	23.72
JH	20.0	22.91	22.93	22.55	22.03	21.57	21.07	20.61	20.18	20.10	20.52	21.48	22.44	22.94	22.98
UCLA	25.0	20.83	20.83	20.28	19.83	19.44	18.89	18.22	16.39	19.72	20.00	20.56	21.22	21.67	21.94
JH	40.0	20.97	21.19	21.36	21.44	21.46	21.38	21.26	21.04	20.85	20.74	20.71	20.80	20.98	21.22
JH	80.0	20.27	20.27	20.25	20.23	20.26	20.27	20.28	20.24	20.21	20.19	20.18	20.19	20.19	20.20

Note—UCLA reference thermoelement ice bath renewed between 0840 and 1030 CST on 19 August.

2.1.b. Change of soil temperature ($°C\ hr^{-1}$) averaged over indicated layers from soil temperature integrators (University of Wisconsin). Values are differences between readings at the end and beginning of 1-hr intervals centered at indicated CST.

Depth (cm)	18 August 1835	2035	2235	19 August 1953 0035	0235	0435	0635	0835	1035	1235	1435	1635	1835	2035
0—5	−2.58	−1.01	0.17	−0.75	−0.11	−0.56	0.69	1.76	1.82	1.31	0.77	−2.28	−2.58	−0.86
5—15	−0.58	−0.68	−0.67	−0.43	−0.40	−0.36	−0.26	0.45	1.07	1.10	0.77	0.06	−0.51	−0.82
15—50	0.13	0.00	−0.05	−0.10	−0.13	−0.13	−0.13	−0.12	0.00	0.12	0.21	0.21	0.14	−0.03

2.2.a. Soil thermal conductivity ($mcal\ cm^{-1}\ sec^{-1}\ deg^{-1}$) computed from soil thermistor response to defined heating pulses (University of Texas, Albrecht heat flux meter No. 2). Values are derived from 60-sec trials beginning at indicated CST.

Depth (cm)	18 August 1840	2040	2240	19 August 1953 0040	0240	0440	0640	0840	1040	1240	1440	1640	1840	2040
0.5	0.76	0.79	0.81	0.82	0.83	0.81	0.80	0.78	0.75	0.70	0.68	0.66	0.68	0.70
1.5	1.06	1.04	1.04	1.00	0.99	0.99	1.05	1.10	1.16	1.17	1.10	1.08	1.03	1.00
2.5	1.21	1.18	1.15	1.16	1.19	1.23	1.23	1.23	1.23	1.24	1.22	1.19	1.16	1.14
3.5	1.35	1.32	1.28	1.28	1.27	1.27	1.26	1.26	1.28	1.28	1.27	1.25	1.24	1.27
4.5	1.90	1.90	1.85	1.82	1.83	1.83	1.79	1.74	1.70	1.73	1.78	1.77	1.65	1.70
5.5	1.40	1.41	1.45	1.45	1.45	1.43	1.44	1.48	1.48	1.53	1.53	1.57	1.57	1.53

2.2.b. Soil moisture (% wet weight) from soil samples at the Johns Hopkins University site. Indicated CST refers to the approximate time of soil sample extraction.

Depth (cm)	18 August 1730	19 August 1930
4	8.0	8.2
10	7.8	6.3
20	5.1	4.4
40	2.8	2.5

2.2.c. Soil heat capacity ($cal\ cm^{-3}\ deg^{-1}$) from soil samples at the University of Wisconsin site (calorimetric determination). Indicated CST refers to the approximate time of soil sample extraction (0-10 cm layer).

19 August 1953 0400	1400	1500
0.35	0.39	0.41

2.3. Soil moisture tension (mb) from tensiometers (Johns Hopkins University). Values are readings at indicated CST.

Depth (cm)	18 August 1835	2035	2235	19 August 1953 0035	0235	0435	0635	0835	1035	1235	1435	1635	1835	2035
5	589	418	224	180	121	95	107	210	395	498	508	608	648	—
10	632	536	388	320	255	200	196	272	434	550	629	674	688	650
20	695	683	578	453	312	129	20	21	130	297	504	639	695	694
40	446	478	407	204	42	10	6	12	37	97	229	370	470	500

2.4. Vertical flux of heat (mcal cm^{-2} min^{-1}) from soil temperature integrators (University of Wisconsin), Albrecht heat flux meter No. 2 (University of Texas-Al), Gier and Dunkle heat flow meters (University of California; University of Texas-GD), and numerical integration of soil temperature profile changes (Johns Hopkins University). UW and JH values are 60-min averages, UCLA values are 15-min averages, and UT values are approximately 2-min averages. All averages are centered at indicated CST.

Inst. Set	Depth (cm)	18 August 1835	2035	2235	19 August 1953 0035	0235	0435	0635	0835	1035	1235	1435	1635	1835	2035
UW	0.0	−77	−68	−47	−70	−60	−70	−28	48	114	130	118	−16	−52	−79
UT-Al	0.0[1]	−39	−55	−83	−53	−60	−80	−95	106	215	248	170	84	−41	−78
JH	0.0[1]	−42	−60	−57	−60	−55	−53	−42	43	100	135	100	15	−50	—
UCLA	0.2[2]	−62	−87	−71	−74	−78	−69	−39	146	248	312	305	112	−39	−91
UT-GD	0.2[2]	−40	−66	−56	−54	−57	−51	−32	109	210	142	184	78	−24	−61
UCLA	1.3	−20	−38	−33	−37	−37	−33	−21	51	93	120	131	64	0	−37
UT-Al	2.0	−29	−44	−40	−40	−42	−42	−30	39	95	107	84	23	−15	−41
UW	5.0	0	−38	−52	−48	−57	−54	−49	−4	60	92	94	83	7	−54
UCLA	10.0	18	−11	−20	−27	−31	−31	−31	−3	29	70	75	59	15	−9
UW	15.0	32	0	−14	−24	−34	−34	−34	−30	0	30	57	51	36	−8

[1] Values are extrapolated to surface.
[2] Approximatine depth; the upper plates of the heat flow meters were "just covered with soil".

3.1. Summary of data on radiation (mcal cm^{-2} min^{-1}). Short-wave radiation from Eppley pyrheliometer (GRD); net radiation from two Gier and Dunkle radiometers (Johns Hopkins University and University of Texas) and the Suomi net radiometer (University of Wisconsin); total radiation from the Gier and Dunkle radiometer (University of Texas). Values are hourly averages centered at indicated CST.

	Inst. Set	18 August 1835	2035	2235	19 August 1953 0035	0235	0435	0635	0835	1035	1235	1435	1635	1835	2035
(Short-	GRD	83[1]	0	0	0	0	0	80	710	1020	1330	1213	700	133	—
Wave)	GRD[2]	90	0	0	0	0	0	80	61[3]	1060	990[3]	1180[3]	700[3]	180	0
	JH	−30	−70	−70	−70	−70	−60	−30	380	630	860	760	560	−20	−70
(Net)	UT	−80	−67	−102	−106	−100	−95	−20	436	789	806	690	345	−11	−104
	UW	−81[4]	−84	−92	−95	−94	−84	−44	422	676	892	759	315	−12	−87[5]
(Total)	UT	534	492	466	449	446	457	550	1209	1614	1642	1692[6]	1189	606	466

[1] Centered at 1845.
[2] 10-min average centered at indicated CST.
[3] Subject to error because of clouds.
[4] 30-min average 1835-1905.
[5] 30-min average 2005-2035.
[6] Centered at 1450.

3.2. Boundary shear-stress (dynes cm^{-2}) from drag recorder (University of California) and Sheppard-type drag plate (Johns Hopkins University); direction of boundary shear-stress (deg from North) from drag recorder (University of California). Values are 10-min means centered at indicated CST.

Inst. Set	18 August 1835	2035	2235	19 August 1953 0035	0235	0435	0635	0835	1035	1235	1435	1635	1835	2035
UCLA	—	0.07[1]	0.49	0.34	0.49	0.73	1.16	1.74	—	—	—	1.91[2]	0.43	0.16
JH	0.06	—	0.12	0.08	—	—	—	0.4	0.7	0.8	—	0.09	0.09	—
UCLA	—	131[1]	138	149	172	182	188	194	—	—	—	134[2]	128	109

[1] For time interval 2037-2043.   [2] For time interval 1630-1642.

3.3. Characteristics of low level smoke-puff drift (Johns Hopkins University); direction of drift (deg from North); time t_{25} (sec) required to cross 25 m circle; lateral width S (deg) at 25 m and time t_D (sec) required to reach threshold of visibility. Values are ensemble averages for 10 smoke puffs fired at approximately 1-min intervals beginning at indicated CST.

	18 August 1800	2000	2200	0000	0200	0400	0600	0800	1000	1200	1400	1600	1800	2000
dd	151	158	141	165	181	177	189	188	190	179	157	156	142	112
t_{25}	9.4	15.0	9.9	9.5	11.5	9.1	6.6	6.1	5.3	5.5	5.2	6.5	11.0	11.6
S	11.3	9.7	12.9	13.2	11.5	11.6	13.0	11.0	12.9	13.2	12.4	12.4	12.3	13.0
t_D	37	—	—	—	—	—	37	20	16	20	13	22	51	—

3.4. Characteristics of surface pressure variations from micro-barograms (GRD, Paulin-type aneroid system); trend (WBAN Synoptic Code number); qualitative index of micro-variations ("a" = calm to "d" = very unruly); trace ratio (trace length relative to trend length); trend ratio (trend length relative to chart length); period (min), amplitude (10^{-2} mb) and number of perceptible waves. Values refer to 2-hr intervals centered at indicated CST.

	18 August 1935	2135	2335	19 August 1953 0135	0335	0535	0735	0935	1135	1335	1535	1735	1935
Trend	3	8	3	8	3	2	2	7	7	7	7	6	2
Index	a	a	a	a	a	a	a-b	b	c	b	b-a	a	a
Trace ratio	1.1	1.2	1.1	1.1	1.1	1.1	1.3	1.2	1.5	1.6	1.4	1.1	1.1
Trend ratio	1.25	1.0	1.1	1.1	1.1	1.2	1.1	1.0	1.2	1.2	1.1	1.2	1.0
Period	30	20	15	10	45	25	40	40	40	30	30	20	60
Ampl.	6	4	3	2.5	5	2.5	4	4	6	5	5	4	6
Number	1	2	3	4	2	2	1	2	2	3	1	2	1
Period	20	15	10	25	10	—	25	—	10	5	10	—	—
Ampl.	4	3	3	2.5	3	—	4	—	3	3	4	—	—
Number	2	3	1	1	2	—	2	—	4	4	2	—	—
Period	10	—	—	—	—	—	15	—	—	—	—	—	—
Ampl.	4	—	—	—	—	—	3.5	—	—	—	—	—	—
Number	1	—	—	—	—	—	1	—	—	—	—	—	—

3.5. Dew desposition data (GRD); Taylor dew gauge trace characteristics and Duvdevani dew block scale-numbers. Values are readings at indicated CST.

Inst. Set	Height (cm)	18 August				19 August 1953						—	2035
		2035	2135	2235	2335	0035	0135	0235	0335	0435	0535		
Gauge	7	#[1]	#[2]	O	O	O	#[3]	#	#	#	#[4]	—	#[5]
Block	100	O	O	O	O	O	—	Tr.	Tr.	1	1	—	O
Block	50	O	O	O	O	O	—	Tr.	1	1	1	—	O
Block	8	Tr.	Tr.	Tr.	Tr.	Tr.	—	1	2a	2a	3a	—	Tr.
Block	2.5	Tr.	1	1	1	2	—	3	5a	5b	6a	—	1

[1] Beginning of trace 2020 CST.   [4] End of trace 0700 CST.
[2] End of trace 2155 CST.   [5] Beginning of trace 2010 CST.
[3] Beginning of trace 0045 CST; heavy trace begins 0115 CST.

4.1.a. Hourly mean wind speed (cm/sec) from standard three-cup anemometers (Mass. Inst. Tech.), ping-pong ball anemometers (Iowa State College) and modified SCS cup anemometers (Johns Hopkins University); centered at indicated CST.

Inst. Set	Height (m)	18 August		19 August 1953										
		1835	2035	2235	0035	0235	0435	0635	0835	1035	1235	1435	1635	1835	2035
MIT	16.0	494	477	509	437	551	573	578	601	696	632	622	575	447	479
MIT	8.0	410	343	402	344	404	437	479	570	651	600	583	540	355	330
ISC	7.0	390	310	386	293	374	404	455	521	634	598	582	547	340	313
JH	6.4	366	286	378	318	360	374	446	532	642	605	592	551	318	294
MIT	4.0	338	225	316	265	307	355	412	524	596	552	540	497	289	222
ISC	4.0	341	214	324	223	299	334	397	483	591	563	547	511	286	226
JH	3.2	314	193	304	249	274	302	381	489	590	562	553	510	265	203
MIT	2.0	287	141	257	208	241	290	352	468	534	507	491	457	235	132
JH	1.6	272	140	251	205	221	253	332	444	533	508	498	460	221	156
ISC	1.0	242	97	215	125	199	339[1]	302	391	474	453	441	403	195	98
JH	0.8	235	106	213	172	187	219	290	387	468	450	438	401	191	120
JH	0.4	199	78	176	144	154	181	241	326	393	381	372	338	162	96

[1] Questionable value; correct value is probably 239.

4.1.b. 15-min mean wind speed (cm sec^{-1}) from standard three-cup anemometers (Mass. Inst. Tech.), modified Sheppard-type anemometers (University of California), and ping-pong ball anemometers (Iowa State College); centered at indicated CST. ISC data are 10-min means centered at indicated CST.

Inst. Set	Height (m)	18 August		19 August 1953										
		1835	2035	2235	0035	0235	0435	0635	0835	1035	1235	1435	1635	1835	2035
MIT	16.0	449	436	517	429	584	611	598	662	682	615	642	567	415	530
MIT	8.0	368	324	412	344	422	466	493	628	638	581	608	537	341	361
UCLA	8.0	378	345	434	365	436	486	557	580	686	652	641	576	348	382
ISC	7.0	357	297	398	326	369	431	468	534	613	568	595	430	330	344
UCLA	4.15	307	245	355	286	334	396	480	528	626	594	590	511	282	272
MIT	4.0	297	206	324	260	321	385	432	571	584	534	557	590	284	246
ISC	4.0	301	209	335	263	312	362	416	497	576	536	559	395	284	250
MIT	2.0	246	121[1]	267	199	253	317	372	507	520	486	507	446	233	162[1]
UCLA	2.0	244	165	282	226	265	326	412	466	548	530	520	480	232	190
UCLA	1.0	204	108	236	182	218	276	356	407	478	460	459	420	197	142
ISC	1.0	206	84	231	163	210	263	314	397	458	431	453	311	203	130
UCLA	0.5	172	78	198	149	180	233	302	348	408	394	394	362	166	116

[1] 10-min mean centered at tabulated time.

4.2. Mean air temperature (°C) from aspirated thermocouples (Mass. Inst. Tech., 15-min means; University of California, average of six readings taken every 3 min), and shielded thermocouples (Johns Hopkins University, average of 20 readings at each level during a 5-min interval) and shielded thermistors (University of Texas, 10-sec means); centered at indicated CST.

Inst. Set	Height (m)	18 August			19 August 1953										
		1835	2035	2235	0035	0235	0435	0635	0835	1035	1235	1435	1635	1835	2035
MIT	16.0	23.42	20.71	19.16	16.52	15.68	14.62	15.32	20.33	23.54	24.62	25.50	26.16	24.28	21.47
MIT	8.0	22.98	19.17	18.50	15.94	14.48	13.87	15.09	20.47	23.73	24.80	25.72	26.32	23.97	19.12
UCLA	8.0	21.50	17.56	16.67	13.94	12.11	11.78	12.50	16.33	22.78	24.17	25.33	26.33	23.33	18.44
JH	6.4	22.28	18.47	18.16	15.47	13.62	13.71	14.88	20.19	23.20	24.77	25.66	25.67	23.40	18.18
MIT	4.0	22.55	17.41	17.80	15.35	13.82	13.44	14.92	20.62	23.93	24.92	25.84	26.40	23.62	17.47
UCLA	4.0	21.06	16.11	16.11	13.33	11.39	11.39	12.39	16.56	23.22	24.67	25.67	26.39	23.06	17.22
JH	3.2	21.98	17.42	17.69	14.89	13.21	13.37	14.85	20.35	23.37	25.39	25.97	25.89	23.18	17.14
MIT	2.0	22.30	16.20	17.40	15.00	13.50	13.20	14.80	20.90	24.40	25.40	26.40	26.70	23.50	16.60
UCLA	2.0	20.56	15.00	15.78	13.17	11.39	11.22	12.22	16.39	23.50	24.78	26.39	26.44	22.78	16.94
JH	1.6	21.60	16.64	17.29	14.54	12.94	13.13	14.66	20.57	23.80	25.78	26.35	26.15	23.03	16.59
UCLA	1.0	20.28	13.94	15.00	12.61	10.83	10.83	11.94	16.67	23.89	25.39	27.11	26.94	22.89	15.67
JH	0.8	21.31	16.07	16.88	14.24	12.67	12.98	14.57	20.81	24.20	26.25	26.82	26.41	22.84	16.17
UT	0.8	20.55	15.65	16.65	14.75	13.6	13.5	14.95	20.65	25.1	27.0	27.85	26.7	23.1	16.1
UCLA	0.5	20.61	13.33	14.44	12.22	10.56	10.72	11.78	17.06	24.28	26.17	27.61	27.11	22.56	15.39
UT	0.5	20.35	14.9	16.4	14.4	13.4	13.3	14.75	20.75	25.55	26.55	28.55	26.8	22.9	15.7
JH	0.4	21.09	15.52	16.47	13.90	12.50	12.78	14.46	21.01	24.67	26.90	27.50	26.69	22.72	15.65
UT	0.3	20.35	14.65	16.35	14.4	13.3	13.3	15.05	21.1	26.0	27.0	28.75	27.1	22.8	13.8
JH	0.2	20.81	15.04	16.09	13.65	12.32	12.59	14.37	21.22	25.03	27.24	28.35	26.89	22.58	15.17
JH	0.1	20.58	14.58	15.81	13.43	12.18	12.44	14.23	21.57	25.57	28.09	29.10	27.18	22.51	14.95
UT	0.1	20.2	14.0	15.6	13.95	12.85	12.95	14.7	21.7	27.3	27.5	29.5	27.5	22.65	15.3

Note—UCLA reference thermoelement ice bath renewed between 0840 and 1030 CST on 19 August.

4.3.a. Mean water vapor pressure (mb) from dew-point apparatus (Johns Hopkins University). Simultaneous air sampling at given intake levels. Values are 5-min averages centered at indicated CST.

Height (m)	18 August			19 August 1953										
	1835	2035	2235	0035	0235	0435	0635	0835	1035	1235	1435[1]	1635	1835	2035
6.4	13.08	12.17	12.40	13.17	12.91	12.44	12.41	13.28	13.63	14.16	13.29	12.54	13.03	13.54
3.2	13.28	12.45	12.54	13.18	12.54	12.67	12.49	13.63	13.90	14.28	13.50	12.60	13.66	13.93
1.6	13.90	12.84	12.60	13.17	12.49	12.72	12.64	13.90	14.43	14.45	13.89	12.78	14.20	14.02
0.8	13.90	13.02	12.66	13.26	12.48	12.73	12.82	14.09	14.68	14.71	14.40	13.16	14.29	14.10
0.4	13.99	13.09	12.76	13.16	12.57	12.67	12.92	14.43	14.84	15.17	15.06	13.35	14.55	14.28
0.2	14.38	13.28	12.95	13.11	12.64	12.64	13.90	14.65	15.20	15.34	15.74	13.92	14.87	14.28
0.1	14.03	13.57	13.02	13.17	12.40	12.72	14.01	15.21	15.55	15.95	16.24	14.25	15.17	14.29

[1] Average of 1335 and 1535 data.

4.3.b. Mean vertical difference (between 82 and 39 cm) of dry-bulb temperature (10^{-3} °C) and water vapor pressure (10^{-3} mb) from double psychrometer lift-apparatus (University of Wisconsin). Values are hourly means (based on one sample every 10 min) centered at indicated CST.

	18 August			19 August 1953										
	1835	2035	2235	0035	0235	0435	0635	0835	1035	1235	1435	1635	1835	2035
10^{-3} °C	281	476	362	284	206	171	136	−313	−421	−596	−531	−237	226	430
10^{-3} mb	−12	−71	−20	43	54	46	−36	−99	−295	−398	−472	−273	−135	38

4.4. Mean ozone concentration (10^{-8} g O_3/g air) from automatic ozone recorders (University of New Mexico). Values are 60-min means estimated from traces on chart recorders centered at indicated CST.

Height (m)	18 August			19 August 1953										
	1830	2030	2230	0030	0230	0430	0630	0830	1030	1230	1430	1630	1830	2030
12.5	5.8	5.5	6.4	5.1	4.5	3.9	4.2	5.4	7.0	7.7	7.5	7.5	6.6	5.7
6.25	—	—	6.2	—	—	—	—	5.9	7.3	8.1	7.9	7.9	6.4	—
1.6	5.9	4.5	5.8	4.9	3.4	3.4	4.2	5.7	7.3	7.9	7.7	7.5	6.0	—
0.4	5.3	3.2	5.5	4.9	3.5	3.3	4.1	5.9	7.5	8.2	7.9	7.6	—	—

5.1. Standard deviation of temperature fluctuations (10^{-2} °C) from fast-response thermocouples (Mass. Inst. Tech., one sample per sec during 11-min periods) and bead thermistors (Iowa State College, 10 samples per sec during 5-min periods). Periods are centered at indicated CST.

Inst. Set	Height (m)	18 August			19 August 1953										
		1835	2035	2235	0035	0235	0435	0635	0835	1035	1235	1435	1635	1835	2035
MIT	12.0	23	6	15	10	13	18	11	20	28	31	27	18	—	14
ISC	8.0	53	35	56	23[1]	47	34	25	46	87	89	74	—	25	—
MIT	6.0	25	9	15	9	13	18	10	25	40	39	37	19	—	8
ISC	4.0	—	25	59	24[1]	37	29	22	51	87	89	82	—	26	43
MIT	3.0	34	20	29	17	16	18	12	28	51	54	56	29	—	16
ISC	2.0	56	20	58	—	34	26	19	54	84	83	85	—	27	38
MIT	1.5	39	20	31	18	13	—	12	34	46	58	60	29	—	15
ISC	1.0	59	21	61	24[1]	29	27	17	57	86	80	88	—	29	27
ISC	0.5	—	—	61	—	18	25	17	77	89	73	88	—	31	20
ISC	0.25	—	12	63	24[1]	23	23	17	76	93	68	84	—	32	20

[1] Period centered at 0135 CST.

5.2.a. Statistics of fluctuation quantities from 1-sec samplings of fast-response probes (Mass. Inst. Tech.). Total air speed V (cm sec^{-1}); standard deviation of horizontal (parallel and perpendicular to 10-min mean wind) and vertical eddy components $S(u)$, $S(v)$, and $S(w)$ (cm sec^{-1}); gustiness ratios $G(x)$, $G(y)$, and $G(z)$; mean cross products of eddy components $\overline{uv}$, $\overline{vw}$, and $\overline{uw}$ (cm^2 sec^{-2}); horizontal Reynolds' stress (parallel to 10-min mean wind) τ (dynes cm^{-2}); linear correlation coefficients between eddy components and air temperature (u,v), (v,w), (u,w), $(u;T)$, $(v;T)$, and $(w;T)$; mean cross product of vertical eddy component and air temperature multiplied by density and specific heat of air Q (mcal cm^{-2} min^{-1}). Values are 10-min means or totals centered at indicated CST.

Date	CST	Height	V	$S(u)$	$S(v)$	$S(w)$	$G(x)$	$G(y)$	$G(z)$	$\overline{uv}$	$\overline{vw}$	$\overline{uw}$	τ	(u,v)	(v,w)	(u,w)	$(u;T)$	$(v;T)$	$(w;T)$	Q
1953 18 Aug.	1835	12.0	411	43	24	14	.10	.06	.03	−60	0	−300	0.3	−0.06	0.00	−0.49	0.10	0.36	0.00	0
		6.0	331	32	39	19	.13	.12	.06	40	−80	−160	0.2	0.03	−0.11	−0.26	0.00	0.21	0.00	0
		3.0	273	36	16	9	.13	.06	.03	40	−10	−80	0.1	0.07	−0.07	−0.25	0.16	0.00	0.00	0
		1.5	221	45	13	9	.20	.06	.05	50	0	−110	0.1	0.09	0.00	−0.27	0.23	0.00	−0.28	−18
	2035	12.0	398	18	20	0	.05	.05	.00	−110	0	0	0.0	−0.30	0.00	0.00	0.93	0.00	0.00	0
		6.0	282	11	29	2	.04	.10	.01	10	−10	0	0.0	0.03	−0.17	0.00	0.00	0.38	0.00	0
		3.0	174	10	4	0	.06	.02	.00	20	0	0	0.0	0.50	0.00	0.00	0.50	1.00	0.00	0
		1.5	100	11	3	2	.11	.03	.02	0	0	0	0.0	0.00	0.00	0.00	0.45	0.00	0.00	0
	2235	12.0	476	55	40	18	.12	.08	.04	60	60	−220	0.2	0.03	0.08	−0.22	0.61	0.00	0.00	0
		6.0	371	46	32	27	.12	.09	.07	400	70	−190	0.2	0.27	0.08	−0.15	0.58	0.21	0.00	0
		3.0	294	43	22	16	.15	.07	.05	220	20	−150	−0.2	0.23	0.06	−0.22	0.56	0.16	0.00	0
		1.5	221	39	17	10	.18	.08	.05	130	0	−10	0.0	0.20	0.00	−0.03	0.66	0.19	0.00	0
19 Aug.	0035	12.0	394	27	28	7	.07	.07	.02	290	0	−30	0.0	0.38	0.00	−0.16	0.37	0.36	0.00	0
		6.0	310	25	9	14	.03	.03	.05	50	−10	−60	0.1	0.22	−0.08	−0.17	0.44	0.00	0.00	0
		3.0	229	22	11	7	.10	.05	.03	20	10	−10	0.0	0.08	−0.13	−0.07	0.27	0.00	0.00	0
		1.5	179	22	11	4	.12	.06	.02	−10	0	0	0.0	−0.04	0.00	0.00	0.25	0.00	0.00	0
	0235	12.0	512	34	26	10	.07	.05	.02	−290	10	−50	0.0	−0.33	0.04	−0.15	0.23	0.00	0.00	0
		6.0	380	35	22	20	.09	.06	.05	−60	0	−140	0.2	−0.08	0.00	−0.20	0.22	0.00	0.00	0
		3.0	296	39	18	14	.13	.06	.05	40	−20	−30	0.0	0.06	−0.08	−0.06	0.48	0.00	0.00	0
		1.5	223	56	21	11	.25	.09	.05	11	0	0	0.0	0.01	0.00	0.00	0.27	0.00	0.00	0
	0435	12.0	543	40	30	17	.07	.06	.03	50	−10	−180	0.2	0.04	−0.02	−0.26	0.28	−0.19	0.00	0
		6.0	425	44	22	27	.10	.05	.06	100	−20	−190	0.2	0.10	−0.03	−0.16	0.13	0.00	−0.21	−18
		3.0	355	44	23	20	.12	.06	.06	30	10	−140	0.2	0.03	0.02	−0.16	0.38	0.00	0.00	0
		1.5	282	45	29	15	.16	.10	.05	230	10	−50	0.1	0.18	0.02	−0.07	—	—	—	—

SITE DESCRIPTION AND DATA TABULATION

Date	CST	Height	V	$S(u)$	$S(v)$	$S(w)$	$G(x)$	$G(y)$	$G(z)$	$\overline{uv}$	$\overline{vw}$	$\overline{uw}$	τ	(u,v)	(v,w)	(u,w)	$(u;T)$	$(v;T)$	$(w;T)$	Q
	0635	12.0	544	58	64	23	.11	.12	.04	−360	−40	−300	0.3	−0.10	−0.03	−0.22	0.47	0.00	0.00	0
		6.0	466	66	50	33	.14	.11	.07	−360	30	−390	0.4	−0.11	0.02	−0.18	0.45	0.00	−0.30	−18
		3.0	400	57	42	22	.14	.11	.06	−240	60	−120	0.1	−0.10	0.07	−0.10	0.58	−0.20	0.00	0
		1.5	335	58	41	18	.17	.12	.05	−260	−80	−110	0.1	−0.11	−0.11	−0.11	0.57	−0.20	0.00	0
	0835	12.0	643	107	91	41	.17	.14	.06	390	−130	−880	1.0	0.04	−0.04	−0.20	0.05	−0.33	0.24	30
		6.0	603	100	91	49	.17	.15	.08	610	370	−1480	1.7	0.07	0.08	−0.30	−0.24	−0.22	0.24	48
		3.0	536	98	80	38	.18	.15	.07	200	100	−950	1.1	0.03	0.03	−0.26	−0.33	−0.09	0.09	18
		1.5	472	95	79	26	.20	.17	.06	880	−90	−510	0.6	0.12	−0.04	−0.21	−0.37	−0.11	0.11	18
	1035	12.0	666	127	91	41	.19	.14	.06	240	−80	−1450	1.6	0.02	−0.02	−0.28	−0.22	−0.12	0.35	66
		6.0	612	128	93	52	.21	.15	.08	1050	−170	−2040	2.3	0.09	−0.04	−0.37	−0.35	−0.11	0.43	144
		3.0	549	121	81	38	.22	.15	.07	340	90	−1420	1.6	0.04	0.03	−0.31	−0.39	−0.10	0.26	78
		1.5	468	112	85	31	.24	.18	.07	−970	60	−840	0.9	−0.10	0.02	−0.24	−0.25	−0.13	0.14	30
	1235	12.0	588	106	148	44	.18	.15	.08	600	−100	−340	0.4	0.04	−0.02	−0.07	0.15	−0.02	0.37	78
		6.0	534	111	162	46	.21	.30	.09	670	280	−480	0.5	0.04	0.04	−0.09	−0.12	−0.08	0.28	78
		3.0	496	112	123	33	.23	.25	.07	1440	0	−830	0.9	0.10	0.00	−0.22	−0.21	0.03	0.28	78
		1.5	433	104	122	27	.24	.28	.06	−190	−270	−690	0.8	−0.02	−0.08	−0.25	−0.22	0.16	0.13	30
	1435	12.0	602	123	163	49	.20	.27	.08	6440	450	−1050	1.2	0.32	0.06	−0.17	0.24	0.36	0.38	78
		6.0	562	124	151	52	.22	.27	.09	5060	40	−980	1.1	0.27	0.01	−0.15	−0.15	0.07	0.31	96
		3.0	515	123	133	38	.24	.26	.07	5230	−200	−1000	1.1	0.32	−0.04	−0.21	−0.25	0.08	0.23	78
		1.5	449	113	129	29	.25	.29	.07	2110	100	620	0.7	0.14	0.03	0.19	−0.22	0.14	0.17	48
	1635	12.0	530	87	162	37	.16	.31	.07	−3680	−710	−520	0.6	−0.26	−0.12	−0.16	−0.06	−0.24	0.30	30
		6.0	493	96	163	42	.20	.33	.09	−3990	−690	−770	0.8	−0.25	−0.10	−0.19	−0.22	−0.23	0.38	48
		3.0	453	91	135	29	.20	.30	.06	−3110	−410	−680	0.7	−0.25	−0.10	−0.26	−0.27	−0.23	0.24	30
		1.5	396	87	121	25	.22	.31	.06	−2230	−10	−540	0.6	−0.21	0.00	−0.25	−0.20	−0.23	0.14	18
	2035	12.0	451	19	15	2	.04	.03	.00	60	0	0	0.0	0.21	0.00	0.00	0.00	−0.48	0.00	0
		6.0	303	13	26	8	.04	.09	.03	50	−40	0	0.0	0.15	−0.19	0.00	0.00	0.00	0.00	0
		3.0	209	16	17	1	.08	.08	.01	10	0	0	0.0	0.04	0.00	0.00	0.39	−0.37	0.00	0
		1.5	125	14	12	1	.11	.10	.01	10	0	0	0.0	0.06	0.00	0.00	0.48	−0.56	0.00	0

5.2.b. Standard deviation ($S(u)$, $S(w)$) of eddy components (in the direction of the estimated mean wind, u, and the vertical; cm/sec) and gustiness ratios $G(x)$, $G(z)$, from rotating pressure tube anemometer (Texas A & M College); one sample per sec during 5-min periods centered at indicated CST.

Date (1953)	CST	Height (m)	u	$S(u)$	$S(w)$	$G(x)$	$G(z)$
19 August	0832	1.2	511	97	31	.19	.061
	1033	1.2	656	126	32	.19	.050
	1232	1.2	412	103	21	.25	.051
	1432	1.2	451	104	29	.23	.065
	1632	1.2	363	85	31	.23	.085

6.1.a. Loeser technique of daytime wind profile measurements (GRD). Mean height Z (m); duration t (sec) of evaluated drift; mean West, South, and upward components u, v, w (m/sec) of drift of individual smoke puffs. Values are t-sec averages centered at indicated $CST + t/2$ sec.

19 August 1953

CST	Z	t	u	v	w	CST	Z	t	u	v	w	CST	Z	t	u	v	w
0630	1397	36	3.7	5.7	−0.8							1040	1177	108	3.0	6.8	−0.2
	1180	30	2.8	5.3	0.1								993	102	4.7	7.5	−0.1
	1019	24	3.3	7.1	0.8								855	96	4.4	7.6	0.4
0830	1330	108	2.6	5.2	0.2	1030	1215	108	2.1	7.0	−0.1	1035	1147	108	2.8	7.2	0.3
	1129	102	4.2	7.8	0.3		982	96	3.3	7.8	−0.1		936	108	4.5	7.5	0.4
	961	6	10.8	7.0	−4.5		812	96	5.4	7.4	0.3		767	102	3.8	7.8	0.3
	849	6	9.4	7.5	8.7		646	66	3.5	8.5	−0.3		623	48	3.0	9.2	0.2
	530	18	5.6	10.7	0.7		430	18	11.9	12.0	1.9		511	42	2.4	8.4	0.1
	472	24	6.9	10.5	0.0		311	18	4.0	8.4	0.8		410	6	1.2	9.2	1.5
	396	24	7.2	10.5	0.3		228	36	2.1	7.6	0.2		233	24	2.2	8.4	0.3
	334	24	6.5	10.0	0.5		152	30	1.4	7.8	0.5		181	24	0.9	7.1	0.5
	292	24	5.6	9.1	0.2		84	30	1.5	6.6	−0.4		130	24	0.8	7.1	0.3
	241	24	5.3	8.0	−0.4		40	30	1.5	5.9	0.2		90	24	1.0	6.8	0.0
													54	12	3.0	6.8	0.5

6.1.b. Loeser technique of night-time wind profile measurements (GRD). Median values of West and South components u, v (m/sec) of drift; number N of balloons of a pibal swarm which cross the indicated levels. Basic data are overlapping 24-sec mean displacements toward the East and North of each of the N balloons at 12-sec intervals during a 4-min period centered at indicated CST.

Height (m)	18 August 2035			2235			19 August 1953 0235			0435		
	u	v	N	u	v	N	u	v	N	u	v	N
1600	—	—	—	1.5	1.6	1	−1.1	2.6	1	—	—	—
1400	1.3	6.5	1	1.5	3.1	3	−0.2	2.5	2	2.0	3.6	1
1200	0.8	7.2	2	1.3	3.9	4	1.3	2.9	3	2.0	7.6	2
1000	−2.0	8.0	3	0.3	6.8	4	2.3	5.4	5	2.5	8.8	2
800	−3.0	7.5	5	−1.1	9.1	4	2.0	8.4	6	1.9	9.9	3
700	−3.3	7.6	6	−2.0	9.3	5	0.8	9.5	7	1.7	11.1	5
600	−3.7	7.6	6	−2.7	9.5	4	0.0	10.5	6	1.4	11.4	5
500	−4.3	7.9	5	−4.0	9.5	6	0.0	11.5	5	0.1	11.5	6
400	−4.4	7.9	5	−5.7	9.3	6	−0.5	12.7	5	−0.1	12.0	5
300	−4.8	8.0	6	−6.3	10.0	5	−0.2	13.8	4	0.1	12.7	5
200	−5.0	8.4	5	−7.0	10.3	4	−0.5	14.9	3	1.2	13.9	5
100	−5.0	8.0	3	−6.4	9.4	2	−0.8	12.4	2	−0.3	12.7	4

6.2. Rawinsonde (GMD-1A) wind speed (m/sec) and direction (deg from North) from 1-min mean drift at 30-sec intervals, for first 7 min of ascent started at indicated CST.

18 August 1953 / 19 August 1953

1835			2035			2235			0035			0235		
m	m/sec	deg	m	m/sec	deg	m	m/sec	deg	m	m/sec	deg	m	m/sec	deg
2248	0.8	315	2125	0.5	233	1550	2.4	215	1923	1.9	158	2294	2.7	180
1967	1.5	275	1828	1.1	157	1347	3.2	226	1650	2.4	160	1982	3.7	145
1812	1.5	127	1678	2.7	175	1247	3.8	197	1513	3.4	166	1828	4.1	155
1657	3.7	146	1520	4.1	180	1138	5.1	184	1374	3.1	171	1657	4.0	152
1503	4.6	164	1366	6.1	191	1023	5.8	180	1238	2.4	199	1486	3.2	148
1351	6.1	173	1212	6.5	183	904	7.7	177	1099	4.3	186	1316	3.6	170
1198	8.4	166	1058	8.2	171	788	9.5	174	952	4.5	188	1146	4.6	188
1027	8.7	161	900	9.5	166	670	10.7	168	806	6.6	187	972	6.3	196
856	8.1	156	739	8.8	156	553	12.0	162	661	10.1	174	798	8.8	192
687	7.7	154	575	10.1	154	438	11.1	156	517	12.8	169	625	11.4	185
528	8.4	152	415	10.2	153	324	10.1	148	372	13.4	165	453	13.5	180
352	8.5	150	255	10.7	152	216	11.4	145	242	12.5	160	284	13.6	176
162	7.4	145	130	8.8	148	107	11.0	143	119	11.6	158	140	13.0	176

19 August 1953

0435			0635			0835			1035			1235		
m	m/sec	deg	m	m/sec	deg	m	m/sec	deg	m	m/sec	deg	m	m/sec	deg
2173	2.8	171	2255	2.0	156	1940	2.0	150	1997	4.8	142	2845	2.7	192
1900	3.6	165	1946	3.1	171	1686	2.4	176	1740	5.0	157	2422	3.3	208
1747	1.8	172	1788	2.6	189	1552	4.6	185	1611	5.0	170	2367	2.4	191
1574	2.1	183	1630	2.6	187	1418	4.5	192	1480	5.0	174	2194	5.1	172
1402	3.8	198	1473	4.0	202	1284	5.6	206	1352	6.2	189	2022	6.5	159
1227	8.3	195	1308	5.6	209	1151	7.3	210	1223	7.5	191	1850	6.8	156
1057	10.8	197	1145	7.5	204	1062	10.9	204	1094	8.8	198	1679	6.8	158
897	10.2	203	975	8.4	206	883	12.4	203	951	9.0	207	1466	6.1	162
738	12.3	194	812	10.4	201	750	10.1	201	797	9.4	209	1254	5.8	186
579	13.3	186	645	12.2	199	617	10.9	203	642	9.8	205	1043	7.4	194
421	13.9	182	487	12.5	198	484	11.6	204	488	9.4	196	773	7.7	192
268	14.3	180	320	14.9	193	345	11.2	206	336	9.0	190	467	7.6	183
133	13.5	179	160	14.1	193	173	9.2	200	168	9.0	190	191	9.5	173

19 August 1953

1435			1635			1835			2035		
m	m/sec	deg	m	m/sec	deg	m	m/sec	deg	m	m/sec	deg
2188	4.8	198	2292	3.5	224	2289	3.4	208	1671	6.2	204
1970	2.8	181	2004	5.6	199	1993	6.9	203	1439	6.5	194
1860	5.4	178	1852	5.4	199	1835	7.1	197	1323	7.0	185
1720	6.6	174	1713	6.8	176	1678	7.0	194	1208	8.0	178
1538	7.3	168	1543	8.3	166	1520	7.8	183	1093	8.7	173
1352	7.0	164	1371	7.8	164	1361	7.2	184	971	8.9	170
1168	6.8	167	1200	6.7	165	1198	6.9	175	849	9.2	167
989	6.1	171	1027	6.1	168	1024	8.6	168	726	9.6	164
822	5.7	168	856	5.6	164	853	8.4	166	603	9.6	160
654	6.1	158	683	6.3	152	682	8.2	159	481	10.2	156
487	5.8	164	512	8.3	144	511	8.1	155	360	10.1	152
322	6.7	169	338	8.4	142	340	8.6	150	240	10.7	149
161	8.8	175	167	7.0	148	171	8.6	144	120	10.3	144

6.3. Double theodolite pibal wind speed (m/sec) and direction (deg from North) from 1-min mean drift at 30-sec intervals, at indicated height (m), for first 7 min of ascent started at indicated CST.

18 August 2130 | 19 August 1953 0035 | 0236 | 0438

m	m/sec	deg	m	m/sec	deg	m	m/sec	deg	m	m/sec	deg
888	9.5	168	745	10.4	172	956	7.1	193	908	8.6	199
836	9.1	167	663	9.8	172	856	9.4	190	841	9.2	196
776	9.4	166	638	8.1	172	805	5.5	193	772	11.4	191
724	9.4	164	583	13.2	163	752	9.4	187	697	12.1	205
657	9.0	161	512	11.2	165	673	11.0	183	630	10.8	195
598	9.2	158	478	9.7	169	624	10.5	180	578	11.8	182
549	10.1	155	423	12.2	162	553	16.0	178	499	13.1	180
468	9.9	152	372	12.3	161	472	11.9	176	435	12.8	179
406	10.3	149	322	11.4	161	425	10.2	175	374	11.1	178
340	11.4	148	282	14.4	158	350	14.9	176	322	12.8	177
274	11.3	146	225	16.7	157	288	14.9	176	249	14.7	179
213	11.3	144	171	15.2	157	218	16.0	176	188	13.5	182
142	11.2	144	117	14.1	157	144	14.5	177	132	14.2	179
68	10.0	141	60	9.6	155	69	11.1	176	74	12.6	178

19 August 1953 0630 | 0830 | 1030 | 1230

m	m/sec	deg	m	m/sec	deg	m	m/sec	deg	m	m/sec	deg
830	11.1	198	908	9.9	203				1197	5.9	178
822	3.4	201	850	10.1	203				1127	7.5	182
778	7.6	195	787	9.8	203				1044	8.2	178
729	7.7	194	736	9.7	203	752	1.1	203	954	7.7	177
677	13.9	193	680	10.5	204	696	7.1	194	866	6.8	181
568	15.7	193	624	12.0	204	605	8.9	188	783	6.3	181
514	12.4	192	543	11.6	202	508	8.6	186	714	5.7	174
449	13.9	194	479	10.4	202	426	8.2	188	635	5.4	172
391	14.8	194	424	11.9	205	374	7.9	189	584	5.2	177
320	15.4	193	364	12.7	207	310	8.7	192	534	5.6	175
256	14.6	192	317	13.9	207	254	8.4	192	436	6.0	167
212	14.8	190	248	9.6	209	204	8.1	190	308	5.5	181
136	14.8	190	192	6.9	209	134	8.3	189	190	6.2	174
66	11.2	191	92	6.7	202	63	8.1	191	64	6.7	186

19 August 1953 1430 | 1630 | 1830

m	m/sec	deg	m	m/sec	deg	m	m/sec	deg
1018	5.8	168	815	7.2	158	896	5.3	160
952	6.7	167	744	7.6	158	864	7.5	162
890	6.1	168	711	7.4	158	767	9.6	164
795	5.2	167	689	7.8	157	708	12.6	156
710	5.7	158	660	9.1	157	551	11.4	155
618	6.2	154	616	9.1	159	519	2.5	172
544	8.4	149	570	8.4	152	516	4.8	162
450	6.8	149	508	7.4	147	462	9.2	154
356	5.9	157	452	6.5	148	395	7.5	152
378	8.6	157	378	6.1	144	344	5.9	148

F

19 August 1953

1430			1630			1830		
m	m/sec	deg	m	m/sec	deg	m	m/sec	deg
312	8.2	156	312	5.8	136	282	8.3	143
225	7.7	150	244	6.0	135	200	10.1	142
146	8.7	142	175	6.4	135	132	8.3	143
76	9.8	139	111	6.6	132	60	6.4	141

6.4. Radiosonde pressure (mb), temperature (°C) and relative humidity (%) at significant levels of ascent started at indicated CST. (M = "motorboating", i.e., a humidity value below the minimum value that the radiosonde can measure at that temperature.)

	18 August		19 August 1953											
	1835	2035	2235	0035	0235	0435	0635	0835	1035	1235	1435	1635	1835	2035
mb	951	952	952	952	952	952	953	953	953	953	951	951	950	950
°C	22.8	15.5	16.5	14.8	12.9	13.2	15.0	21.5	25.5	26.4	27.9	27.0	23.2	16.0
%	53	81	74	82	90	87	75	51	49	46	43	38	53	76
mb	801	932	938	940	429	936	933	918	892	798	860	766	936	940
°C	10.9	21.3	21.3	19.8	20.2	19.6	19.6	18.3	18.6	12.3	18.5	8.4	24.2	22.2
%	72	50	58	68	63	65	53	50	53	80	61	83	38	52
mb	786	874	880	873	864	920	916	914	866	784	788	734	821	923
°C	11.6	16.5	17.6	16.2	16.5	19.9	19.2	19.8	17.2	12.5	11.3	6.1	14.2	21.2
%	33	55	54	54	42	53	43	48	57	62	84	87	60	42
mb	778	792	852	859	818	856	853	782	808	728	756	694	754	816
°C	11.5	11.3	15.6	15.9	13.0	15.4	14.5	10.1	12.0	7.2	8.6	4.0	7.4	12.2
%	43	26	38	42	62	65	63	58	76	65	67	68	82	58
mb	731	768	784	798	778	818	827	734	782	702	743	676	666	745
°C	7.1	9.3	10.2	10.9	9.8	13.4	13.5	5.4	10.9	6.1	8.1	2.0	1.7	5.4
%	50	52	67	65	28	51	67	70	68	63	45	79	81	80
mb	692	700	774	791	750	777	754	729	742	669	670	660	659	720
°C	3.8	2.4	10.2	10.2	7.4	9.2	6.8	6.0	6.9	3.2	3.1	3.2	3.5	4.7
%	78	75	33	65	50	70	72	38	73	80	80	25	33	70
mb	681	682	760	777	663	748	746	658	728	645	653	636	647	682
°C	2.8	0.1	9.2	10.4	0.0	7.4	7.1	0.0	6.9	2.1	1.8	1.1	2.1	1.7
%	78	78	48	39	85	34	38	75	44	74	58	35	25	69
mb	654	650	706	705	652	736	738	635	690	626	648	608	624	668
°C	2.3	1.8	4.1	3.2	0.4	6.1	6.6	−1.5	3.5	2.2	2.7	−1.1	−0.1	2.4
%	26	25	62	65	44	55	32	70	76	28	45	87	25	22
mb	618	608	692	666	628	666	693	624	653	592	640	546	611	634
°C	0.3	−2.0	3.7	1.0	0.4	0.4	2.4	−1.0	0.2	−1.2	2.5	−7.0	−1.1	−0.4
%	M	M	38	39	24	85	71	25	84	62	29	82	46	M
mb	—	—	666	656	612	650	667	614	633	583	604	—	—	610
°C	—	—	1.2	−0.1	−1.4	1.3	0.7	−1.9	0.9	−2.2	−0.3	—	—	−1.5
%	—	—	64	37	M	25	73	42	60	51	57	—	—	23
mb	—	—	653	644	598	626	643	598	620	558	567	—	—	600
°C	—	—	1.7	0.2	−2.5	0.2	0.7	−2.7	−0.4	−4.0	−3.9	—	—	−2.8
%	—	—	23	25	31	M	22	21	39	67	72	—	—	42
mb	—	—	618	602	570	594	594	594	595	—	548	—	—	—
°C	—	—	−0.9	−2.1	−4.9	−2.3	−2.9	−3.2	−1.9	—	−5.4	—	—	—
%	—	—	M	M	35	26	M	M	37	—	70	—	—	—

6.5. Air temperature T (°C) and mixing ratio W (g water vapor/kg air) at altitude Z (m) from aerograph (L-20) data. CST of start, top level, and end of flight is indicated.

18 August (1840–1913–1935)

Z	T	W
17	22.7	11.3
35	22.6	11.0
51	22.7	11.1
65	23.3	11.2
95	22.9	10.8
125	22.8	9.2
155	22.7	9.2
240	22.7	9.3
310	21.2	8.5
470	20.0	9.6
630	18.5	10.0
790	16.6	9.5
940	15.1	9.1
1260	12.8	9.6
1580	12.8	5.5
1900	10.2	6.5
1580	12.8	5.9
1260	12.8	9.2
1100	14.3	10.3
940	15.4	9.7
790	16.4	9.4
630	18.2	9.6
470	19.7	9.6
310	21.2	9.6
95	22.9	9.4
35	21.8	11.5
17	22.0	11.0

19 August 1953 (0621–0637–0653)

Z	T	W
17	15.2	9.7
35	15.4	10.1
51	15.5	9.8
65	15.7	10.0
95	16.1	9.8
125	17.7	9.1
155	19.4	8.9
240	19.9	8.4
310	19.3	7.9
790	15.8	9.3
940	14.9	10.3
1260	13.8	7.3
1580	11.5	8.4
1260	13.3	9.0
940	14.7	10.3
630	16.7	10.1
310	19.4	8.2
240	19.7	8.5
155	18.2	8.2
125	17.6	8.6
95	16.5	8.8
65	15.5	9.4
51	15.2	9.5
35	15.0	9.8
17	15.0	9.8

(0819–0842–0859)

Z	T	W
17	18.8	11.2
35	19.2	10.3
65	19.5	10.4
95	18.5	9.9
125	18.4	9.7
155	17.6	9.6
240	17.7	9.6
310	19.1	9.8
630	16.7	8.4
940	14.4	9.3
1260	13.1	9.4
1580	10.5	8.6
1260	12.8	10.6
940	14.6	10.1
630	17.1	9.3
310	17.9	9.2
240	17.8	9.0
155	18.6	9.4
125	19.0	9.7
95	19.6	10.0
65	19.9	10.1
51	20.0	10.1
35	20.2	10.3
17	20.8	10.6

(———1042–1100)

Z	T	W
1580	10.5	8.5
1260	12.4	9.9
940	15.1	9.5
620	16.8	10.1
470	18.2	10.2
310	19.8	10.7
240	20.8	10.8
155	21.5	10.1
125	21.2	10.6
95	22.3	10.0
65	22.6	10.6
51	22.8	10.8
35	22.8	10.6
17	23.0	10.7

19 August 1953 (1216–1237–1249)

Z	T	W
17	23.8	11.3
51	23.3	11.4
65	23.7	11.5
95	22.7	10.7
155	22.2	10.6
240	21.0	10.3
310	20.6	10.5
630	17.7	10.7

(1412–1432–1446)

Z	T	W
17	24.8	10.7
51	24.2	10.7
65	23.9	10.2
95	23.2	9.8
155	22.9	9.9
240	21.9	9.8
310	21.2	10.1
630	18.2	10.3

(1620–1634–1648)

Z	T	W
155	23.5	9.4
240	22.5	8.9
310	22.0	9.2
630	19.6	9.5
940	16.1	9.3
1260	13.6	9.7
1580	10.4	9.2
1260	13.6	10.1

(1813–1832–1848)

Z	T	W
17	24.6	9.3
35	24.2	9.1
65	24.4	8.6
95	24.0	8.5
125	23.7	8.2
155	23.5	8.1
310	21.9	7.6
630	19.6	8.2

19 August 1953

(1216–1237–1249)			(1412–1423–1446)			(1620–1634–1648)			(1813–1832–1848)		
940	15.3	10.3	940	15.8	9.9	630	19.2	9.8	940	16.2	8.4
1260	12.8	9.6	1260	13.5	9.5	310	22.5	9.8	1260	14.0	8.9
1580	11.0	7.9	1580	10.6	7.7	125	23.7	8.4	1580	10.5	8.8
1260	13.1	9.7	1260	13.4	9.4	95	24.6	9.0	1260	13.6	9.2
940	15.1	10.3	940	15.6	10.6	35	24.9	8.8	940	16.1	8.7
590	16.6	10.2	630	18.8	10.5	17	25.5	9.0	630	19.1	8.6
310	20.7	10.8	310	21.3	10.7				310	22.2	7.8
65	23.2	10.4	155	23.6	10.5				155	23.8	8.3
35	23.7	10.6	125	23.7	10.1				125	24.2	8.2
26	23.7	10.6	95	24.6	10.6				95	24.2	8.2
			65	24.7	9.8				65	24.2	8.2
			51	24.5	10.0				35	23.7	8.7
			26	25.1	10.2				17	23.7	9.8

7.1. Representative values of West and South components of the wind u, v (m/sec) at standard heights. Values are estimated from the combination of smoke puff or pibal swarm, rawinsonde and double theodolite pibal data at or near the indicated CST.

	Height (m)	18 August		19 August 1953											
		1835	2035	2235	0035	0235	0435	0635	0835	1035	1235	1435	1635	1835	2035
u	2000	0.5	0.6	0.0	−0.9	−2.4	−1.1	−0.7	−1.4	−3.0	−3.0	−0.2	1.3	2.5	3.4
	1750	−0.8	0.2	0.5	−0.6	−2.1	−0.3	0.4	−0.4	−1.9	−2.3	−0.7	0.1	1.5	2.5
	1500	−1.3	0.6	1.6	−0.2	−1.0	0.8	1.7	0.7	−0.4	−1.6	−1.0	−1.2	0.5	1.4
	1250	−1.5	1.2	0.3	0.3	0.5	2.0	3.0	2.8	1.5	0.3	−1.1	−1.7	−0.5	0.1
	1000	−2.6	−1.7	0.1	0.7	1.9	3.0	3.5	5.2	4.0	1.5	−1.0	−1.9	−1.6	−1.3
	800	−3.2	−3.1	−1.0	0.4	1.8	3.1	3.6	5.9	4.5	1.5	−1.0	−2.3	−2.4	−2.4
	700	−3.5	−3.5	−2.0	−0.9	1.1	2.3	3.7	5.9	4.3	1.3	−1.4	−2.9	−2.9	−3.0
	600	−3.8	−3.9	−3.0	−1.9	0.4	1.5	3.8	5.8	3.8	1.1	−1.8	−3.4	−3.2	−3.5
	500	−4.0	−4.2	−4.0	−2.8	−0.1	0.9	3.7	5.6	3.2	0.6	−1.7	−3.8	−3.5	−4.0
	400	−4.1	−4.5	−5.2	−3.6	−0.5	0.4	3.5	5.2	2.6	0.0	−1.7	−4.1	−4.0	−4.6
	300	−4.1	−4.7	−6.3	−4.2	−0.6	0.3	3.3	4.7	2.1	−0.5	−2.0	−4.2	−4.6	−5.2
	200	−4.2	−4.9	−6.8	−4.6	−0.7	0.2	3.1	4.0	1.8	−0.6	−2.3	−4.1	−5.0	−5.7
	100	−4.3	−5.0	−6.4	−4.6	−0.8	0.2	2.5	2.4	1.4	−0.7	−2.6	−4.0	−4.8	−5.6
v	2000	−0.2	1.3	1.5	1.2	3.3	3.0	3.2	1.8	4.0	6.1	6.4	6.6	6.2	3.5
	1750	1.8	2.5	1.7	1.6	3.0	2.5	2.7	2.1	4.5	5.7	6.2	6.9	6.6	5.1
	1500	4.5	4.5	2.2	2.2	2.6	2.6	3.2	4.0	5.4	5.7	6.1	7.2	7.1	6.5
	1250	7.2	6.6	3.7	3.5	3.1	6.0	5.5	6.0	6.7	6.1	6.0	7.4	7.6	7.6
	1000	8.2	8.2	6.5	4.5	5.5	9.2	7.9	8.2	7.7	7.1	6.0	7.2	7.9	8.8
	800	8.0	8.4	9.2	6.5	8.4	10.7	10.0	9.4	8.2	7.6	5.9	7.0	8.0	9.2
	700	7.8	8.5	10.0	9.6	9.8	11.6	11.1	10.0	8.7	7.9	5.9	6.8	8.0	9.2
	600	7.6	8.5	10.3	11.6	11.2	12.1	12.1	10.5	9.1	8.0	6.0	6.6	7.9	9.2
	500	7.3	8.5	10.1	12.4	12.3	12.6	13.1	10.8	9.3	8.1	6.1	6.4	7.7	9.1
	400	7.0	8.4	9.9	12.8	13.3	13.0	14.1	10.8	9.3	8.3	6.3	6.2	7.5	9.0
	300	6.6	8.2	9.6	12.9	14.2	13.5	15.0	10.3	8.7	8.5	6.9	6.0	7.3	8.8
	200	6.1	8.0	9.3	12.4	14.9	13.9	15.0	9.0	8.1	8.7	8.0	5.7	7.0	8.5
	100	5.6	7.7	8.5	11.0	12.5	13.4	12.1	7.3	7.5	8.7	7.8	5.2	6.4	7.9

7.2.a. Air temperature (°C) at standard heights. Values are interpolated and averaged from radiosonde and airplane (L-20) data at or near the indicated CST.

Height (m)	18 August			19 August 1953										
	1835	2035[1]	2235[1]	0035[1]	0235[1]	0435[1]	0635	0835	1035	1235	1435	1635	1835	2035[1]
2000	9.5	8.3	8.9	9.2	8.0	8.0	7.8	7.4	8.2	9.3	7.8	7.0	7.9	6.5
1750	11.3	10.2	10.2	10.3	9.9	9.4	9.6	9.5	10.1	11.0	9.8	9.3	10.1	8.7
1500	12.2	12.0	11.7	11.2	11.7	11.8	11.8	11.3	11.3	11.9	11.8	11.6	12.2	10.9
1250	12.8	13.5	13.6	13.2	13.8	13.8	13.8	13.2	13.0	13.7	14.1	14.0	14.2	13.1
1000	14.9	15.1	15.5	15.2	16.2	15.1	14.6	14.6	15.3	15.7	16.1	16.3	16.2	15.2
800	16.8	16.3	16.9	16.2	17.2	16.5	15.8	16.0	16.6	17.1	17.9	18.2	18.0	16.9
600	18.5	17.9	18.3	17.2	18.1	17.9	17.2	17.4	17.7	18.6	19.7	20.1	19.9	18.6
400	20.1	19.6	19.6	18.3	18.9	19.4	18.7	18.5	19.8	20.6	21.6	22.0	21.6	20.3
200	22.0	21.0	21.0	19.4	19.8	19.7	19.4	18.5	22.2	22.7	23.7	23.7	23.5	21.8
100	22.5	18.2	19.8	18.6	19.5	17.0	16.9	19.6	23.4	23.7	24.8	25.3	24.0	20.6

[1] Radiosonde data only.

7.2.b. Mixing ratio (g water vapor/kg air) at standard heights. Values are interpolated and averaged from radiosonde and airplane (L-20) data at or near the indicated CST.

Height (m)	18 August			19 August 1953										
	1835	2035[1]	2235[1]	0035[1]	0235[1]	0435[1]	0635	0835	1035	1235	1435	1635	1835	2035[1]
2000	6.0	4.8	4.6	3.7	3.9	4.5	8.0	6.4	6.6	6.1	5.9	7.8	7.7	6.1
1750	5.6	3.8	3.5	4.2	2.8	6.0	8.0	7.2	7.4	7.0	7.5	8.3	8.0	6.2
1500	6.8	3.3	6.2	6.2	5.4	6.0	7.9	8.0	8.4	8.7	8.4	8.8	8.3	6.3
1250	8.7	4.7	5.4	5.9	6.8	6.6	8.0	8.9	9.0	9.6	9.4	9.3	8.7	6.5
1000	9.0	6.1	5.0	5.7	5.8	8.2	9.0	8.8	8.8	9.9	9.9	9.1	8.3	6.8
800	9.2	7.2	6.9	6.8	6.6	8.5	8.5	8.6	8.9	10.1	10.2	9.2	8.2	7.0
600	9.5	7.8	8.3	8.0	7.6	8.6	8.3	8.5	9.5	10.3	10.3	9.3	8.2	7.2
400	9.4	8.2	9.1	9.1	8.6	8.6	7.8	8.6	10.0	10.4	10.4	9.3	7.9	7.4
200	9.5	8.7	9.9	10.3	9.7	9.8	8.4	9.2	10.3	10.4	10.4	9.0	8.0	8.6
100	10.0	9.1	10.8	10.3	10.0	9.5	8.9	9.9	10.3	10.5	10.3	9.0	8.5	9.4

[1] Radiosonde data only.

7.3.a. Summary of heat budget constituents (mcal cm^{-2} min^{-1}) of the earth-air interface according to the theoretical models by Suomi, Halstead, and Lettau. Net radiation flux R, heat transfer to the soil S, sensible heat transfer to the air Q, and latent heat transfer to the air (heat equivalent of evaporation) E. Values are hourly means centered at indicated CST.

	18 August			19 August 1953										
	1835	2035	2235	0035	0235	0435	0635	0835	1035	1235	1435	1635	1835	2035
Suomi														
R_0	81	85	92	95	94	84	44	−422	−677	−892	−760	−315	12	87
S_0	−77	−68	−47	−70	−60	−70	−28	48	114	130	118	16	−52	−79
Q_0	−4	−21	−49	−20	−24	−10	−29	245	260	360	259	102	—	−7
E_0	0	5	4	−5	−10	−4	13	129	302	401	382	197	—	−1
Halstead														
R_0	30	70	70	70	70	60	30	−380	−630	−860	−760	−560	20	—
S_0	−42	−60	−57	−60	−55	−53	−42	43	100	135	100	15	−50	—
Q_0	−65	−117	−97	−67	−48	−55	−37	93	257	305	262	125	−35	—
E_0	130	88	50	0	30	20	58	217	320	343	610[1]	295	118	—
Lettau														
R_0	64	76	86	88	87	78	35	−410	−680	−867	−748	−402	14	84
S_0	−54	−66	−60	−63	−61	−64	−44	78	157	176	156	39	−44	−78
Q_0	−15	−6	−23	−6	−18	−18	−20	145	277	495	509	134	−11	−9
E_0	6	11	10	−3	−1	−9	28	78	126	196	281	119	26	7

[1] Interpolated value.

7.3.b. Representative logarithmic height derivatives of wind speed (zV', mm sec^{-1}, from UCLA and JH data), potential temperature ($z\theta'$, 10^{-3} °C, from JH and UW data), and water vapor pressure (ze', 10^{-3} mb, from JH and UW data); representative values of Karman number k (from zV' and UCLA, JH, and MIT stress data), interpolated ground drag τ_0 (dynes cm^{-2}, from zV' and representative k values), and ratio of heat and momentum diffusivities N_Q; representative ground-flux ratio F_0 and inverse Bowen ratio B. Values refer to indicated CST and are employed in the computation of the heat budget constituents Q_0 and E_0 (Lettau model; see Table 7.3.a).

	18 August			19 August 1953										
	1835	2035	2235	0035	0235	0435	0635	0835	1035	1235	1435	1635	1835	2035
zV'	494	433	532	443	494	542	683	834	989	909	900	848	424	405
$z\theta'$	352	673	503	395	281	229	158	−337	−545	−738	−706	−320	252	586
ze'	−37	−126	−64	−31	9	46	−113	−234	−322	−488	−680	−359	−200	−59
k	0.34	0.28	0.33	0.29	0.36	0.36	0.37	0.40	0.40	0.42	0.43	0.39	0.35	0.32
τ_0	0.31	0.16	0.36	0.19	0.37	0.45	0.74	1.22	1.70	1.60	1.63	1.23	0.24	0.20
N_Q	0.48	0.18	0.46	0.26	0.60	0.66	0.80	2.06	2.06	2.65	2.78	1.99	0.54	0.22
F_0	0.31	0.27	0.53	1.01	0.86	0.51	−0.36	4.66	3.86	3.69	3.20	5.43	−1.46	0.14
B	−0.17	−0.30	−0.20	0.13	0.05	0.32	−1.15	1.11	0.94	1.05	1.53	1.78	−1.26	−0.16

7.4. Richardson number (Ri; units of 10^{-3}) from Mass. Inst. Tech. and Johns Hopkins University data on simultaneous temperature and wind velocity differences, centered at indicated CST and mean height z_m (meters). (Ri') = average height derivative of Richardson number (10^{-3} m^{-1}).

Inst. Set	Height (m)	18 August			19 August 1953										
		1835	2035	2235	0035	0235	0435	0635	0835	1035	1235	1435	1635	1835	2035
MIT	8.0	136	202	152	284	122	102	73	−106	−91	−165	−157	−66	145	219
MIT	4.0	79	132	108	100	61	63	43	−73	−74	−150	−144	−82	91	127
JH	3.2	122	132	85	116	65	65	31	−63	−67	−149	−105	−75	66	129
JH	1.6	82	136	75	85	56	45	27	−31	−40	−49	−46	−31	48	109
JH	0.8	36	111	55	66	38	26	10	−12	−16	−25	−26	−13	50	99
(Ri')		26	41	27	37	20	17	10	−16	−16	−25	−27	−15	23	39

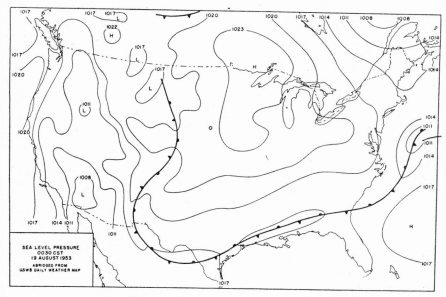

Fig. B.3.1. Continental scale synoptic chart. Sea level pressure distribution for the third general observation period.

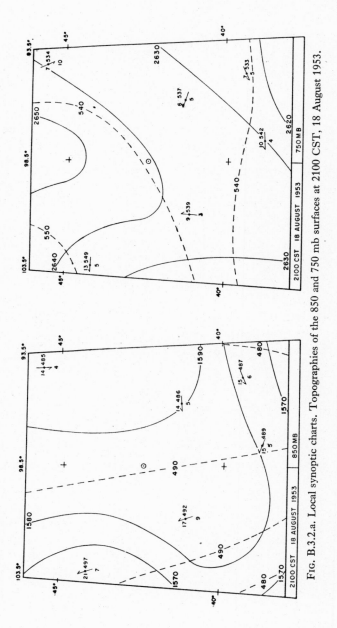

FIG. B.3.2.a. Local synoptic charts. Topographies of the 850 and 750 mb surfaces at 2100 CST, 18 August 1953.

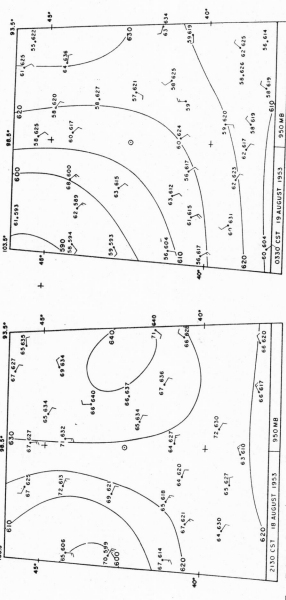

FIG. B.3.3.a. Local synoptic charts. Topography of the 950 mb surface at 2130 CST, 18 August, and 0330 CST, 19 August 1953.

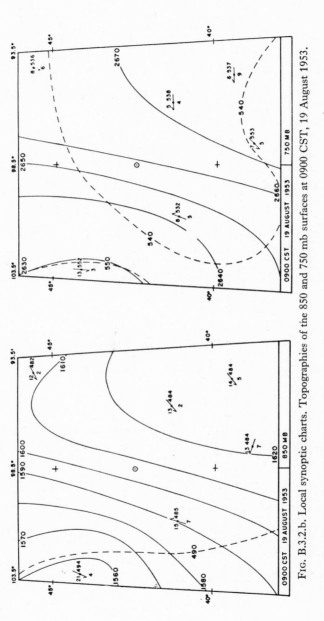

Fig. B.3.2.b. Local synoptic charts. Topographies of the 850 and 750 mb surfaces at 0900 CST, 19 August 1953.

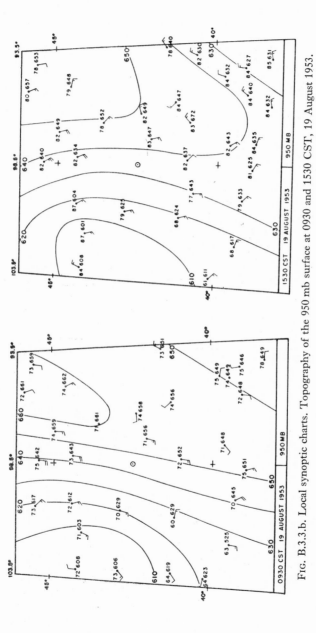

Fig. B.3.3.b. Local synoptic charts. Topography of the 950 mb surface at 0930 and 1530 CST, 19 August 1953.

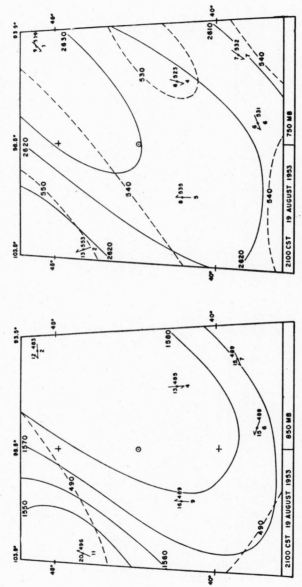

Fig. B.3.2.c. Local synoptic charts. Topographies of the 850 and 750 mb surfaces at 2100 CST, 19 August 1953.

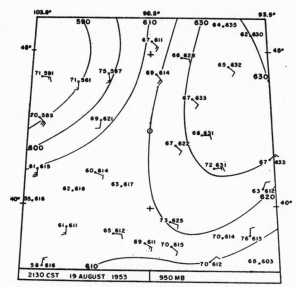

FIG. B.3.3.c. Local synoptic chart. Topography of the 950 mb surface at 2130 CST, 19 August 1953.

FOURTH GENERAL OBSERVATION PERIOD

0405 CST 22 August through 1505 CST 22 August 1953

Solar Data for the Field Site near O'Neill, Nebraska

	Sun's elevation angle at apparent noon	Sunrise CST	Apparent noon CST	Sunset CST
22 August	59° 13′	0548	1237	1926

Summary of Synoptic Conditions

The stationary front in Western Nebraska stayed in that position through 22 August. The air flow on 19, 20, 21, and 22 August was dominated by a blocking high-pressure cell over Wisconsin. Rain fell east of the front in Western Nebraska and South Dakota on the 19th and 20th. The winds were generally southerly at 5 to 10 mph increasing to 10 to 15 mph. The skies had broken clouds in the afternoon and became generally clear on the 21st. The fourth general observation was begun at 0405 on the 22nd under favorable conditions. However, by 1030 CST of the 22nd the sky over the test site became nine-tenths covered with cirro-stratus type clouds. This dense cloud cover made the conditions for smoke-puff photography so poor that the fourth general observation period was terminated at 1505 CST. The stationary front in Western Nebraska weakened on the 23rd while the high-pressure cell over Wisconsin started to move eastward. Some precipitation persisted in Western Nebraska. The wind was from the south initially and then backed to southeast at 5 to 15 mph. On the 23rd the sky cover varied from broken to overcast.

1.1.a. Mean geopotential H (dynamic m above 601 = geopotential of test site), West and South components of the geostrophic wind u_g, v_g (m/sec) at indicated pressure (mb) levels. Values are estimated for the O'Neill site from local synoptic charts.

22 August 0900

mb	H	u_g	v_g
750	2022	2.7	10.8
800	1475	2.6	12.2
850	962	3.2	12.9
900	468	4.3	12.6
950	9	2.5	13.1

1.1.b. Direction (deg from North) and speed (m/sec) of the 950 mb geostrophic wind. Values are estimated for the O'Neill site from local synoptic charts.

22 August 1953

0330	0630	0930	1230	1530
186	186	191	189	189
11.1	12.5	13.3	14.3	16.7

1.2. Direction (deg from North) of the mean surface wind from standard vane recordings at 1-min intervals (Mass. Inst. Tech., 16 m level). Hourly and 15-min averages centered at indicated CST.

22 August 1953

	0435	0635	0835	1035	1235	1435[1]
60-min mean:	170	168	170	181	172	157
15-min mean:	171	173	170	181	170	157

[1] Period 1405 to 1443 CST.

1.3. Standard shelter temperature (°F), relative humidity (%); station pressure (inches) and air density (mg cm^{-3}); amount (tenths) and types of clouds.

Month	Day	CST	Temp.	RH	Pressure	Density	Clouds	Remarks
Aug.	22	0430	61	59	28.030	1.14	3 AcCs	Clear overhead. Some clouds to E
		0630	59	66	.035	1.14	3 AcCs	Some Cs in all directions. Clear overhead
		0830	67	54	.030	1.12	1 Cs	Some haze. Clouds dissipating except heavier to far W
		1030	75	60	.030	1.10	9 AcCs	Light haze. Cs to W coming up
		1230	82	41	.020	1.09	8 Cs	Cs coming overhead, mostly to W
		1430	84	35	27.990	1.08	9 CuCs	Sun variable. Thin shadows

2.1.a. Soil temperature (°C) from thermistors (University of Texas) and soil thermocouples (University of California and Johns Hopkins University). Values are readings at indicated CST.

Inst. Set	Depth (cm)	0435	0635	0835	1035	1235	1435
UT	0.5	16.53	16.25	22.01	33.23	39.00	36.57
UCLA	1.3	16.17	15.61	20.44	30.56	37.67	36.11
UT	1.5	17.31	17.09	20.64	28.48	34.06	33.61
UT	2.5	18.38	17.73	20.08	26.28	31.37	31.77
JH	2.5	18.83	18.30	19.21	22.50	26.18	27.33
UT	3.5	18.94	18.25	19.89	25.92	29.76	30.75
UT	4.5	19.27	18.63	19.79	24.15	28.70	29.93
JH	5.0	19.62	19.04	19.30	21.36	24.40	26.10
UT	5.5	19.77	19.11	19.98	23.46	27.56	29.13
UCLA	10.0	19.83	19.17	18.44	20.33	23.28	25.00
JH	10.0	20.77	20.16	19.86	20.64	22.49	24.24
JH	20.0	21.73	21.30	20.86	20.70	21.06	21.88
UCLA	25.0	21.39	20.67	20.00	20.00	20.28	20.56
JH	40.0	21.56	21.46	21.32	21.16	21.06	20.98
JH	80.0	20.13	20.15	20.15	20.13	20.10	20.10

Above the data columns: 22 August 1953

2.1.b. Change of soil temperature (°C hr^{-1}) averaged over indicated layers from soil temperature integrators (University of Wisconsin). Values are differences between readings at the end and beginning of 1-hr intervals centered at indicated CST.

Depth (cm)	0435	0635	0835	1035	1235	1435
0–5	−0.55	0.72	1.75	2.17	1.02	0.40
5–15	−0.52	−0.26	0.29	0.95	1.18	0.60
15–50	−0.16	−0.13	−0.12	−0.03	0.12	0.16

Above the data columns: 22 August 1953

2.2.a. Soil thermal conductivity (mcal cm^{-1} sec^{-1} deg^{-1}) computed from soil thermistor response to defined heating pulses (University of Texas, Albrecht heat flux meter No. 2). Values are derived from 60-sec trials beginning at indicated CST.

Depth (cm)	22 August 1953 0440	0640	0840	1040	1240
0.5	0.60	0.56	0.62	0.59	0.61
1.5	0.82	0.80	0.80	0.85	0.80
2.5	0.96	1.06	0.96	1.01	0.99
3.5	1.04	1.06	0.97	1.01	1.05
4.5	1.45	1.24	1.10	1.28	1.45
5.5	1.40	1.53	1.48	1.58	1.43

2.2.b. Soil moisture (% wet weight) from soil samples at the Johns Hopkins University site. Indicated CST refers to the approximate time of soil sample extraction.

Depth (cm)	21 August 1230	1530	2030	22 August 1953 0530	1500
4	7.1	6.3	6.6	6.5	5.5
10	6.0	6.6	5.6	5.2	4.5
20	4.0	5.4	5.0	4.2	4.6
40	2.9	2.5	2.6	2.3	3.2

2.3. Soil moisture tension (mb) from tensiometers (Johns Hopkins University). Values are readings at indicated CST.

Depth (cm)	22 August 1953 0435	0635	0835	1035	1235	1435
5	597	557	550	600	650	683
10	660	636	625	650	684	710
20	535	442	388	424	533	631
40	233	49	11	32	118	289

2.4. Vertical flux of heat (mcal cm^{-2} min^{-1}) from soil temperature integrators (University of Wisconsin), Albrecht heat flux meter No. 2 (University of Texas-A*l*), Gier and Dunkle heat flow meters (University of California; University of Texas-*GD*; Johns Hopkins University-*GD*), and numerical integration of soil temperature profile changes (Johns Hopkins University). UW and JH values are 60-min averages, UCLA values are 15-min averages, and UT and JH-*GD* values are approximately 2-min averages. All averages are centered at indicated CST.

Inst. Set	Depth (cm)	22 August 1953 0435	0635	0835	1035	1235	1435
UW	0.0	−85	−27	38	110	126	85
UT-A*l*	0.0[1]	−99	−46	116	383	250	—
JH	0.0[1]	−50	−42	3	85	127	100
UCLA	0.2[2]	−72	−46	123	292	312	206
UT-*GD*	0.2[2]	−42	−25	79	194	184	120

Inst. Set	Depth (cm)	22 August 1953 0435	0635	0835	1035	1235	1435
UCLA	1.3	−34	−25	39	112	143	105
UT-A*l*	2.0	−64	−36	30	123	145	—
JH-*GD*	2.5	−38	−33	0	67	112	85
UW	5.0	−69	−49	−14	46	97	74
UCLA	10.0	−24	−27	−10	28	65	66
UW	15.0	−40	−34	−30	−8	30	40

[1] Values are extrapolated to surface.

[2] Approximative depth; the upper plates of the flow meters were "just covered with soil".

3.1. Summary of data on radiation (mcal cm^{-2} min^{-1}). Short-wave radiation from Eppley pyrheliometer (GRD); net radiation from two Gier and Dunkle radiometers (Johns Hopkins University and University of Texas) and the Suomi net radiometer (University of Wisconsin); total radiation from the Gier and Dunkle radiometer (University of Texas). Values are hourly averages centered at indicated CST.

	Inst. Set	22 August 1953 0435	0635	0835	1035	1235	1435
(Short-Wave)	GRD	0	103	677	1133	1263	987
	GRD[1]	0	90	680	1140	1320[2]	950[2]
	JH	−80	−40	340	680	820	560
(Net)	UT	−96	13	455	832	1016	714
	UW	−108	−32	376	724	785	580
(Total)	UT	456	570	1252	1793	2061	1616

[1] 10-min average centered at indicated CST.   [2] Subject to error because of clouds.

3.2. Boundary shear-stress (dynes cm^{-2}) from drag recorder (University of California) and Sheppard-type drag plate (Johns Hopkins University); direction of boundary shear-stress (deg from North) from drag recorder (University of California). Values are 10-min means centered at indicated CST.

Inst. Set	22 August 1953 0435	0635	0835	1035	1235	1435
UCLA	0.97	1.95	—	—	—	—
JH	0.6	1.4	2.5	1.5	2.6	2.5
UCLA	152	170	—	—	—	—

3.3. Characteristics of low level smoke-puff drift (Johns Hopkins University); direction of drift (deg from North); time t_{25} (sec) required to cross 25 m circle; lateral width S (deg) at 25 m and time t_D (sec) required to reach threshold of visibility. Values are ensemble averages for 10 smoke puffs fired at approximately 1-min intervals beginning at indicated CST.

G

22 August 1953

	0400	0600	0800	1000	1200	1400
dd	—	172	173	170	183	154
t_{25}	—	6.0	5.1	5.4	5.4	5.1
S	—	15.7	14.7	9.3	10.7	13.1
t_D	—	30	15	13	22	19

4.1.a. Hourly mean wind speed (cm/sec) from standard three-cup anemometers (Mass. Inst. Tech.), modified Sheppard-type anemometers (University of California), ping-pong ball anemometers (Iowa State College), and modified SCS cup anemometers (Johns Hopkins University); centered at indicated CST.

Inst. Set	Height (m)	22 August 1953 0435	0635	0835	1035	1235	1435
MIT	16.0	641	723	832	668	791	806
MIT	8.0	536	620	766	623	733	743
UCLA	8.0	516	636	798	659	760	802
ISC	7.0	499	603	763	607	718	746
JH	6.4	450	564	752	619	698	757
UCLA	4.15	438	562	723	602	697	736
MIT	4.0	469	554	700	578	675	679
ISC	4.0	444	549	710	573	669	703
JH	3.2	385	508	689	576	651	700
MIT	2.0	403	487	630	519	607	619
UCLA	2.2	368	486	633	536	616	648
JH	1.6	328	450	611	516	583[1]	624
UCLA	1.0	313	420	552	472	538	566
ISC	1.0	328	418	552	454	526	549
JH	0.8	278	389	533	456	512	547
UCLA	0.5	263	356	470	406	460	484
JH	0.4	233	326	455	389	435[1]	464

[1] Interpolated values.

4.1.b. 15-min mean wind speed (cm/sec) from standard three-cup anemometers (Mass. Inst. Tech.), modified Sheppard-type anemometers (University of California), ping-pong ball anemometers (Iowa State College), and semi-cylindrical anemometers (Johns Hopkins University); centered at indicated CST.

Inst. Set	Height (m)	22 August 1953 0435	0635	0835	1035	1235	1435
MIT	16.0	618	730	841	669	770	784
MIT	8.0	513	622	777	618	706	723
UCLA	8.0	506	654	780	640	762	784
ISC	7.0	481	619	778	607	720	729
UCLA	4.15	434	576	704	582	702	721

Inst. Set	Height (cm)	22 August 1953 0435	0635	0835	1035	1235	1435
MIT	4.0	449	554	709	567	645	662
ISC	4.0	426	554	720	572	674	680
JH	3.2	308[1]	455[2]	641[3]	544[4]	673[5]	695[6]
MIT	2.0	385	490	638	507	578	605
UCLA	2.0	366	495	618	518	623	634
JH	1.6	282[1]	406[2]	—	490[4]	604[5]	622[6]
UCLA	1.0	318	427	538	457	540	552
ISC	1.0	316	423	558	457	527	530
JH	0.8	—	337[2]	496[3]	—	—	—
UCLA	0.5	264	362	458	393	460	472
JH	0.4	206[1]	294[2]	409[3]	341[4]	414[5]	442[6]
JH	0.2	176[1]	246[2]	338[3]	290[4]	352[5]	367[6]
JH	0.1	113[1]	176[2]	258[3]	222[4]	271[5]	276[6]
JH	0.05	77[1]	117[2]	179[3]	156[4]	—	141[6]

[1] 0430–0445. [3] 0830–0845. [5] 1230–1245.
[2] 0630–0645. [4] 1030–1045. [6] 1430–1445.

4.2. Mean air temperature (°C) from aspirated thermocouples (Mass. Inst. Tech., 15-min means; University of California, average of six readings taken every 3 min), shielded thermocouples (Johns Hopkins University, average of 20 readings at each level during a 5-min interval), and shielded thermistors (University of Texas, 10-sec means); centered at indicated CST.

Inst. Set	Height (m)	22 August 1953 0435	0635	0835	1035	1235	1435
MIT	16.0	16.48	15.87	19.75	24.14	26.97	28.00
MIT	8.0	16.24	15.75	19.92	24.34	27.30	28.26
UCLA	8.0	15.22	14.72	18.61	23.44	26.89	27.61
JH	6.4	15.31	14.99	19.79	24.11	26.94	28.11
MIT	4.0	16.03	15.67	20.06	24.65	27.66	28.43
UCLA	4.0	15.67	14.72	18.67	23.67	27.50	28.00
JH	3.2	15.01	14.94	20.20	24.44	27.52	28.59
MIT	2.0	15.80	15.60	20.40	25.20	28.30	28.90
UCLA	2.0	14.94	14.67	18.89	24.17	27.94	28.11
JH	1.6	14.77	14.80	20.39	24.83	28.00	28.75
UCLA	1.0	14.56	14.50	19.11	24.28	28.33	28.61
JH	0.8	14.57	14.67	20.73	25.37	28.49	29.19
UT	0.8	15.05	15.35	20.5	25.6	28.35	29.35
UCLA	0.5	14.06	14.06	19.72	25.33	29.39	29.17
UT	0.5	15.0	15.25	20.85	26.55	29.05	29.4
JH	0.4	14.30	14.54	21.01	25.98	28.90	29.69
UT	0.3	15.05	15.25	21.1	27.0	29.5	29.75
JH	0.2	14.08	14.36	21.45	26.76	29.65	30.01
JH	0.1	13.87	14.28	21.80	27.53	30.29	30.29
UT	0.1	14.6	14.9	21.7	28.0	30.5	30.5

4.3.a. Mean water vapor pressure (mb) from dew-point apparatus (Johns Hopkins University). Simultaneous air sampling at given intake levels. Values are 5-min averages centered at indicated CST.

Height (m)	22 August 1953 0435	0635	0835	1035	1235	1435
6.4	10.42	10.99	12.01	13.46	12.16	11.42
3.2	10.57	11.08	11.99	13.90	12.38	11.60
1.6	10.50	11.06	12.12	14.04	12.50	11.82
0.8	10.61	11.11	12.31	14.29	12.72	12.13
0.4	10.62	11.15	12.64	14.88	13.13	12.50
0.2	10.66	11.32	12.70	15.06	13.47	12.76
0.1	10.71	11.36	12.93	15.61	13.74	13.00

4.3.b. Mean vertical difference (between 82 and 39 cm) of dry-bulb temperature (10^{-3} °C) and water vapor pressure (10^{-3} mb) from double psychrometer lift-apparatus (University of Wisconsin). Values are hourly means (based on one sample every 10 min) centered at indicated CST.

	22 August 1953 0435	0635	0835	1035	1235	1435	1635
10^{-3} °C	200	98	−277	−590	−615	−421	−260
10^{-3} mb	−31	−4	−153	−339	−335	−317	−256

4.4. Mean ozone concentration (10^{-8} g O_3/g air) from automatic ozone recorders (University of New Mexico). Values are 60-min means estimated from traces on chart recorders centered at indicated CST.

Height (m)	22 August 1953 0430	0630	0830	1030	1230	1430
12.5	6.8	6.3	6.4	7.7	8.3	9.1
6.25	—	—	5.7	6.9	7.7	7.8
1.6	—	—	6.4	7.7	8.4	8.8
0.4	6.4	6.1	6.2	7.7	8.4	8.8

5.1. Standard deviation of temperature fluctuations (10^{-2} °C) from bead thermistors (Iowa State College, 10 samples per sec during 10-min periods). Periods are centered at indicated CST.

Inst. Set	Height (m)	22 August 1953 0435	0635	0835	1035	1235	1435
ISC	8.0	17	21	—	87	105	65
ISC	4.0	15	21	—	97	128	67
ISC	2.0	9	23	51	95	131	68
ISC	1.0	10	23	50	100	161	76
ISC	0.5	6	27	50	156	—	64
ISC	0.25	11	27	49	161	155	65

5.2.b. Standard deviation $S(u)$, $S(w)$ of eddy components (in the direction of the estimated mean wind, u, and the vertical; m/sec) and gustiness ratios $G(x)$, $G(z)$, from rotating pressure tube anemometer (Texas A & M College); one sample per sec during 5-min periods centered at indicated CST.

Date (1953)	CST	Height (m)	u	$S(u)$	$S(w)$	$G(x)$	$G(z)$
22 August	0632	3.1	500	83	20	0.16	0.040
	0832	3.1	330	69	19	0.21	0.058
	1034	3.1	392	92	32	0.23	0.081
	1232	3.1	525	145	42	0.28	0.080
	1432	3.1	520	132	38	0.25	0.073

5.3. Statistics of fluctuation quantities from aircraft (PBY-6A) data (Woods Hole Ocean. Inst.). Potential temperature θ (°K); mixing ratio W (g water vapor/kg air); standard deviation of eddy components $S(u)$ and $S(w)$ (cm sec^{-1}); horizontal Reynolds' stress τ_{xz} (dynes cm^{-2}); linear correlation coefficient between eddy wind components $(u;w)$; standard deviation of temperature $S(T)$ (°C); mean cross product of vertical eddy component and temperature multiplied by density and specific heat of air Q_z (mcal cm^{-2} min^{-1}). Values are averages over horizontal upwind courses of 2 to 3 miles extent. CST of flight at lowest and highest level is indicated.

22 August 1953   1450 to 1540 CST

Height (m)	θ	W	$S(u)$	$S(w)$	τ_{xz}	$(u;w)$	$S(T)$	Q_z
1676	307.0	7.3	73	72	1.0	−0.17	0[1]	0[1]
1219	307.4	7.2	69	64	−1.1	0.22	0[1]	0[1]
914	307.5	7.2	104	92	−6.2	0.59	0[1]	0[1]
610	307.9	7.3	102	65	3.1	−0.42	0[1]	0[1]
305	308.0	7.4	92	90	1.1	−0.12	0.15	64
152	307.3	7.5	76	64	−1.5	0.14	0.13	50
61	307.2	7.8	71	87	1.3	−0.18	0.18	159
30	307.2	7.8	122	56	0.9	−0.12	0.16	75

[1] Very small value. Not measured but estimated to be zero.

6.1.a. Loeser technique of daytime wind profile measurements (GRD). Mean height Z (m); duration t (sec) of evaluated drift; mean West, South, and upward components u, v, w (m/sec) of drift of individual smoke puffs. Values are t-sec averages centered at indicated CST$+t/2$ sec.

22nd August 1953

CST	Z	t	u	v	w	CST	Z	t	u	v	w	CST	Z	t	u	v	w
0630	1292	108	3.6	10.1	0.0	0635	765	84	2.8	14.0	0.0	0640	1201	108	3.8	10.0	0.1
	1100	108	4.0	10.1	−0.1		623	78	2.9	16.6	0.1		1011	102	3.9	10.2	0.0
	944	102	2.9	10.5	0.0		514	78	2.9	17.2	0.2		888	96	2.9	10.5	0.3
	817	102	3.0	13.1	0.1		377	72	2.0	18.3	0.2		747	96	2.5	12.8	0.1
	696	96	2.8	15.3	0.0		314	72	2.4	18.5	0.2		630	96	2.4	15.0	0.3
	591	90	3.0	17.0	0.2								367	78	1.5	17.7	0.5

22 August 1953

CST	Z	t	u	v	w	CST	Z	t	u	v	w	CST	Z	t	u	v	w
0830	1026	108	2.0	11.8	0.4	0835	1369	108	2.0	9.8	−0.1	0840	1368	120	1.6	10.6	0.3
	848	102	0.9	11.5	0.4		1165	102	1.4	11.0	0.0		1164	120	1.6	11.4	0.1
	704	96	1.0	11.9	0.4		1030	96	2.1	11.9	0.2		1014	120	2.0	12.2	0.1
	565	96	1.1	12.3	0.3		909	96	1.7	11.7	0.0		871	120	1.0	11.7	0.1
	459	96	1.7	12.6	0.3		793	90	0.6	11.6	0.0		756	120	1.0	12.2	0.1
	366	90	2.3	12.7	0.3		545	90	1.4	12.4	0.0		646	120	0.9	12.0	0.2
	288	90	3.1	12.6	0.5		473	84	1.6	12.3	−0.1		543	120	1.4	12.2	0.1
	188	48	0.2	10.8	0.3		430	84	2.0	12.1	0.0		465	120	2.0	12.4	0.1
							359	84	2.6	12.4	0.1		385	120	2.1	12.6	0.1
													323	120	2.4	12.3	0.1
													268	120	3.1	12.2	0.0
													219	66	1.5	11.5	−0.2
1030	1314	108	−2.2	11.8	0.4	1035	1220	108	−1.4	11.5	0.2	1040	1263	120	−1.5	11.7	0.6
	1135	102	−0.2	12.6	0.4		1011	102	1.7	12.6	0.6		1055	120	1.1	12.8	0.3
	987	96	1.3	12.7	0.7		606	96	1.9	12.4	0.0		893	114	2.2	12.3	0.3
	847	96	1.5	12.6	0.6		437	60	2.0	8.7	−1.1		751	114	2.2	12.5	0.4
	746	90	1.6	13.0	0.5		108	6	−0.5	4.3	3.2		646	108	2.8	12.5	0.6
	650	90	2.6	13.1	0.5		45	24	−0.5	5.0	0.8		536	54	2.6	8.7	0.4
	530	78	3.2	10.4	0.2								420	6	−0.8	8.7	1.2
	467	84	1.2	9.1	0.0												
	429	84	2.0	7.2	0.8												
1230	1250	102	−1.8	11.3	−0.6							1240	1285	84	−1.0	11.2	0.1
	1020	96	−1.2	10.3	−0.6								1001	42	−1.4	11.9	−2.0
	835	90	−0.7	9.3	−1.0								769	66	−0.8	12.0	−2.7
	716	90	0.2	8.8	−0.4								642	72	0.2	11.7	−2.2
	559	66	0.1	8.4	−0.6								477	66	0.4	10.9	−3.1
	436	54	0.7	8.0	−1.1								402	54	0.6	10.0	−2.3
	341	42	0.6	7.6	−0.6								326	60	0.8	9.8	−1.8
	245	36	−1.2	8.6	−0.6								262	54	−0.2	9.4	−1.2
	190	18	−0.9	8.1	0.4								221	54	0.4	9.2	−0.8
	118	12	−4.2	7.9	−0.2								179	54	0.3	9.0	−0.5
	70	12	−4.1	8.8	0.5								138	54	0.5	8.9	−0.4
	23	12	−2.2	8.7	0.2								107	48	0.2	8.8	−0.4

6.2. Rawinsonde (GMD-1A) wind speed (m/sec) and direction (deg from North) from 1-min mean drift at 30-sec intervals, for first 7 min of ascent started at indicated CST.

22 August 1953

0435			0700			0835		
m	m/sec	deg	m	m/sec	deg	m	m/sec	deg
2790	7.2	168	2355	7.9	159	2296	10.5	163
2392	2.7	72	1997	8.1	127	1963	11.7	135
2194	4.8	62	1831	8.2	143	1803	12.2	159
1988	2.9	119	1662	8.1	160	1642	10.4	167
1781	6.0	185	1495	7.5	175	1480	12.2	181
1575	8.0	193	1328	9.2	184	1318	13.2	187
1379	8.6	205	1161	11.4	193	1158	12.0	186
1180	11.9	191	995	12.2	199	999	13.6	185
982	15.2	198	829	12.3	196	841	13.7	184
788	19.1	190	663	14.4	188	683	13.4	186
591	22.1	182	498	17.3	184	526	13.2	188
395	24.9	176	332	20.4	185	378	13.2	190
199	22.3	172	157	18.8	180	184	14.3	182

1035 m	m/sec	deg	1235 m	m/sec	deg	1435 m	m/sec	deg
2112	8.0	160	2535	10.0	183	2087	13.7	196
1856	10.9	154	2165	14.2	158	1867	10.6	199
1728	12.6	160	1977	14.6	171	1696	12.2	190
1579	13.4	158	1792	14.7	170	1530	11.0	185
1441	12.5	164	1615	14.3	173	1367	10.8	178
1304	12.4	173	1435	12.7	177	1198	11.7	170
1153	12.6	179	1256	11.4	181	1049	11.7	167
995	13.5	177	1076	10.2	184	908	12.2	168
838	14.5	186	888	9.6	180	767	11.9	164
679	12.4	189	704	9.1	173	622	10.5	163
525	9.2	189	515	8.8	171	479	9.7	164
361	8.3	187	327	10.3	171	337	9.7	165
180	7.6	184	167	11.7	169	165	9.3	162

6.3. Double theodolite pibal wind speed (m/sec) and direction (deg from North) from 1-min mean drift at 30-sec intervals, for first 7 min of ascent started at indicated CST.

22 August 1953

0630 m	m/sec	deg	0830 m	m/sec	deg	1030 m	m/sec	deg	1230 m	m/sec	deg	1430 m	m/sec	deg
964	10.3	194	1029	10.8	187	1083	12.7	182	1080	5.6	181	889	10.3	174
908	11.9	191	964	12.6	189	1011	13.5	185	1028	7.4	180	845	10.5	172
804	14.5	189	871	11.7	186	965	13.3	185	978	7.7	180	769	10.2	169
757	15.1	188	804	11.3	182	892	13.3	184	894	6.9	179	694	10.9	168
680	17.3	189	732	11.7	181	831	12.4	183	808	10.5	172	620	10.2	168
613	17.0	188	661	11.8	182	768	13.4	184	648	11.9	167	554	9.2	163
548	18.5	186	588	12.3	183	662	13.4	186	535	8.0	163	494	8.8	165
476	15.7	185	514	12.8	183	569	12.7	190	460	9.4	167	449	9.8	156
434	17.9	182	446	11.9	183	464	11.3	194	375	10.2	168	390	10.3	159
365	22.2	181	383	12.5	183	370	9.6	193	288	8.4	169	317	9.8	159
278	20.3	177	310	13.5	186	296	8.9	191	224	6.8	177	249	11.2	156
213	19.0	178	242	12.7	187	225	7.6	191	171	7.1	177	184	10.8	159
150	16.9	176	172	11.2	182	146	7.3	188	116	7.8	167	136	10.7	154
78	13.4	168	92	9.8	174	82	7.6	181	70	8.2	163	72	10.3	147

6.4. Radiosonde pressure (mb), temperature (°C), and relative humidity (%) at significant levels of ascent started at indicated CST. (M = "motorboating", i.e., a humidity value below the minimum value that the radiosonde can measure at that temperature.)

22 August 1953

	0435	0700	0835	1035	1235	1435
mb	949	949	949	949	949	948
°C	14.6	16.7	21.2	25.0	28.0	29.5
%	68	64	53	47	39	35
mb	918	942	937	890	866	825
°C	20.2	16.6	19.7	18.7	19.0	16.6
%	37	61	54	52	47	56

22 August 1953

	0435	0700	0835	1035	1235	1435
mb	864	930	919	870	751	764
°C	17.0	20.8	22.2	18.7	7.2	10.3
%	47	58	38	44	66	71
mb	828	872	910	746	720	716
°C	14.8	18.9	21.6	8.0	5.8	5.5
%	43	38	—	59	51	88
mb	762	833	—	729	688	684
°C	9.1	16.1	—	7.6	6.4	6.6
%	67	42	—	30	28	33
mb	706	731	851	706	664	666
°C	3.4	6.4	19.5	5.8	4.6	5.3
%	82	72	38	59	48	28
mb	668	685	767	694	653	629
°C	1.1	4.1	10.0	5.5	4.4	3.5
%	57	58	55	47	27	37
mb	648	658	737	684	637	584
°C	2.0	3.4	7.6	6.3	3.6	−1.6
%	25	27	65	28	27	42
mb	628	634	692	673	587	—
°C	0.5	2.3	5.0	6.3	−2.4	—
%	24	24	54	27	38	—
mb	558	590	670	614	—	—
°C	−6.4	−1.8	5.5	1.0	—	—
%	M	27	25	27	—	—
mb	—	545	646	—	—	—
°C	—	−6.0	4.1	—	—	—
%	—	26	25	—	—	—
mb	—	505	604	—	—	—
°C	—	−9.9	0.4	—	—	—
%	—	M	25	—	—	—

6.5. Air temperature T (°C) and mixing ratio W (g water vapor/kg air) at altitude Z (m) from aerograph (L-20) data. CST of start, top level, and end of flight is indicated.

22 August 1953

(0625-0642-0655)			(0817-0838-0853)			(1019-1036-1049)			(1217-1238-1253)			(1417-1436-1450)		
Z	T	W	Z	T	W	Z	T	W	Z	T	W	Z	T	W
17	15.2	7.9	17	18.6	9.0	35	23.1	10.3	17	26.3	8.9	17	27.8	7.5
35	15.7	8.2	35	18.4	8.9	65	22.5	9.9	35	26.2	8.6	51	27.1	7.5
51	15.7	8.2	51	18.7	8.9	100	22.2	10.0	51	26.1	8.6	65	27.1	7.5
65	16.0	8.0	65	18.2	8.7	130	22.1	9.7	65	25.4	8.8	100	26.3	6.9
240	20.2	6.2	100	17.8	8.6	165	21.7	10.1	130	24.9	8.0	130	26.4	7.2
320	20.7	6.1	130	17.5	8.4	240	20.8	9.7	165	24.3	7.9	165	25.9	7.0
640	18.6	6.8	165	17.7	8.4	320	20.1	9.5	240	24.2	8.1	240	24.8	6.6
960	16.6	6.4	240	20.7	7.9	640	19.5	6.8	320	23.6	8.2	320	24.0	6.8

22 August 1953

(0625-0642-0655)	(0817-0838-0835)	(1019-1036-1049)	(1217-1238-1253)	(1417-1436-1450)
1260 14.8 6.8	320 21.3 7.0	960 17.1 6.8	640 20.7 8.4	640 21.3 5.9
1590 12.5 7.4	640 20.0 6.4	1260 14.7 6.8	960 17.2 8.2	960 18.3 7.5
1260 14.6 7.2	960 17.2 6.3	1590 11.8 6.4	1260 14.8 7.4	1260 15.6 7.8
960 17.1 7.3	1260 14.7 6.8	1260 14.5 7.4	1590 11.9 7.9	1590 13.0 7.9
640 19.4 7.5	1590 12.2 6.7	960 16.6 7.3	1260 14.7 8.5	1260 15.6 8.9
320 20.9 7.7	1260 14.4 7.6	640 19.2 6.9	960 17.1 8.2	960 18.4 8.7
165 19.3 7.7	960 16.9 7.2	320 20.8 9.9	640 20.4 8.3	600 21.4 8.0
100 17.2 7.8	640 19.3 6.6	100 23.0 10.1	320 23.7 7.9	320 24.5 7.9
51 16.1 8.1	320 21.5 7.6	65 23.7 10.3	165 25.2 8.1	165 26.5 7.8
35 15.9 8.0	165 18.5 8.6	51 23.7 10.1	130 24.9 7.2	130 26.7 8.0
17 15.9 8.2	130 18.8 9.1	17 23.7 10.1	100 26.2 7.8	100 27.2 7.3
	100 18.2 8.8		51 26.2 7.6	35 27.6 7.4
	65 19.7 9.5		26 26.8 7.6	17 27.9 7.3
	35 19.7 9.5			
	17 19.8 9.5			

7.1. Representative values of West and South components of the wind u, v, (m/sec) at standard heights. Values are estimated from the combination of smoke puff, rawinsonde and double theodolite pibal data at or near the indicated CST.

	Height (m)	22 August 1953 0435	0635	0835	1035	1235	1435
u	2000	−0.8	−6.5	−10.0	−5.6	−2.1	3.7
	1750	0.6	−3.1	−4.2	−4.6	−2.2	2.3
	1500	2.2	−0.3	0.1	−3.4	−1.4	0.5
	1250	3.6	3.0	1.6	−1.4	−0.6	−1.0
	1000	4.0	3.6	1.9	1.1	−0.2	−2.2
	800	3.2	3.1	1.8	1.9	−0.2	−2.7
	700	2.1	2.8	1.8	2.0	−0.3	−4.0
	600	1.0	2.3	1.8	2.1	−0.4	−3.0
	500	−0.1	2.0	1.8	2.1	−0.5	−3.0
	400	−1.2	1.6	2.0	1.8	−0.6	−3.0
	300	−2.3	0.8	2.1	1.5	−0.8	−3.0
	200	−3.1	0.0	1.5	1.0	−1.0	−3.1
	100	−3.5	−1.0	−1.0	0.3	−1.5	−3.4
v	2000	2.3	5.1	9.9	10.0	14.5	12.3
	1750	5.2	6.6	10.6	10.9	14.0	11.9
	1500	8.5	8.1	11.3	11.7	13.0	11.6
	1250	11.5	10.2	11.9	12.2	11.6	11.3
	1000	14.3	11.0	12.4	12.9	10.5	11.0
	800	17.9	12.8	12.6	13.1	10.1	10.7
	700	21.1	14.7	12.8	12.5	9.9	10.4
	600	22.8	16.7	12.9	11.3	9.6	10.1
	500	23.7	18.3	12.9	9.8	9.4	9.9
	400	24.1	20.0	12.9	8.5	9.1	9.6
	300	23.8	20.5	12.8	8.0	8.9	9.3
	200	22.5	19.3	12.7	7.5	8.6	9.0
	100	20.2	16.8	12.3	7.1	8.5	8.5

7.2.a. Air temperature (°C) at standard heights. Values are interpolated and averaged from radiosonde and airplane (L-20) data at or near the indicated CST.

Height (m)	22 August 1953 0435[1]	0635	0835	1035	1235	1435
2000	8.5	9.2	9.1	7.9	8.0	9.6
1750	10.5	11.2	11.1	10.5	10.3	11.7
1500	12.5	13.1	13.2	12.8	12.6	13.9
1250	14.5	15.0	15.3	15.1	14.9	15.9
1000	16.0	17.1	17.2	16.7	17.0	18.4
800	17.3	18.4	18.9	18.3	18.9	20.2
600	18.5	19.3	20.2	19.1	21.0	22.1
400	19.7	20.2	21.2	20.3	23.0	24.1
200	18.1	20.1	19.7	22.0	24.9	26.3
100	16.3	17.1	18.7	23.0	26.0	27.1

[1] Radiosonde data only.

7.2.b. Mixing ratio (g water vapor/kg air) at standard heights. Values are interpolated and averaged from radiosonde and airplane (L-20) data at or near the indicated CST.

Height (m)	22 August 1953 0435[1]	0635	0835	1035	1235	1435
2000	6.3	6.7	6.3	5.6	6.5	7.1
1750	6.2	6.6	6.3	5.9	7.0	7.6
1500	5.9	6.8	6.5	6.5	7.3	8.0
1250	5.6	6.6	6.9	6.9	7.4	8.3
1000	6.2	6.2	6.7	6.7	7.8	8.2
800	6.7	6.3	6.8	6.8	8.0	7.8
600	6.4	6.6	6.9	7.3	8.3	7.7
400	6.2	7.1	7.2	8.8	8.4	8.0
200	6.6	7.5	8.2	9.8	8.4	8.0
100	7.0	7.7	8.7	10.0	8.5	7.8

[1] Radiosonde data only.

7.3.a. Summary of heat budget constituents (mcal cm^{-2} min^{-1}) of the earth-air interface according to the theoretical models by Suomi, Halstead, and Lettau. Net radiation flux R, heat transfer to the soil S, sensible heat transfer to the air Q, and latent heat transfer to the air (heat equivalent of evaporation) E. Values are hourly means centered at indicated CST.

	22 August 1953 0435	0635	0835	1035	1235	1435
Suomi						
R_0	108	32	−376	−724	−785	−580
S_0	−85	−27	38	110	126	85
Q_0	−24	0	178	316	349	222
E_0	8	0	160	297	310	273

22 August 1953

	0435	0635	0835	1035	1235	1435
Halstead						
R_0	80	40	−340	−680	−820	−560
S_0	−50	−42	3	85	127	100
Q_0	−82	−48	202	312	340	253
E_0	40	68	237	343	275	285
Lettau						
R_0	97	27	−377	−727	−835	−596
S_0	−69	−36	56	180	179	116
Q_0	−32	−27	161	458	443	292
E_0	14	11	117	190	181	185

7.3.b. Representative logarithmic height derivatives of wind speed (zV', mm sec^{-1}, from UCLA and JH data), potential temperature ($z\theta'$, 10^{-3} °C, from JH and UW data), and water vapor pressure (ze', 10^{-3} mb, from JH and UW data); representative values of Karman number k (from zV' and UCLA, JH, and MIT stress data), interpolated ground drag τ_0 (dynes cm^{-2}, from zV' and representative k values), and ratio of heat and momentum diffusivities N_Q; representative ground-flux ratio F_0 and inverse Bowen ratio B. Values refer to indicated CST and are employed in the computation of the heat budget constituents Q_0 and E_0 (Lettau model; see Table 7.3.a).

22 August 1953

	0435	0635	0835	1035	1235	1435
zV'	683	885	1121	909	1064	1140
$z\theta'$	286	153	−371	−744	−679	−567
ze'	−59	−32	−266	−489	−418	−423
k	0.37	0.37	0.39	0.41	0.40	0.39
τ_0	0.72	1.26	2.13	1.54	2.01	2.18
N_Q	0.74	0.88	1.59	2.52	2.39	1.86
F_0	0.64	−0.28	3.16	3.01	3.56	3.07
B	−0.33	−0.34	1.15	1.05	0.98	1.18

7.4. Richardson number (Ri; units of 10^{-3}) from Mass. Inst. Tech. and Johns Hopkins University data on simultaneous temperature and wind velocity differences, centered at indicated CST and mean height z_m (meter). (Ri') = average height derivative of Richardson number (10^{-3} m^{-1}).

Inst. Set	Height (m)	22 August 1953 0435	0635	0835	1035	1235	1435
MIT	8.0	72	41	−55	−113	−118	−69
MIT	4.0	50	23	−41	−125	−96	−75
JH	3.2	60	28	−41	−92	−110	−48
JH	1.6	30	15	−16	−46	−36	−18
JH	0.8	20	7	−9	−26	−15	−13
(Ri')		13	6	−9	−23	−21	−13

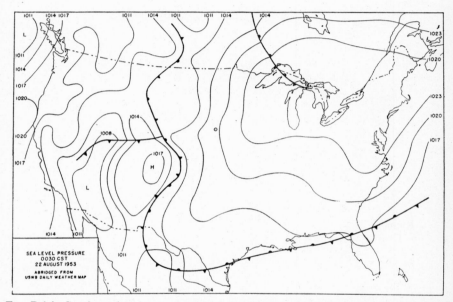

FIG. B.4.1. Continental scale synoptic chart. Sea level pressure distribution for the fourth general observation period.

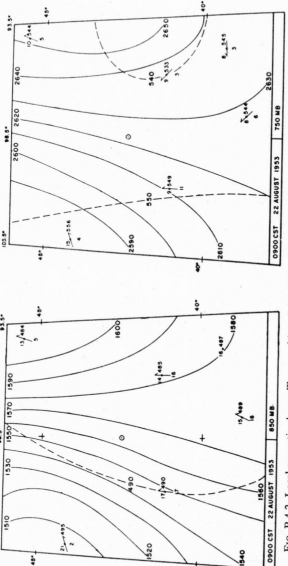

FIG. B.4.2. Local synoptic charts. Topographies of the 850 and 750 mb surfaces at 0900 CST, 22 August 1953.

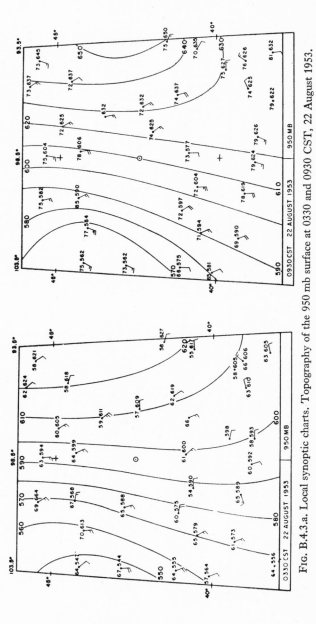

FIG. B.4.3.a. Local synoptic charts. Topography of the 950 mb surface at 0330 and 0930 CST, 22 August 1953.

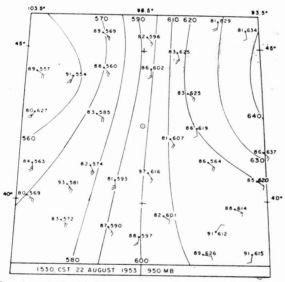

FIG. B.4.b. Local synoptic chart. Topography of the 950 mb surface at 1530 CST, 22 August 1953.

FIFTH GENERAL OBSERVATION PERIOD

1205 CST 24 August through 2105 CST 25 August 1953

Solar Data for the Field Site near O'Neill, Nebraska

	Sun's elevation angle at apparent noon	Sunrise CST	Apparent noon CST	Sunset CST
24 August	58° 32′	0551	1236	1922
25 August	58° 12′	0552	1236	1921

Summary of Synoptic Conditions

On 24 and 25 August there was an extensive high-pressure system centered over Ohio and covering the central and eastern parts of the United States. Conditions were favorable enough to begin the fifth general observation period at 1205 CST on 24 August and continue it until 2105 CST of the 25th. The high remained almost stationary during the first part of the period and started to move eastward slowly at 0930 CST of the 25th. Winds were southerly at 15 to 25 mph. The skies were clear for most of the period with scattered altocumulus clouds during both afternoons over all of Nebraska. A low-pressure system was located in Montana with a cold front in the Rocky Mountains moving slowly eastward over the Northern Great Plains. At 0030 CST of the 25th a pre-frontal squall line developed in association with this front. This squall line extended from Saskatchewan to Chadron, Nebraska, with thunderstorms, lightning, and rain showers. By 0330 CST this squall line had disappeared. The cold front continued to move into the eastern part of the Dakotas. By 0330 CST of the 25th a wave developed on the southern portion of the front over Casper, Wyoming. On the 26th, this development had moved to Southeastern Montana.

1.1.a. Mean geopotential H (dynamic m above 601 = geopotential of test site), West and South components of the geostrophic wind u_g, v_g (m/sec) at indicated pressure (mb) levels. Values are estimated for the O'Neill site from local synoptic charts.

mb	H	24 Aug. 0900 u_g	24 Aug. 0900 v_g	24 Aug. 2100 u_g	24 Aug. 2100 v_g	25 Aug. 0900 u_g	25 Aug. 0900 v_g	25 Aug. 2100 u_g	25 Aug. 2100 v_g
750	2011	12.9	12.9	13.3	12.4	10.2	8.6	12.0	11.6
800	1430	13.8	9.3	12.5	9.1	11.3	8.8	9.0	8.7
850	909	11.9	8.0	9.3	6.0	9.4	7.1	8.1	5.9
900	407	10.2	5.9	6.1	9.2	9.5	5.7	12.9	8.4
950	−61	8.0	11.9	11.2	12.4	8.8	11.3	9.7	9.1

1.1.b. Direction (deg from North) and speed (m/sec) of the 950 mb geostrophic wind. Values are estimated for the O'Neill site from local synoptic charts.

24 August					25 August 1953								
0930	1230	1530	1830	2130	0030	0330	0630	0930	1230	1530	1830	2130
214	217	218	224	222	220	216	222	218	222	214	223	227
14.3	16.7	16.7	14.3	16.7	20.0	22.2	16.7	14.3	14.3	15.4	14.3	13.3

1.2. Direction (deg from North) of the mean surface wind from standard vane recordings at 1-min intervals (Mass. Inst. Tech., 16 m level). Hourly and 15-min averages centered at indicated CST.

	24 August						25 August 1953										
	1235	1435	1635	1835	2035	2235	0035	0235	0435	0635	0835	1035	1235	1435	1635	1835	2035
60-min mean:	187	189	184	180	172	171	174	184	179	182	192	190	192	184	181	172	162
15-min mean:	186	192	181	180	169	172	174	181	179	182	194	191	186	178	182	173	163

1.3. Standard shelter temperature (°F) and relative humidity (%); station pressure (inches) and air density (mg cm^{-3}); amount (tenths) and types of clouds.

Month	Day	CST	Temp.	RH	Pressure[1]	Density	Clouds	Remarks
Aug.	24	1235	88	39	27.785	1.07	0 —	Wind gusty 10 to 22 mph
		1435	90	35	.750	1.06	0 —	Wind gusty up to 27 mph
		1635	90	33	.725	1.06	1 Ac	Some very small Cu to S. Sky clear
		1835	86	39	.730	1.07	0 —	High clouds noticeable to W
		2035	79	56	.735	1.08	0 Ac	Clouds not visible after sunset
		2235	76	60	.780	1.09	0 —	Some As overhead
	25	0035	75	59	.760	1.09	0 —	Wind increasing. Gusts to 20 mph. No clouds visible
		0235	74	60	.770	1.09	0 —	Wind gusty to 20 mph
		0435	71	68	.780	1.10	0 —	Gusty winds
		0635	71	71	.780	1.10	0 —	Gusty winds
		0835	75	66	.795	1.09	0 —	Gusts to 30 mph
		1035	82	54	.810	1.08	0 —	Gusts to 29 mph
		1235	90	46	.815	1.07	0 —	
		1435	95	35	.800	1.06	0 —	Hot; light haze
		1635	94	34	.800	1.06	0 —	
		1835	90	37	.785	1.07	0 —	Some small clouds to N seem to be moving up
		2035	80	54	.790	1.08	0 —	

[1] Observer noted on Form 10 that pressure computations were unreliable.

H

2.1.a. Soil temperature (°C) from thermistors (University of Texas) and soil thermocouples (University of California and Johns Hopkins University). Values are readings at indicated CST.

Inst. Set	Depth (cm)	24 August						25 August 1953										
		1235	1435	1635	1835	2035	2235	0035	0235	0435	0635	0835	1035	1235	1435	1635	1835	2035
UT	0.5	41.94	41.31	36.18	29.70	25.39	—	22.70	21.91	21.04	20.81	25.68	36.05	43.47	43.34	37.78	30.94	26.48
UCLA	1.3	40.22	40.83	35.78	28.61	24.56	—	21.83	21.11	20.11	20.17	25.00	33.56	41.78	45.94	37.89	30.28	25.72
UT	1.5	36.74	37.73	34.80	29.82	26.15	—	23.33	22.43	21.68	21.23	24.40	31.88	38.11	39.63	36.55	31.11	27.19
UT	2.5	33.60	35.26	33.60	29.72	26.52	—	23.72	22.92	22.11	21.56	23.77	29.45	34.86	36.90	35.31	31.04	27.60
JH	2.5	27.52	29.58	29.48	27.82	25.62	24.44	23.52	22.80	22.22	21.74	22.50	25.30	29.36	31.04	31.14	29.58	27.22
UT	3.5	31.44	33.44	32.63	29.62	26.78	—	24.02	23.14	22.44	21.80	23.27	27.84	32.53	34.91	34.16	30.85	27.84
UT	4.5	30.24	32.42	32.00	29.49	26.92	—	24.18	23.31	22.63	21.98	23.07	26.83	31.16	33.76	33.47	30.69	27.99
JH	5.0	25.50	27.73	28.30	27.44	25.84	24.70	23.85	23.15	22.61	22.13	22.28	23.91	26.64	29.06	29.80	29.04	27.34
UT	5.5	29.02	31.29	31.39	29.41	26.14	—	24.55	23.70	23.05	22.37	23.05	26.02	29.90	32.50	32.72	30.52	28.23
UCLA	10.0	24.33	26.61	27.22	26.83	25.83	—	23.67	23.06	22.56	22.22	22.22	23.06	25.44	27.61	28.61	28.33	26.94
JH	10.0	23.36	25.18	26.21	26.30	25.60	24.76	24.12	23.50	23.01	22.60	22.37	22.92	24.44	26.31	27.40	27.61	26.92
JH	20.0	21.70	22.46	23.24	23.77	24.04	23.92	23.70	23.40	23.12	22.86	22.58	22.46	22.70	23.42	24.17	24.80	25.04
UCLA	25.0	21.00	21.61	21.94	22.50	23.00	—	22.78	22.78	22.44	22.50	22.22	21.78	22.06	22.50	23.06	23.56	23.61
JH	40.0	21.27	21.28	21.35	21.50	21.73	21.92	22.05	22.12	22.12	22.12	22.04	21.96	21.90	21.92	22.01	22.16	22.37
JH	80.0	20.19	20.18	20.16	20.18	20.19	20.19	20.20	20.20	20.22	20.26	20.27	20.28	20.22	20.26	20.30	20.36	20.38

2.1.b. Change of soil temperature (°C hr^{-1}) averaged over indicated layers from soil temperature integrators (University of Wisconsin). Values are differences between readings at the end and beginning of 1-hr intervals centered at indicated CST.

Depth (cm)	24 August						25 August 1953						
	1235	1435	1635	1835	2035	2235	0035	0235	0435	0635	0835	1035	1235[1]
0–5	1.64	0.03	−1.06	−1.27	−0.83	−0.43	−0.37	−0.29	−0.29	0.03	1.72	2.22	1.63
5–15	1.07	0.73	0.17	−0.46	−0.55	−0.40	−0.33	−0.30	−0.26	−0.15	0.29	0.82	1.05
15–50	0.10	0.19	0.19	0.13	0.07	0.01	−0.03	−0.05	−0.06	−0.06	−0.06	−0.01	0.10

[1] No data after 1235 on 25 August.

2.2.a. Soil thermal conductivity (mcal cm^{-1} sec^{-1} deg^{-1}) computed from soil thermistor response to defined heating pulses (University of Texas, Albrecht heat flux meter No. 2). Values are derived from 60-sec trials beginning at indicated CST.

Depth (cm)	24 August 1953				
	0440	0640	0840	1040	1240
0.5	0.57	0.58	0.60	0.58	0.61
1.5	0.59	0.68	0.66	0.70	0.72
2.5	0.90	0.90	0.84	0.87	0.86
3.5	0.96	0.91	0.90	0.90	0.90
4.5	0.99	0.95	1.06	1.11	1.15
5.5	1.38	1.40	1.41	1.25	1.23

2.2.b. Soil moisture (% wet weight) from soil samples at the Johns Hopkins University site. Indicated CST refers to the approximate time of soil sample extraction.

Depth (cm)	24 Aug. 1400	25 Aug. 0700	25 Aug. 1400
4	5.4	4.6	4.0
10	4.5	4.0	3.9
20	4.5	3.3	3.3
40	3.9	2.7	2.3

2.2.c. Soil heat capacity (cal cm^{-3} deg^{-1}) from soil samples at the University of Wisconsin site (calorimetric determination). Indicated CST refers to the approximate time of soil sample extraction (0–10 cm layer).

24 August		25 August
1500	2200	1400
0.32	0.40	0.40

2.3. Soil moisture tension (mb) from tensiometers (Johns Hopkins University). Values are readings at indicated CST.

Depth (cm)	24 August						25 August 1953									
	1235	1435	1635	1835	2035	2235	0035	0235	0435	0635	0835	1035	1235	1435	1635	1835
10	728	731	737	754	768	768	767	769	771	772	—	756	749	743	746	763
20	661	678	697	715	732	734	734	733	734	734	—	718	714	712	717	732
40	438	528	602	645	672	678	681	681	682	683	—	663	667	678	699	721

2.4. Vertical flux of heat (mcal cm^{-2} min^{-1}) from soil temperature integrators (University of Wisconsin), Albrecht heat flux meter No. 2 (University of Texas-Al), Gier and Dunkle heat flow meters (University of California; University of Texas-GD; John Hopkins University-GD), and numerical integration of soil temperature profile changes (Johns Hopkins University). UW and JH values are 60-min averages, UCLA values are 15-min averages, and UT and JH-GD values are approximately 2-min averages. All averages are centered at indicated CST.

Inst. set	Depth (cm)	24 August						25 August 1953										
		1235	1435	1635	1835	2035	2235	0035	0235	0435	0635	0835	1035	1235	1435	1635	1835	2035
UW	0.0	135	89	25	-32	-38	-34	-37	-38	-39	-23	51	110	130	—	—	—	—
UT-Al	0.0[1]	—	—	—	—	—	—	—	—	-34	-23	88	267	483	—	—	—	—
JH	0.0[1]	306	225	100	17	-46	—	-10	-20	-18	-15	15	73	118	110	70	25	-2
UCLA	0.2[2]	251	181	71	-24	-36	—	-35	-33	-39	-21	100	243	281	234	97	-33	-45
UT-GD	0.2[2]	—	—	—	—	—	—	-33	-32	-34	-23	98	231	217	189	68	-28	-40
UCLA	1.3	134	116	67	9	-13	—	-13	-12	-12	-8	34	90	133	125.	71	12	-12
UT-Al	2.0	—	—	—	—	—	—	—	—	-19	-16	28	115	153	—	—	—	—
JH-GD	2.5	98	97	58	17	-7	-8	-13	-13	-13	-13	10	58	97	98	67	22	-5
UW	5.0	87	88	56	6	-13	-21	-26	-29	-30	-24	0	44	79	—	—	—	—
UCLA	10.0	63	75	62	32	3	2	-4	-7	-10	-17	3	32	61	82	66	36	12
UW	15.0	26	47	47	32	8	—	-8	-12	-16	-16	-16	-2	24	—	—	—	—

[1] Values are extrapolated to surface. [2] Approximative depth; the upper plates of the flow meters were "just covered with soil".

3.1. Summary of data on radiation (mcal cm⁻² min⁻¹). Short-wave radiation from Eppley pyrheliometer (GRD); net radiation from two Gier and Dunkle radiometers (Johns Hopkins University and University of Texas) and the Suomi net radiometer (University of Wisconsin); total radiation from the Gier and Dunkle radiometer (University of Texas). Values are hourly averages centered at indicated CST.

	Inst. Set	24 August						25 August 1953										
		1235	1435	1635	1835	2035	2235	0035	0235	0435	0635	0835	1035	1235	1435	1635	1835	2035
(Short-Wave)	GRD[1]	1277	1133	710	150	0	0	0	0	0	113	670	1130	1303	1122	690	120	0
	GRD[2]	1280	1110	670	110	0	0	0	0	0	100	670	1130	1310	1120	690	120	0
(Net)	JH	800	690	330	−30	−70	−60	−90	−80	−90	−40	340	690	820	700	340	−30	−80
	UT	895	760	379	−56	−108	—	−131	−121	−123	−16	458	879	985	837	331	−80	−120
	UW	919	734	304	−75	−118	−118	−120	−116	−118	−33	375	750	870	—	—	—	—
(Total)	UT	1925	1739	1210	579	474	—	447	456	453	560	1249	1844	2156	1843	1223	594	496

[1] The values on 24 August are 30-min average centered at indicated CST minus 10 min. [2] 10-min average centered at indicated CST.

3.2. Boundary shear-stress (dynes cm^{-2}) from drag recorder (University of California) and Sheppard-type drag plate (Johns Hopkins University); direction of boundary shear-stress (deg from North) from drag recorder (University of California). Values are 10-min means centered at indicated CST.

	24 August	25 August 1953											
	2035[1]	2235	0035	0235	0435	0635	0835	1035	1235	1435	1635	1835	2035
UCLA	1.58	—	—	—	—	—	—	—	—	—	—	—	1.22
JH	0.8	1.8	1.4	1.6	1.7	1.8	3.4	2.6	3.3	3.1	2.6	1.0	0.7
UCLA	164	—	—	—	—	—	—	—	—	—	—	—	154

[1] No data prior to 2035 due to strong winds.

3.3. Characteristics of low level smoke-puff drift (Johns Hopkins University); direction of drift (deg from North); time t_{25} (sec) required to cross 25 m circle; lateral width S (deg) at 25 m and time t_D (sec) required to reach threshold of visibility. Values are ensemble averages for 10 smoke puffs fired at approximately 1-min intervals beginning at indicated CST.

	24 August						25 August 1953										
	1200	1400	1600	1800	2000	2200	0000	0200	0400	0600	0800	1000	1200	1400	1600	1800	2000
dd	200	195	188	184	176	174	174	185	184	187	197	190	192	189	188	179	158
t_{25}	3.3	3.6	4.1	4.7	5.7	4.3	4.8	4.3	4.6	4.8	3.1	3.4	3.1	3.4	3.4	4.3	17.8
S	10.9	9.6	10.6	13.3	9.3	12.6	16.3	17.0	12.2	12.8	11.3	11.5	13.3	10.6	11.0	10.7	16.6
t_D	8	10	15	16	—	—	—	—	—	24	11	13	9	10	13	15	—

3.4. Characteristics of surface pressure variations from micro-barograms (GRD Paulin-type aneroid system); trend (WBAN Synoptic Code number); qualitative index of micro-variations ("a" = calm to "d" = very unruly); trace ratio (trace length relative to trend length); trend ratio (trend length relative to chart length); period (min), amplitude (10^{-2} mb), and number of perceptible waves. Values refer to 2-hr intervals centered at indicated CST.

	24 August						25 August 1953						
	1335	1535	1735	1935	2135	2335	0135	0335	0535	0735	0935	1135	1335
Trend	7	7	5	2	2	1	2	0	2	2	1	6	7
Index	d	d	d-b	a	a-c	c	c	c-b	c	c-d	d-c	c-d	d
Trace ratio	2.0	1.8	1.55	1.1	—	—	1.3	1.3	1.4	2.0	1.85	1.75	2.3
Trend ratio	1.25	1.3	1.0	1.2	—	—	1.1	1.1	1.1	1.05	1.2	1.0	1.05
Period	30	15	20	30	—	—	35	25	50	45	30	55	20
Ampl.	6	6	6	4	—	—	5	5	6	9	6	5.5	6
Number	2	2	2	2	—	—	1	1	1	1	1	2	1
Period	15	—	—	—	—	—	15	35	30	30	20	5	10
Ampl.	4.5	—	—	—	—	—	4	4	5	5	4	4	4
Number	1	—	—	—	—	—	3	1	1	1	1	3	5
Period	—	—	—	—	—	—	—	—	15	20	10	—	—
Ampl.	—	—	—	—	—	—	—	—	3.5	5	4	—	—
Number	—	—	—	—	—	—	—	—	2	2	2	—	—

4.1.a. Hourly mean wind speed (cm/sec) from standard three-cup anemometers (Mass. Inst. Tech.), modified Sheppard-type anemometers (University of California), ping-pong ball anemometers (Iowa State College) and modified SCS cup anemometers (Johns Hopkins University); centered at indicated CST.

Inst. Set	Height (m)	24 August 1235	1435	1635	1835	2035	2235	25 August 1953 0035	0235	0435	0635	0835	1035	1235	1435	1635	1835	2035
MIT	16.0	1151	1280	1200	822	786	938	943	974	1002	1015	1299	1216	1265	1205	1121	752	722
MIT	8.0	1057	1167	1087	725	681	825	829	864	887	905	1182	1112	1160	1108	1024	657	607
UCLA	8.0	1116	1196	1157	754	710	878	882	915	938	940	1351	1165	—	1149	1099	696	640
ISC	7.0	1015	—	1051	679	654	787	807	829	841	870	1111	1061	1119	1046	997	638	575
JH	6.4	1086	1104	1050	702	645	804	817	832	836	856	1165	1057	1086	1080	1000	659	572
UCLA	4.15	1011	1076	1036	669	622	778	784	815	833	838	1114	1045	—	1034	986	614	562
MIT	4.0	966	1063	988	648	602	735	739	774	789	818	1074	1015	1057	1011	929	579	529
ISC	4.0	953	998	975	622	597	724	739	756	773	802	1032	988	1044	972	922	584	521
JH	3.2	997	1017	955	634	576	729	736	754	750	770	1057	966	993	990	914	592	506
MIT	2.0	860	945	882	568	529	649	651	681	693	720	956	905	940	904	825	508	464
UCLA	2.0	878	939	892	580	538	676	674	702	720	720	974	919	—	908	858	528	480
JH	1.6	890	908	850	555	502	645	649	662	664	680	944	867	892	888	815	524	440
UCLA	1.0	764	818	783	500	464	582	585	605	623	627	846	802	—	791	746	456	412
ISC	1.0	745	769	755	476	450	547	564	580	589	616	796	774	815	761	715	443	389
JH	0.8	784	798	744	483	435	557	562	572	576	590	832	761	785	784	718	456	378
UCLA	0.5	652	700	669	426	393	492	496	516	530	536	726	686	—	678	650	386	346
JH	0.4	660	672	625	405	369	472	473	479	483	493	695	640	660	659	603	381	318

4.1.b. 15-min mean wind speed (cm/sec) from standard three-cup anemometers (Mass. Inst. Tech.), modified Sheppard-type anemometers (University of California) and ping-pong ball anemometers (Iowa State College); centered at indicated CST. ISC data are 10-min means centered at indicated CST.

Inst. Set	Height (m)	24 August						25 August 1953										
		1235	1435	1635	1835	2035	2235	0035	0235	0435	0635	0835	1035	1235	1435	1635	1835	2035
MIT	16.0	1145	1338	1240	831	764	956	939	993	1044	993	1345	1199	1169	1230	1125	784	726
MIT	8.0	1057	1226	1118	730	659	841	828	885	932	885	1220	1105	1071	1132	1037	693	601
UCLA	8.0	1122	828	1210	776	698	859	902	927	968	922	1308	1170	1220	1149	1126	750	646
ISC	7.0	1025	—	1057	680	647	806	817	854	865	854	1141	1078	1080	1075	1036	698	581
UCLA	4.15	1012	744	1083	680	616	754	800	820	866	820	1166	1050	1094	1036	1009	660	560
MIT	4.0	970	1112	1007	649	578	750	736	794	777	797	1098	1010	976	1034	949	611	520
ISC	4.0	959	1055	980	624	586	741	750	765	795	789	1055	1002	1017	997	956	642	524
MIT	2.0	868	987	895	567	507	665	652	699	730	699	980	899	885	926	841	540	459
UCLA	2.0	883	654	942	597	532	662	685	710	743	705	1020	928	964	904	880	574	484
UCLA	1.0	768	568	816	512	460	571	593	615	645	614	884	810	841	786	764	496	418
ISC	1.0	746	822	765	481	441	560	574	631	609	609	815	787	797	782	738	487	392
UCLA	0.5	658	490	688	434	390	484	504	524	550	522	760	694	720	672	654	422	349

4.2. Mean air temperature (°C) from aspirated thermocouples (Mass. Inst. Tech., 15-min means; University of California, average of six readings taken every 3 min), shielded thermocouples (Johns Hopkins University, average of 20 readings at each level during a 5-min interval) and shielded thermistors (University of Texas, 10-sec means); centered at indicated CST.

Inst. Set	Height (m)	24 August 1235	1435	1635	1835	2035	2235	25 August 1953 0035	0235	0435	0635	0835	1035	1235	1435	1635	1835	2035
MIT	16.0	29.32	30.62	31.29	—	27.09	25.36	24.40	23.52	22.30	21.23	23.67	27.19	31.24	32.81	33.55	31.69	28.32
MIT	8.0	29.63	30.94	31.43	—	26.88	25.25	24.26	23.43	22.22	21.19	23.83	27.47	31.60	33.06	33.68	31.61	27.98
UCLA	8.0	29.22	31.39	31.39	29.44	25.94	—	23.78	22.94	21.78	20.83	23.28	26.78	31.50	33.39	33.50	31.39	27.61
JH	6.4	29.14	30.97	31.28	29.42	25.87	24.93	23.98	23.20	21.94	21.12	23.64	27.48	31.09	33.20	33.65	31.35	27.54
MIT	4.0	29.94	31.20	31.54	—	26.70	25.13	24.15	23.33	22.13	21.14	23.99	27.72	31.93	33.30	33.80	31.51	27.68
UCLA	4.0	29.67	31.39	31.56	29.39	25.83	—	23.61	22.83	21.56	21.00	23.44	27.00	31.67	33.83	33.89	31.28	27.28
JH	3.2	29.95	31.61	31.47	29.36	25.55	24.83	23.80	23.00	21.82	21.09	24.00	27.78	31.51	33.61	33.86	31.23	27.26
MIT	2.0	30.70	31.90	31.90	—	26.50	25.00	24.00	23.20	22.00	21.10	24.40	28.40	32.80	34.00	34.20	31.40	27.50
UCLA	2.0	30.17	31.72	31.56	29.17	25.72	—	23.61	22.94	21.61	21.00	23.89	27.39	32.22	33.94	33.89	31.11	27.22
JH	1.6	30.53	31.94	31.77	29.20	25.39	24.71	23.59	22.88	21.71	21.04	24.24	28.18	32.29	34.10	34.15	31.10	27.02
UCLA	1.0	30.89	32.67	31.78	29.22	25.39	—	23.39	22.67	21.39	20.61	23.89	28.00	32.56	34.72	34.28	31.06	26.78
JH	0.8	31.11	32.36	32.06	29.08	25.20	24.51	23.39	22.76	21.50	21.00	24.50	28.75	32.65	34.59	34.47	31.01	26.82
UT	0.8	31.55	33.2	32.1	29.4	25.6	—	23.85	22.85	21.65	21.02	24.70	29.4	33.2	34.85	34.5	31.05	27.1
UCLA	0.5	32.39	33.44	32.50	28.89	25.06	—	23.17	22.39	21.11	20.33	24.17	28.72	33.83	36.00	34.89	30.72	26.56
UT	0.5	31.7	32.9	32.65	29.4	25.3	—	23.5	22.6	21.25	21.5	24.7	29.8	33.7	35.7	34.55	31.1	27.05
JH	0.4	31.94	33.07	32.32	28.94	24.96	24.24	23.26	22.54	21.40	20.90	24.85	29.21	33.46	35.13	34.73	30.83	26.61
UT	0.3	33.75	33.5	32.8	29.6	25.1	—	23.55	22.7	21.35	21.1	25.0	29.6	34.3	35.6	34.9	31.35	26.7
JH	0.2	32.69	33.63	32.53	28.80	24.76	24.18	23.06	22.36	21.20	20.85	25.04	29.76	34.17	35.95	34.97	30.67	26.39
JH	0.1	33.51	33.94	32.78	28.69	24.61	23.94	22.90	22.19	21.05	20.81	25.39	30.27	34.86	36.55	35.29	30.55	26.25
UT	0.1	33.55	34.5	33.3	29.4	25.1	—	22.9	22.4	21.2	21.1	25.35	30.95	35.15	36.6	35.15	30.7	26.5

4.3.a. Mean water vapor pressure (mb) from dew-point apparatus (Johns Hopkins University). Simultaneous air sampling at given intake levels. Values are 5-min averages centered at indicated CST.

Height (m)	24 August 1235	1435	1635	1835	2035	2235	25 August 1953 0035	0235	0435	0635	0835	1035	1235	1435	1635	1835	2035
6.4	16.13	15.92	14.84	15.18	15.54	17.13	16.38	16.36	16.95	17.47	18.60	18.97	18.74	17.13	14.93	16.95	17.12
3.2	16.43	16.03	14.92	15.06	15.34	17.09	16.14	16.49	17.11	17.51	18.66	19.12	19.24	17.62	15.00	17.04	17.10
1.6	16.68	16.13	14.94	14.94	15.34	17.18	16.34	16.47	17.02	17.53	18.76	19.20	19.12	17.88	15.04	17.13	17.13
0.8	17.02	16.13	15.12	15.02	15.33	17.20	16.26	16.50	17.02	17.56	18.72	19.32	19.12	17.39	15.02	17.18	17.01
0.4	17.31	16.33	15.24	15.16	15.32	17.22	16.62	16.43	17.08	17.65	18.61	19.51	19.36	17.48	15.07	17.20	17.00
0.2	17.33	16.54	15.26	15.30	15.22	17.23	16.36	16.39	17.09	17.65	18.65	19.71	19.36	17.90	15.18	17.27	16.98
0.1	17.90	16.94	15.30	15.70	15.46	17.26	16.32	16.54	17.16	17.67	18.85	20.00	19.61	17.85	15.26	17.31	17.20

4.3.b. Mean vertical difference (between 82 and 39 cm) of dry-bulb temperature (10^{-3} °C) and water vapor pressure (10^{-3} mb) from double psychrometer lift-apparatus (University of Wisconsin). Values are hourly means (based on one sample every 10 min) centered at indicated CST.

	24 August						25 August 1953						
	1235	1435	1635	1835	2035	2235	0035	0235	0435	0635	0835	1035	1235[1]
10^{-3} °C	−657	−560	−281	84	195	137	181	141	140	68	−296	−552	−648
10^{-3} mb	−106	−67	−1	−6	26	94	88	33	60	65	−59	−87	−99

[1] No data 1435 to 2035 due to instrumental failure.

4.4. Mean ozone concentration (10^{-8} g O_3/g air) from automatic ozone recorders (University of New Mexico). Values are 60-min means estimated from traces on chart recorders centered at indicated CST.

Height (m)	24 August						25 August 1953										
	1230	1430	1630	1830	2030	2230	0030	0230	0430	0630	0830	1030	1230	1430	1630	1830	2030
12.5	7.8	8.2	8.2	7.6	7.4	7.4	7.2	6.7	6.8	5.9	5.8	6.7	7.6	8.2	8.2	—	—
6.25	8.0	8.3	7.9	7.3	7.0	7.2	6.9	6.5	6.3	5.9	5.7	6.6	7.6	8.0	—	—	7.7
1.6	7.5	7.7	7.6	7.2	6.8	7.2	6.8	6.4	6.3	5.8	5.7	6.5	7.5	7.9	7.8	—	7.7
0.4	8.2	8.3	8.1	7.5	7.2	7.3	7.0	6.5	6.4	6.1	5.9	6.5	8.0	8.5	8.3	8.0	7.5

5.1. Standard deviation of temperature fluctuations (10^{-2} °C) from fast-response thermocouples (Mass. Inst. Tech., one sample per sec during 11-min periods) and bead thermistors (Iowa State College, 10 samples per sec during 10-min periods. Periods are centered at indicated CST.

Inst. Set	Height (m)	24 August						25 August 1953									
		1235	1435	1635	1835	2035	2235	0035	0235	0435	0635	0835	1035	1235	1435	1635	1835[2]
MIT	12.0	—	—	—	—	15	12	10	11	8	7	—	—	—	—	—	—
ISC	8.0	85	82	—	41	45	34	31	34	—	16	44	84	100	87	45	—
MIT	6.0	—	—	—	—	15	12	13	12	13	11	—	—	—	—	—	12
ISC	4.0	95	88	—	36	46	34	30	33	—	15	45	89	106	92	45	—
MIT	3.0	—	—	—	—	25	19	19	18	18	10	—	—	—	—	—	16
ISC	2.0	91	86	—	30	44	34	27[1]	33	—	15	46	86	105	93	44	—
MIT	1.5	—	—	—	—	25	19	19	17	18	10	—	—	—	—	—	16
ISC	1.0	92	87	—	28	43	28	27[1]	31	—	15	47	83	103	87	44	—
ISC	0.5	90	83	—	27	—	—	29[1]	32	—	15	51	97	112	90	49	—
ISC	0.25	90	87	—	28	41	30	31	31	—	18	54	99	114	91	49	—

[1] Considerable noise in recordings. [2] No data at 2035 CST.

5.2.a. Statistics of fluctuation quantities from 1-sec samplings of fast-response probes (Mass. Inst. Tech.). Total air speed V (cm sec⁻¹); standard deviation of horizontal (parallel and perpendicular to 10-min mean wind) and vertical eddy components $S(u)$, $S(v)$, and $S(w)$ (cm sec⁻¹); gustiness ratios $G(x)$, $G(y)$, and $G(z)$; mean cross products of eddy components $\overline{uv}$, $\overline{vw}$, and $\overline{uw}$ (cm² sec⁻²); horizontal Reynolds' stress (parallel to 10-min mean wind) τ (dynes cm⁻²); linear correlation coefficients between eddy components and air temperature $(u;v)$, $(v;w)$, $(u;w)$, $(u;T)$, $(v;T)$, and $(w;T)$; mean cross product of vertical eddy component and air temperature multiplied by density and specific heat of air Q (mcal cm⁻² min⁻¹). Values are 10-min means or totals centered at indicated CST.

Date	CST	Height	V	$S(u)$	$S(v)$	$S(w)$	$G(x)$	$G(y)$	$G(z)$	$\overline{uv}$	$\overline{vw}$	$\overline{uw}$	τ	(u,v)	$(v;w)$	$(u;w)$	$(u;T)$	$(v;T)$	$(w;T)$	Q
1953 24 Aug.	2035	12.0	718	134	50	48	.19	.07	.07	1150	80	−1390	1.5	0.17	0.03	−0.22	0.50	0.00	−0.28	−30
		6.0	624	126	66	37	.20	.11	.06	670	−50	−870	1.2	0.08	−0.02	−0.19	0.63	0.07	−0.18	−18
		3.0	546	127	60	37	.23	.11	.07	360	20	−1130	1.2	0.05	0.01	−0.24	0.66	0.07	−0.11	−18
		1.5	459	125	66	32	.27	.14	.07	−780	70	−950	1.0	−0.10	0.03	−0.24	0.67	−0.06	0.00	0
	2235	12.0	894	157	73	64	.18	.08	.07	−2400	280	−1750	1.9	−0.21	0.06	−0.17	0.42	−0.11	−0.13	−18
		6.0	793	132	93	39	.17	.12	.05	−1160	70	−1400	1.5	0.00	0.02	−0.27	0.51	−0.09	0.00	0
		3.0	710	144	89	50	.20	.13	.07	−2170	110	−1200	1.3	−0.09	0.03	−0.17	0.51	0.00	0.00	0
		1.5	599	139	89	47	.23	.15	.08	30	−20	−1690	1.9	0.00	0.00	−0.26	0.57	−0.06	0.00	0
1953 25 Aug.	0035	12.0	880	144	64	64	.16	.07	.07	1480	300	−1780	2.0	0.16	0.07	−0.19	0.63	0.16	−0.16	−18
		6.0	783	137	94	46	.17	.12	.06	1300	−200	−1530	1.7	0.10	−0.05	−0.24	0.62	0.08	−0.17	−18
		3.0	696	139	66	45	.20	.10	.07	600	−80	−1200	1.3	0.07	−0.03	−0.19	0.68	−0.48	−0.12	−18
		1.5	597	130	89	45	.22	.15	.08	200	190	−1700	1.9	0.02	0.05	−0.29	0.65	0.00	−0.12	−18
	0235	12.0	986	152	93	70	.15	.09	.07	1490	−30	−2220	2.4	0.11	−0.01	−0.21	0.48	0.00	−0.13	−18
		6.0	837	136	60	43	.16	.07	.05	200	60	−1020	1.1	0.03	0.02	−0.17	0.55	0.00	0.00	0
		3.0	747	148	86	52	.20	.12	.07	−300	80	−1230	1.4	−0.03	0.02	−0.16	0.60	−0.07	−0.11	−18
		1.5	648	138	93	56	.21	.14	.09	800	−80	−1930	2.1	0.06	−0.02	−0.25	0.51	−0.06	−0.11	−18
	0435	12.0	1007	166	97	73	.16	.10	.07	580	−320	−3080	3.4	0.04	−0.05	−0.25	0.68	0.00	−0.17	−18
		6.0	868	153	81	46	.18	.09	.05	470	10	−1990	2.2	0.04	0.00	−0.28	0.65	−0.10	−0.17	−18
		3.0	764	160	90	50	.21	.12	.07	−690	110	−1650	1.8	−0.05	0.02	−0.21	0.73	−0.06	−0.11	−18
		1.5	654	156	102	50	.24	.16	.08	90	90	−1570	1.7	0.01	0.02	−0.20	0.71	−0.05	0.00	0
	0635	12.0	942	155	98	70	.16	.10	.07	410	20	−3030	3.4	0.03	0.00	−0.28	0.74	0.00	−0.20	−18
		6.0	843	145	74	49	.17	.09	.06	820	50	−1640	1.8	0.08	0.01	−0.23	0.56	0.00	0.00	0
		3.0	755	159	88	55	.21	.12	.07	−1790	200	−2170	2.4	−0.13	0.04	−0.25	0.57	0.00	−0.18	−18
		1.5	636	139	97	52	.22	.15	.08	940	430	−1950	2.2	0.07	0.09	−0.27	0.65	0.00	−0.19	−18
	1835[1]	6.0	659	120	57	65	.18	.09	.10	400	−470	−2760	3.0	0.06	−0.13	−0.35	0.42	0.00	−0.26	−30
		3.0	580	124	43	41	.21	.07	.07	−10	80	−1110	1.2	0.00	0.05	−0.22	0.55	0.00	−0.15	−18
		1.5	493	107	71	39	.22	.14	.08	−450	160	−1410	1.5	−0.06	0.06	−0.34	0.47	0.00	−0.16	−18

[1] Data at 12 m level missing.

5.2.b. Standard deviation $S(u)$, $S(w)$ of eddy components (in the direction of the estimated mean wind, u, and the vertical; cm/sec) and gustiness ratios $G(x)$, $G(z)$, from rotating pressure tube anemometer (Texas A & M College); one sample per sec during 5-min periods centered at indicated CST.

Date (1953)	CST	Height (m)	u	$S(u)$	$S(w)$	$G(x)$	$G(z)$
24 August	1448	3.1	1089	128	45	.12	.046
	1632	3.1	1003	138	29	.14	.029
	1832	3.1	867	100	28	.12	.032
	2032	3.1	723	87	28	.12	.039
	2232	3.1	758	127	29	.17	.038
25 August	0032	3.1	775	148	27	.19	.035
	0232	3.1	676	90	28	.13	.041
	0832	3.1	858	163	32	.19	.037
	1032	3.1	897	126	29	.14	.032
	1232	3.1	907	121	28	.13	.031
25 August	1432	3.1	928	125	26	.13	.028
	1633	3.1	906	120	29	.13	.032
	1832	3.1	658	170	41	.26	.062
	2032	3.1	539	114	38	.21	.070

5.3. Statistics of fluctuation quantities from aircraft (PBY-6A) data (Woods Hole Ocean. Inst.). Potential temperature θ (°K); mixing ratio W (g water vapor/kg air); standard deviation of eddy components $S(u)$ and $S(w)$ (cm/sec); horizontal Reynolds' stress τ_{xz} (dynes cm^{-2}); linear correlation coefficient between eddy wind components $(u;w)$; standard deviation of temperature $S(T)$ (°C); mean cross product of vertical eddy component and temperature multiplied by density and specific heat of air Q_z (mcal cm^{-2} min^{-1}). Values are averages over horizontal upwind courses of two to three miles extent. CST of flight at lowest and highest level is indicated.

24 August 1953; 1547 to 1649 CST

Height (m)	θ	W	$S(u)$	$S(w)$	τ_{xz}	$(u;w)$	$S(T)$	Q_z
1829	311.4	10.1	49	50	−0.6	0.22	0[1]	0[1]
1676	311.6	10.1	68	57	1.3	−0.30	0[1]	0[1]
1219	311.9	10.2	47	76	0.2	−0.05	0[1]	0[1]
1036	311.6	10.4	125	76	−3.0	0.29	0[1]	0[1]
610	312.0	10.5	43	65	0.1	−0.02	0[1]	0[1]
305	311.2	10.8	52	55	−1.6	0.50	0.05	23
152	311.9	10.9	88	93	0.9	−0.10	0.13	16
61	312.3	10.5	107	93	1.5	−0.14	0.18	120
30	312.1	11.3	127	77	1.8	−0.16	0.17	82

25 August 1953; 1045 to 1115 CST

Height (m)	θ	W	$S(u)$	$S(w)$	τ_{xz}	$(u;w)$	$S(T)$	Q_z
914	312.3	—	5	16	−0.1	0.84	0[1]	0[1]
610	312.0	—	17	13	−0.1	0.51	0.01	3
610	312.0	—	165	76	−1.3	0.09	0.93	790
305	307.3	—	84	125	3.2	−0.28	0.13	13
152	307.1	—	65	103	2.5	−0.33	0.11	77
61	307.2	—	102	82	3.0	−0.32	0.25	225
30	307.4	—	114	79	4.0	−0.40	0.40	188

25 August 1953; 1600 to 1650 CST

Height (m)	θ	W	S(u)	S(w)	τ_{xz}	$(u;w)_z$	S(T)	Q
914	312.7	—	67	78	−0.3	0.05	0^1	0^1
610	312.5	—	46	47	−1.1	0.48	0^1	0^1
305	312.6	—	36	37	−0.1	0.05	0^1	0^1
152	—	—	46	60	−0.5	0.16	0.06	53
61	—	—	78	65	1.4	−0.25	0.09	39
30	—	—	91	71	1.1	−0.16	0.08	0
18	—	—	121	57	2.3	−0.30	0.09	−33
18	—	—	129	60	3.0	−0.35	0.14	−21

[1] Very small value. Not measured but estimated to be zero.

6.1.a. Loeser technique of daytime wind profile measurements (GRD). Mean height Z (m); duration t (sec) of evaluated drift; mean West, South, and upward components u, v, w (m/sec) of drift of individual smoke puffs. Values are t-sec averages centered at indicated $\text{CST}+t/2$ sec.

24 August 1953

CST	Z	t	u	v	w
1230	1194	108	6.8	13.8	−0.6
	901	96	5.4	12.3	−1.7
	582	84	2.5	12.1	−1.3
	486	84	1.6	13.2	−0.8
	358	90	2.6	14.4	−0.5
	290	78	0.8	13.4	−0.4
	207	54	1.6	11.1	−0.4
	136	24	1.1	11.9	0.6
	72	24	3.5	10.8	0.6
	18	6	2.7	8.7	1.0
1430	1280	102	4.1	14.9	0.5
	1056	90	4.0	14.9	0.3
	836	96	3.8	14.2	−0.7
	658	96	4.3	14.3	−1.0
	425	66	3.9	14.1	−1.3
	276	42	3.9	13.2	−0.7
	187	18	2.2	13.8	−1.8
	133	18	3.4	14.3	−1.3
	86	18	3.4	13.2	−1.3
	56	18	3.6	14.2	−0.6
1630	1265	108	6.1	12.9	0.2
	1014	102	5.3	13.5	−0.6
	794	96	4.3	12.5	−1.4
	700	90	5.1	13.1	−0.4
	561	90	4.6	13.7	−0.8
	470	66	3.7	14.4	−0.5
	446	72	3.6	14.9	0.4
	365	78	4.1	15.6	0.6
	271	18	4.4	15.6	0.4
	226	12	−3.2	12.7	−0.5
	190	6	4.0	11.5	0.5
	157	6	0.8	11.8	1.2

CST	Z	t	u	v	w
1235	1276	108	5.6	12.2	−0.4
	1148	108	2.9	12.8	0.7
	880	96	3.3	12.6	−0.8
	788	102	3.4	11.8	0.3
	695	96	4.0	11.8	0.8
	534	54	4.6	11.1	0.4
	480	48	5.5	10.8	1.6
	448	48	5.7	11.4	2.6
	404	54	5.2	10.0	3.4
	338	54	4.8	10.3	3.0
	236	42	2.9	11.2	1.6
	155	12	2.6	11.4	1.8
1435	1287	108	4.1	12.7	0.1
	1124	96	3.8	13.3	0.3
	857	96	4.0	15.6	−1.4
	729	96	3.1	16.0	−1.6
	652	66	3.3	15.4	−1.0
	577	72	3.2	16.8	−0.6
	425	72	5.5	15.4	−1.6
	353	66	5.0	16.1	−1.5
	298	30	6.3	12.9	−1.2
	242	30	6.1	12.8	−1.0
	205	30	6.4	13.2	−1.0
	159	12	6.4	13.3	−2.5
1635	1331	102	4.7	14.4	0.5
	1081	102	3.7	14.4	0.1
	895	66	4.6	17.3	0.5
	795	54	4.0	15.6	1.3
	684	60	4.7	15.3	2.0
	579	60	3.4	13.6	2.5
	338	36	1.2	14.5	0.9
	225	36	1.2	14.0	1.4
	95	12	3.9	12.2	0.4

CST	Z	t	u	v	w
1240	1289	120	5.2	13.5	0.2
	1102	120	3.9	14.7	0.6
	921	120	3.1	14.2	0.9
	752	120	3.7	13.8	0.5
	621	114	3.1	12.9	0.6
	437	66	1.7	12.7	−0.7
	337	60	1.3	12.5	−0.8
	264	60	2.8	12.4	−0.4
	165	18	0.5	14.3	0.6
	113	12	7.7	8.7	1.7
1440	1340	120	4.0	14.4	−0.2
	1114	120	4.1	15.0	−0.4
	904	120	4.6	14.0	−1.2
	747	120	4.0	14.1	−1.4
	613	120	4.2	14.1	−1.5
	550	120	4.1	14.7	−0.9
	408	108	4.6	14.9	−0.4
	323	90	4.9	15.5	−0.8
	294	78	4.8	15.7	−0.4
	194	84	4.6	14.7	−0.7
1640	1323	120	7.1	11.8	0.9
	1010	108	6.5	13.3	−0.6
	879	90	5.0	13.8	−0.2
	690	102	3.0	13.9	−0.7
	648	78	2.2	15.2	0.5
	559	108	1.4	15.3	0.2
	473	108	2.0	15.3	0.8

CST	Z	t	u	v	w
1830	1281	120	6.3	14.8	0.4
	1015	120	5.5	15.8	0.4
	848	114	4.6	15.9	0.5
	712	102	5.4	16.9	1.4
	513	108	2.7	16.8	0.6
	337	18	10.7	17.3	0.4

25 Augusr 1953

CST	Z	t	u	v	w
0630	1370	102	6.6	9.8	0.0
	1150	102	8.1	10.1	0.1
	974	108	8.3	10.0	-0.1
	824	108	9.0	9.9	0.1
	701	96	13.4	10.1	0.0
	452	66	11.6	20.9	-0.3
	382	78	8.5	20.3	0.0
	325	60	7.4	19.5	0.4
	259	48	4.8	17.9	0.7
	148	18	3.0	14.3	0.0
0830	1196	54	8.2	13.2	-0.1
	1006	78	7.8	13.4	0.0
	842	96	7.2	13.0	-0.2
	686	90	7.8	11.9	-0.2
	564	84	10.2	10.8	-0.2
	444	60	12.0	14.0	-0.6
	370	72	7.3	15.3	-0.5
	280	84	5.2	12.5	0.3
	215	60	5.9	11.8	0.1
	188	54	5.5	13.1	0.8
1030	1181	96	7.9	14.1	-0.1
	1011	102	7.9	15.2	0.0
	862	96	7.9	15.6	0.0
	751	96	8.1	15.7	0.0
	661	78	8.6	15.2	-0.2
	590	90	8.6	14.6	0.1
	491	108	5.1	13.4	0.6
	392	108	4.5	12.6	0.4
	311	84	4.4	13.0	0.1
	266	84	4.2	13.2	0.0
	204	84	3.1	14.3	0.1
	165	84	3.3	14.0	-0.1
1230	1081	108	7.5	12.3	-0.4
	894	102	8.3	15.0	-0.3
	778	96	5.4	15.2	0.3
	590	72	3.6	13.8	-0.3
	515	72	4.4	14.0	1.2
	366	90	4.9	13.5	0.2
	200	60	3.6	14.2	-1.5
	188	54	2.1	13.1	0.5
	104	36	2.8	12.9	1.1
	40	18	2.6	11.3	2.0

CST	Z	t	u	v	w
1835	1372	120	6.9	13.8	0.5
	1130	120	5.7	15.0	0.3
	917	114	5.5	15.5	0.0
	798	108	4.9	15.5	0.4
	656	108	4.6	16.6	0.2
	550	102	4.9	16.1	0.5
	458	102	4.4	15.4	0.5
	372	102	3.9	15.5	1.3
	286	54	3.8	15.3	0.1
	233	42	3.2	15.1	0.3
	174	36	3.1	14.6	0.4
0635	1217	84	7.6	10.6	0.1
	1039	96	8.0	10.2	0.3
	861	96	9.3	9.8	0.0
	737	90	12.1	9.6	0.2
	512	54	13.9	16.6	0.2
	428	60	9.8	20.4	0.3
	358	60	7.5	19.8	0.4
	255	48	4.7	16.8	0.8
	211	24	3.8	15.3	1.6
	152	18	2.3	13.6	0.7
0835	1268	54	8.4	13.0	0.0
	1060	78	8.0	13.6	-0.1
	899	84	7.2	13.9	0.0
	776	78	7.1	12.8	0.1
	456	60	10.0	15.0	-0.1
	401	72	6.7	14.1	0.2
	265	72	5.9	13.8	0.1
	222	72	6.2	14.3	0.8
1035	1291	102	7.7	12.5	-0.4
	1111	108	8.0	14.5	0.0
	954	114	7.5	15.2	0.1
	779	108	8.4	16.2	-0.1
	645	102	8.2	15.9	-0.3
	508	108	6.6	14.5	-0.5
	421	108	3.4	13.8	-0.2
	370	60	2.9	13.9	0.0
	297	54	3.2	12.2	0.1
1235	1347	108	3.4	9.1	-0.4
	1117	102	6.9	12.8	-0.4
	940	96	7.3	15.4	-0.7
	825	96	5.2	12.8	0.1
	672	90	5.3	13.8	-0.1
	541	66	4.5	10.9	-0.5
	466	60	5.3	10.6	-0.2
	406	54	4.1	12.1	0.3
	383	54	2.9	12.2	1.3
	308	48	1.8	12.8	1.8
	252	48	0.0	12.4	2.0
	219	48	0.0	12.3	2.4

CST	Z	t	u	v	w
1840	1318	120	5.5	15.9	0.4
	1066	120	5.1	15.1	0.2
	911	114	4.8	16.2	0.4
	749	114	5.1	16.3	0.2
	654	108	4.8	16.4	0.4
	536	96	4.5	16.6	0.3
	412	96	3.5	15.9	-0.1
	356	90	3.8	16.0	0.2
0640	1272	54	7.5	10.5	0.2
	1056	90	7.7	10.0	0.2
	888	96	8.5	10.1	0.2
	719	84	11.9	9.5	0.0
	606	54	16.0	11.6	0.0
	498	54	13.4	17.4	-0.4
	421	60	9.7	20.1	0.2
	350	60	8.0	20.0	0.4
	270	30	5.7	18.7	0.1
	234	36	4.6	17.9	0.1
	195	36	2.9	16.7	0.1
	148	6	2.2	16.7	-0.8
0840	1329	90	7.8	12.6	-0.3
	1119	114	7.8	13.3	-0.3
	804	108	7.6	13.7	-0.2
	686	102	8.4	12.8	-0.1
	572	102	10.8	10.9	0.0
	472	84	10.9	14.3	-0.3
	370	96	6.7	15.2	-0.3
	296	30	5.2	15.0	-0.7
	267	96	4.9	14.5	0.1
	174	96	5.3	14.4	-0.1
1040	1179	84	8.7	13.8	-0.4
	952	96	7.9	15.7	-0.1
	788	90	7.2	16.8	0.0
	616	90	7.6	16.8	-0.4
	477	90	7.3	13.9	-0.8
	433	114	5.1	11.2	0.2
	297	72	4.3	11.7	-0.4
	237	36	3.6	12.5	-0.1
	202	36	3.5	12.1	1.1
	158	54	2.7	13.2	0.8
	108	54	2.4	13.3	0.8
	56	18	-0.8	12.4	0.7
1240	1309	114	4.4	9.7	-0.3
	1132	114	6.4	11.8	0.1
	942	102	7.6	14.8	-0.1
	792	102	5.0	15.0	-0.1
	649	84	4.2	14.4	-0.3
	532	96	1.8	14.1	0.0
	410	78	2.8	13.5	-0.3
	352	60	2.7	12.7	0.1
	227	54	3.9	12.6	-1.2
	198	24	4.2	11.5	-1.2
	179	30	2.5	10.9	0.3
	132	24	1.8	11.2	0.4

CST	Z	t	u	v	w
1430	1163	108	3.6	11.7	0.4
	938	102	4.4	11.6	0.3
	738	96	4.0	12.2	−0.2
	552	96	3.6	13.2	−1.0
	432	90	2.9	12.7	−1.2
	371	60	2.8	14.8	0.3
	308	60	1.0	14.1	0.9
	247	54	−0.1	13.9	1.7
	161	36	−0.8	13.8	1.5
	112	30	−0.7	16.6	2.2
	36	24	−1.4	12.2	1.1
1630	1355	108	2.9	13.9	0.2
	1121	102	3.4	14.6	0.2
	956	96	2.8	14.8	0.2
	795	96	2.5	14.6	−0.2
	557	90	2.9	14.8	−0.4
	482	90	1.9	13.9	−0.5
	199	42	2.1	12.5	−0.3
1830	1253	114	3.8	14.9	0.1
	1073	102	3.1	14.3	0.8
	893	102	2.9	15.2	0.3
	753	90	3.0	16.5	0.6
	627	84	2.4	15.9	0.7
	513	96	2.0	15.8	0.5
	392	96	1.9	15.7	0.1

CST	Z	t	u	v	w
1435	1332	108	4.3	12.7	−0.5
	1175	102	5.4	12.3	0.5
	1011	90	4.7	12.1	0.9
	830	96	3.5	12.0	−0.4
	724	90	2.2	12.8	−0.3
	670	90	2.7	14.1	1.0
	553	84	2.4	14.1	0.5
	480	78	2.8	14.9	0.4
	392	84	1.5	15.1	−0.3
	349	42	0.3	14.6	0.4
	319	36	−0.4	14.3	1.0
	300	42	0.2	12.8	1.7
1635	1334	72	3.3	13.0	0.4
	1070	66	4.3	13.8	−0.4
	897	60	3.6	14.5	−0.2
	706	60	3.5	14.0	−0.9
	595	54	2.5	14.0	−0.5
	524	54	2.3	14.8	0.5
	411	54	2.8	15.0	−0.4
	323	42	1.9	15.2	−0.4
	261	48	1.8	15.0	−0.1
	203	48	0.9	14.1	−0.1
	145	48	1.0	14.0	−0.5
	84	48	1.0	14.0	−0.8

CST	Z	t	u	v	w
1440	1271	120	4.4	10.0	0.6
	1001	120	4.8	14.5	−0.1
	885	120	2.9	13.3	−0.1
	723	120	2.3	13.2	−0.5
	579	120	2.2	12.6	−0.4
	503	120	2.0	12.8	0.0
	355	120	1.2	12.8	−0.7
	255	72	0.8	13.3	−1.6
	223	42	0.4	13.1	−1.5
	191	42	−1.2	13.4	−0.5
	169	42	−0.9	14.1	0.1
	132	42	−0.4	14.7	−0.1
1640	1262	120	3.9	14.4	0.0
	1022	114	2.9	14.5	−0.6
	872	108	2.5	14.6	−0.6
	708	108	2.2	14.3	−1.2
	586	108	2.0	13.7	−0.9
	494	102	2.0	14.5	−0.3
	402	102	2.2	14.7	−0.3
	363	102	2.0	14.5	0.1
	286	72	1.9	14.1	−0.1
	239	72	2.8	14.5	0.1
	193	72	2.8	14.6	0.0
	162	72	2.1	14.5	0.1
1835	1307	120	3.6	14.6	−0.1
	1108	120	3.6	15.3	0.0
	955	120	3.7	16.0	0.5
	822	114	2.3	15.6	0.6
	692	120	1.8	16.0	0.2
	552	120	1.4	16.1	0.0
	458	120	0.9	16.1	−0.1
	375	114	0.8	15.9	−0.1

6.1.b. Loeser technique of night-time wind profile measurements (GRD). Median values of West and South components u, v (m/sec) of drift; number N of balloons of a pibal swarm which cross the indicated levels. Basic data are overlapping 24-sec mean displacements toward the East and North of each of the N balloons at 12-sec intervals during a 4-min period centered at indicated CST.

Height (m)	24 August 2035			2235			25 August 1953 0035			0235			0435		
	u	v	N	u	v	N	u	v	N	u	v	N	u	v	N
1600	—	—	—	—	—	—	—	—	—	5.8	8.8	1	—	—	—
1400	—	—	—	—	—	—	—	—	—	9.4	11.2	3	—	—	—
1200	—	—	—	10.0	17.0	1	9.2	17.0	2	13.2	13.5	3	8.2	11.2	2
1000	—	—	—	10.2	18.5	2	10.8	27.0	2	16.2	13.8	3	10.9	11.5	3
800	—	—	—	9.2	19.6	2	10.3	31.0	1	18.1	17.6	3	15.0	12.3	4
700	4.7	17.5	1	7.5	21.2	1	12.4	24.0	2	16.9	21.3	3	16.3	13.8	3
600	4.2	18.1	2	7.4	22.3	1	11.6	24.9	2	13.6	24.1	3	15.8	16.2	4
500	3.3	19.0	2	7.1	25.3	3	10.3	25.4	3	11.6	25.2	5	13.3	20.6	4
400	2.6	20.2	4	4.1	25.3	4	5.8	24.6	5	8.9	23.3	5	9.4	22.4	3
300	1.1	21.1	5	1.7	22.3	4	3.8	21.3	4	5.8	21.5	4	6.3	21.9	4
200	−0.2	19.5	4	−0.4	18.6	4	2.1	18.3	4	3.6	17.5	3	3.3	18.3	3
100	−0.9	14.9	3	−1.1	14.8	2	0.7	13.4	4	2.0	14.0	1	2.5	15.2	3

6.2. Rawinsonde (GMD-1A) wind speed (m/sec) and direction (deg from North) from 1-min mean drift at 30-sec intervals, at indicated height (m), for first 7 min of ascent started at indicated CST.

24 August 1953

1235			1435			1635			1835			2035		
m	m/sec	deg	m	m/sec	deg	m	m/sec	deg	m	m/sec	deg	m	m/sec	deg
1922	11.4	212	1868	12.6	207	2247	13.7	207	2462	16.1	211	2142	5.7	234
1686	17.9	213	1561	19.9	201	1934	13.4	208	2122	17.5	210	1910	10.8	224
1561	13.1	214	1400	16.3	202	1774	17.7	202	1954	17.5	209	1799	6.5	251
1438	15.1	217	1237	17.6	196	1581	21.7	205	1782	16.6	204	1665	9.6	227
1313	17.1	211	1078	17.9	191	1384	19.1	199	1627	17.0	202	1535	18.2	210
1189	17.3	203	949	17.7	192	1188	18.2	187	1454	19.1	202	1405	16.4	209
1064	15.4	198	828	19.8	196	1000	16.6	190	1289	19.3	201	1278	16.6	209
939	14.8	201	708	19.6	196	864	17.9	189	1123	19.0	198	1150	21.2	201
790	14.7	204	588	16.7	194	729	20.3	193	945	18.7	196	950	25.8	197
641	13.9	198	469	14.9	196	593	17.6	194	755	18.4	195	738	25.4	196
492	15.0	194	350	15.0	202	458	13.7	189	570	20.3	192	525	25.6	191
342	15.8	188	232	16.4	203	323	12.8	188	375	19.5	190	312	22.1	189
195	18.5	184	117	15.2	200	169	14.7	188	185	14.8	188	142	17.4	182

24 August   25 August 1953

2235			0035			0235			0435		
m	m/sec	deg	m	m/sec	deg	m	m/sec	deg	m	m/sec	deg
1917	6.8	211	1597	11.3	215	2326	5.3	240	2235	7.1	241
1637	10.0	209	1378	9.0	212	2021	10.4	225	1928	8.1	226
1496	10.3	214	1267	5.9	220	1868	13.6	221	1774	7.9	229
1356	11.5	214	1156	9.0	219	1706	18.8	214	1621	8.5	226
1213	13.3	212	1047	15.0	218	1537	22.1	216	1467	10.0	219
1080	14.7	212	932	21.5	216	1368	23.2	219	1309	11.7	218
945	17.3	212	812	27.3	211	1198	23.4	223	1152	14.4	219
810	17.6	208	693	30.2	208	1029	23.7	225	997	16.2	224
675	18.6	204	573	31.8	203	861	25.7	224	837	19.0	228
540	19.8	200	455	29.1	198	693	27.7	219	662	23.3	226
418	28.0	191	337	23.1	194	527	26.7	209	489	25.2	214
170	23.3	186	219	18.1	186	359	23.5	200	318	22.9	199
138	10.1	180	109	14.1	182	185	19.5	193	148	18.1	189

0635			0835			1035			1235		
m	m/sec	deg	m	m/sec	deg	m	m/sec	deg	m	m/sec	deg
2325	3.4	262	1789	5.7	233	1958	1.8	232	2155	3.2	140
—	—	—	1552	9.0	212	1716	6.2	225	1891	2.7	143
1857	4.8	253	1438	11.9	209	1588	6.3	225	1758	3.7	147
—	—	—	1324	15.1	210	1459	5.9	219	1602	3.7	168
1531	8.4	210	1211	17.3	210	1331	8.4	214	1446	6.0	196
—	—	—	1097	18.1	210	1202	14.7	200	1290	8.8	204
1201	11.9	211	983	18.5	209	1075	19.6	208	1144	12.0	203
—	—	—	857	19.0	207	921	18.4	205	976	16.4	207
864	15.9	212	714	17.5	208	770	18.1	203	817	16.7	203
—	—	—	569	14.7	216	612	19.1	203	651	14.8	202
492	18.0	221	425	15.4	216	460	15.6	204	488	15.8	201
—	—	—	280	17.0	205	309	14.3	199	326	17.2	196
140	16.6	194	138	17.5	200	155	15.3	192	163	17.1	191

1435			1650			1835			2035		
m	m/sec	deg	m	m/sec	deg	m	m/sec	deg	m	m/sec	deg
2203	4.6	171	2386	6.8	179	1719	15.2	202	2325	21.2	219
1882	5.4	165	2078	10.1	184	1463	18.4	198	2000	15.2	220
1722	5.5	172	1923	10.7	187	1336	17.1	195	1835	15.0	220
1561	8.0	185	1768	13.6	190	1206	14.7	193	1675	16.6	212
1403	9.9	192	1619	15.1	190	1079	12.3	194	1505	16.0	211
1242	11.0	200	1471	14.6	189	975	14.0	195	1380	18.8	203
1080	14.9	206	1322	13.7	183	856	17.4	190	1180	23.1	196
919	16.4	205	1174	11.9	182	748	18.4	188	1020	21.2	194
769	16.2	201	1037	13.7	187	639	18.5	188	850	22.2	191
617	14.1	198	822	15.9	190	531	18.0	185	680	22.2	187
467	12.4	190	618	16.1	194	422	18.5	184	515	23.3	182
316	13.2	188	414	16.0	193	314	19.7	182	340	21.5	181
159	13.8	183	216	14.8	191	170	16.7	178	180	17.2	190

6.3. Double theodolite pibal wind speed (m/sec) and direction (deg from North) from 1-min mean drift at 30-sec intervals, at indicated height (m), for first 7 min of ascent started at indicated CST.

24 August 1953

1430			1835			2030			2240			2330		
m	m/sec	deg	m	m/sec	deg	m	m/sec	deg	m	m/sec	deg	m	m/sec	deg
835	16.2	195	890	17.4	197	804	27.2	196	824	23.4	203	1106	18.3	207
808	15.8	195	816	16.2	195	721	20.1	197	753	24.2	200	1010	23.5	210
778	16.7	194	757	16.3	194	680	9.1	197	707	25.8	198	941	18.6	211
728	16.3	196	693	16.3	193	671	14.8	192	634	24.7	198	878	20.6	205
709	14.8	197	622	16.3	190	584	22.2	190	598	21.3	197	805	26.2	205
672	15.4	199	540	16.8	190	528	17.8	188	542	25.2	197	737	20.5	205
591	15.8	198	473	17.7	189	468	20.5	187	508	28.4	194	716	22.9	203
496	14.1	193	409	16.5	187	402	22.1	186	450	26.8	193	615	28.4	201
402	13.9	182	356	16.3	188	362	19.1	183	415	26.7	188	564	25.4	199
318	15.9	189	294	15.8	188	312	18.9	182	334	24.9	185	485	26.7	197
253	16.5	188	232	14.1	188	254	20.5	182	304	20.6	182	428	25.4	193
214	13.7	188	176	13.8	186	206	18.5	178	240	20.2	179	358	23.8	187
160	13.8	189	129	12.8	185	146	16.4	175				260	19.6	182
74	15.0	190	68	11.1	182	90	13.1	172				164	18.3	177

25 August 1953

0230			0830			1030			1230		
m	m/sec	deg	m	m/sec	deg	m	m/sec	deg	m	m/sec	deg
884	22.2	228				924	19.3	202	1028	15.3	204
836	27.3	222				850	17.6	202	956	18.1	202
745	29.3	221	764	12.2	205	778	16.4	203	866	18.5	203
692	26.8	222	672	18.7	209	694	17.7	203	814	17.7	204
636	29.7	215	592	12.2	212	604	17.8	204	739	18.8	201
572	29.0	210	558	9.6	222	526	17.9	204	678	18.0	200
526	28.2	205	502	16.7	224	442	16.4	202	596	17.8	198
465	29.2	201	398	18.8	217	374	13.8	198	508	15.6	194
402	25.9	198	348	17.0	204	308	13.6	194	420	14.2	192
343	22.7	195	302	16.5	199	226	16.7	179	345	13.3	191
263	21.0	192	242	14.7	196	161	14.9	193	275	13.3	190
213	18.7	189	192	13.6	195	135	14.8	208	214	12.4	188
134	16.0	188	112	13.9	198	108	14.4	190	153	13.1	189
83	14.2	189	67	14.0	199	58	14.1	190	70	14.1	191

1430			1630			1730			1930		
m	m/sec	deg	m	m/sec	deg	m	m/sec	deg	m	m/sec	deg
1512	6.2	187	792	15.7	185	934	22.3	193			
1448	12.8	197	760	15.0	184	872	14.1	186			
1345	16.9	199	722	16.0	184	816	12.3	186	732	4.3	175
1276	13.3	201	667	15.7	185	747	15.5	187	716	11.2	183
1162	13.2	201	605	14.5	184	694	14.0	185	676	18.7	184
1070	12.7	201	542	13.3	186	642	14.0	186	591	19.1	182
974	12.7	199	492	14.6	186	581	15.2	185	520	16.6	181
882	13.2	196	420	16.1	185	509	14.6	183	460	16.7	179
724	13.5	196	374	15.2	185	421	13.0	182	406	19.8	179
549	13.9	196	332	15.1	186	342	11.4	181	329	18.5	178
376	14.8	190	292	15.1	186	267	10.9	181	270	17.1	175
280	15.3	184	240	14.8	184	216	10.2	182	202	16.4	172
184	10.5	185	162	12.7	183	143	10.0	181	140	13.5	167
146	11.9	182	78	11.0	185	70	9.2	177	69	11.1	163

6.4. Radiosonde pressure (mb), temperature (°C), and relative humidity (%) at significant levels of ascent started at indicated CST. (M = "motorboating", i.e., a humidity value below the minimum value that the radiosonde can measure at that temperature.)

	24 August						25 August 1953										
	1235	1435	1635	1835	2035	2235	0035	0235	0435	0635	0835	1035	1235	1435	1650	1835	2035
mb	941	940	939	938	939	940	940	940	941	941	942	942	942	941	941	941	941
°C	31.3	33.5	33.0	28.5	25.5	24.2	23.7	23.2	21.5	21.0	25.0	29.4	33.8	35.0	35.2	31.5	26.5
%	39	35	33	43	50	58	60	67	71	78	63	52	40	34	31	40	53
mb	828	813	896	918	915	875	928	890	931	901	906	895	871	835	805	896	901
°C	18.1	18.8	27.6	27.6	25.6	23.0	23.7	21.4	22.1	19.5	21.7	23.9	25.4	21.9	20.8	28.4	28.6
%	63	63	40	—	54	—	60	71	70	—	70	63	50	60	55	42	45
mb	800	786	843	804	880	800	872	846	900	894	894	884	826	812	735	836	795
°C	17.5	16.2	22.6	17.3	23.9	16.6	22.0	21.9	20.5	20.9	23.9	26.6	24.9	20.9	16.2	22.9	20.0
%	57	65	52	64	50	61	59	69	70	—	60	47	20	34	27	51	55
mb	760	768	746	728	774	706	826	787	879	886	884	812	786	771	711	776	742
°C	14.4	15.4	13.2	10.0	14.5	10.8	19.5	17.9	23.6	20.5	27.2	20.5	22.0	18.2	14.4	17.0	14.7
%	56	56	77	85	70	23	63	53	62	—	49	42	19	26	21	64	65
mb	718	731	689	723	735	658	780	773	836	870	818	791	677	723	698	734	718
°C	9.9	11.6	9.6	10.0	11.8	8.2	16.9	17.1	22.2	25.0	21.7	20.6	10.7	14.0	15.1	13.2	12.8
%	63	74	54	80	64	22	38	38	55	—	42	24	21	21	20	48	42
mb	634	675	638	638	724	642	752	744	771	799	792	772	659	694	631	722	693
°C	4.0	9.0	7.0	4.5	11.6	6.1	14.2	14.0	18.2	19.1	21.3	19.1	11.2	12.3	9.5	13.6	14.0
%	64	53	47	49	58	M	42	55	23	—	19	37	21	M	M	25	20
mb	546	622	622	604	707	610	740	733	654	770	763	749	619	678	538	707	600
°C	-3.0	4.6	5.5	2.6	10.5	3.8	13.4	13.6	6.9	18.2	18.1	17.3	7.0	12.4	0.6	12.7	7.0
%	58	58	35	27	55	M	25	31	22	—	37	28	25	M	M	22	M
mb	—	610	569	—	675	—	695	713	613	745	750	666	603	641	—	658	—
°C	—	4.2	0.9	—	8.8	—	10.8	12.0	5.5	15.4	18.0	9.3	5.7	9.5	—	10.6	—
%	—	52	43	—	25	—	22	25	M	—	25	23	23	M	—	M	—
mb	—	586	555	—	645	—	638	—	582	678	734	645	542	605	—	618	—
°C	—	1.5	0.2	—	6.9	—	7.1	—	2.0	9.0	16.4	9.8	1.9	5.4	—	6.4	—
%	—	55	46	—	24	—	M	—	M	—	25	23	M	M	—	M	—
mb	—	528	—	—	610	—	584	658	563	660	685	603	—	595	—	601	—
°C	—	-3.7	—	—	4.6	—	3.0	8.1	1.6	8.3	11.0	5.1	—	6.2	—	6.0	—
%	—	27	—	—	M	—	M	26	M	—	28	28	—	M	—	M	—
mb	—	—	—	—	—	—	546	645	—	636	649	—	—	581	—	—	—
°C	—	—	—	—	—	—	-1.0	7.5	—	7.9	10.1	—	—	5.7	—	—	—
%	—	—	—	—	—	—	M	24	—	20	—	—	M	—	—	—	—
mb	—	—	—	—	—	—	—	611	—	610	612	—	—	—	—	—	—
°C	—	—	—	—	—	—	—	4.5	—	5.0	6.2	—	—	—	—	—	—
%	—	—	—	—	—	—	—	M	—	—	23	—	—	—	—	—	—

6.5. Air temperature T (°C) and mixing ratio W (g water vapor/kg air) at altitude Z (m) from aerograph (L-20) data. CST of start, top level, and end of flight is indicated.

24 August 1953

(1220-1239-1249)			(1420-1435-1448)			(1606-1619-1631)			(1820-1833-1845)		
Z	T	W	Z	T	W	Z	T	W	Z	T	W
17	28.4	11.5	26	30.6	10.5	17	31.9	11.0	17	30.7	10.8
70	28.2	11.7	100	29.6	10.4	100	30.8	10.4	100	30.2	10.6
100	27.7	11.7	330	27.4	10.1	170	30.0	9.6	170	29.7	10.3
135	27.6	11.9	660	24.6	11.6	330	28.7	9.9	250	29.3	10.2
170	27.5	11.9	990	21.1	11.5	660	25.7	10.7	330	28.7	9.9
250	26.4	11.8	1310	18.8	11.5	990	22.9	11.8	660	25.6	9.8
330	25.4	11.4	1630	16.0	9.8	1310	19.8	11.7	990	22.8	10.7
660	22.9	12.2	1780	15.3	9.2	1630	16.5	11.5	1310	19.5	11.0
990	20.5	12.0	1950	13.9	10.4	1310	19.9	12.6	1630	16.4	11.1
1310	17.7	10.3	1630	15.8	10.7	990	22.8	12.4	1310	19.7	11.8
1630	16.3	10.0	1310	18.5	11.7	660	26.3	12.2	990	22.7	11.7
1310	17.5	11.0	990	21.6	12.0	330	28.6	10.4	660	25.7	10.8
990	20.1	12.6	660	24.5	12.3	170	30.9	10.4	330	28.7	10.5
660	23.2	12.3	330	27.7	11.5	35	32.7	10.7	135	30.5	10.8
330	26.3	13.0	250	28.7	11.5	17	32.7	10.7	100	30.3	10.6
100	28.4	12.7	170	29.1	10.6				17	29.7	10.2
17	29.7	11.6	135	29.7	10.6						
			100	30.2	10.8						
			17	31.6	11.4						

25 August 1953

(0624-0638-0646)			(0816-0831-0844)			(1020-1032-1042)			(1224-1235-1244)		
Z	T	W	Z	T	W	Z	T	W	Z	T	W
16	22.2	14.4	16	24.1	15.6	16	27.7	14.9	16	30.7	13.5
130	21.6	11.6	48	24.0	15.3	48	27.3	14.4	65	29.6	12.7
330	20.6	12.5	165	22.7	14.6	100	27.0	14.1	240	28.2	12.5
660	25.5	12.3	330	21.2	14.4	165	25.9	13.8	490	26.1	13.4
990	23.7	8.4	660	26.4	9.5	240	25.0	14.3	660	24.7	11.7
1300	21.0	8.0	990	23.7	8.5	330	24.5	13.9	990	23.6	7.3
1630	20.5	4.7	1300	21.1	6.4	660	26.4	9.0	1300	22.6	5.1
990	24.2	11.1	1630	20.9	4.8	990	23.5	7.8	1630	20.6	3.9
330	20.7	13.6	1300	21.8	7.6	1300	21.5	6.0	1140	22.5	7.5
165	21.6	14.6	990	24.3	10.4	1630	19.1	6.2	820	24.2	13.1
65	22.1	14.7	660	27.0	11.7	1300	21.8	6.9	660	24.0	12.8
16	22.5	14.9	330	21.8	14.6	990	23.7	10.4	490	26.1	14.4
			165	23.2	15.5	660	26.5	10.4	165	29.6	14.7
			100	23.9	15.5	330	24.2	13.1	100	29.9	13.6
			65	24.1	15.4	165	26.3	15.1	33	30.7	13.5
			48	24.7	15.6	33	27.7	15.2			
			25	25.4	15.5						

(1417-1431-1441)				(1620-1635-1646)				(1815-1832-1843)		
Z	T	W		Z	T	W		Z	T	W
33	32.4	11.3		33	32.2	9.5		48	32.0	11.4
65	31.6	10.4		100	31.5	9.8		100	31.0	10.8
165	31.2	10.9		165	31.1	9.7		230	30.8	10.8
330	29.5	10.7		280	30.1	9.5		330	29.9	10.3
660	27.1	12.4		330	29.9	9.7		660	27.3	10.3
990	23.5	12.9		490	27.9	8.8		990	24.1	10.7
1300	21.4	9.6		660	27.5	9.8		1300	21.0	10.7
1630	19.2	7.4		990	23.9	10.7		1630	18.5	10.9
1300	20.9	6.8		1140	20.8	11.0		1300	21.4	11.8
820	25.4	12.8		1630	18.8	7.9		990	24.0	12.2
660	25.9	12.4		1300	21.3	10.9		660	27.2	11.8
330	29.5	13.6		990	24.1	12.5		490	28.8	11.1
165	30.9	12.6		490	28.6	10.7		330	30.1	10.8
100	32.2	12.2		330	29.9	10.1		165	30.6	10.9
33	32.7	11.8		100	31.7	9.9		115	30.8	10.7
				65	32.5	9.7		57	30.9	10.6

7.1. Representative values of West and South components of the wind u, v (m/sec) at standard heights. Values are estimated from the combination of smoke puff or pibal swarm, rawinsonde and double theodolite pibal data at or near the indicated CST.

	Height (m)	24 August					25 August 1953											
		1235	1435	1635	1835	2035	2235	0035	0235	0435	0635	0835	1035	1235	1435	1635	1835	2035
u	2000	6.1	5.9	7.3	7.7	7.1	3.1	2.9	5.7	6.0	5.4	3.6	1.0	-2.0	-1.3	1.5	4.0	10.7
	1750	6.0	5.7	6.8	7.2	7.4	4.5	4.3	7.1	6.0	4.4	4.8	2.7	-0.5	-0.4	1.9	5.6	9.5
	1500	5.9	5.3	6.2	6.7	7.6	6.1	5.8	10.5	6.2	4.6	6.0	5.0	1.7	1.4	2.1	5.5	8.3
	1250	5.7	4.8	5.5	6.1	7.5	7.6	7.5	13.9	7.9	6.3	8.0	7.4	4.8	4.3	2.5	4.1	6.4
	1000	5.0	4.5	4.8	5.5	7.2	9.5	10.7	16.3	11.0	8.1	8.5	8.2	6.8	5.7	2.8	3.3	4.6
	800	4.4	4.4	4.3	5.0	6.6	9.0	13.0	18.0	14.6	9.7	8.4	7.6	6.0	4.7	2.9	2.7	3.5
	700	4.0	4.4	3.9	4.8	5.9	8.1	13.4	17.5	16.2	10.9	8.6	7.7	5.5	4.1	2.8	2.4	2.5
	600	3.7	4.4	3.6	4.4	5.0	7.3	12.4	14.9	16.5	12.3	8.9	7.5	5.0	3.6	2.6	2.0	1.5
	500	3.3	4.5	3.1	4.0	4.0	6.3	10.0	11.5	14.0	12.2	9.5	6.5	4.5	3.0	2.4	1.5	0.6
	400	2.9	4.5	2.8	3.5	3.0	4.6	7.1	8.5	10.0	10.4	8.9	5.5	4.0	2.2	2.2	1.1	-0.1
	300	2.4	4.5	2.6	2.9	2.0	2.6	4.1	6.2	6.8	7.6	7.1	4.4	3.5	1.3	2.0	0.6	-1.1
	200	1.9	4.3	2.5	2.2	0.8	0.7	1.9	3.9	3.4	4.6	5.9	3.4	3.0	0.4	1.5	-0.3	-2.5
	100	1.5	3.8	2.6	1.5	-1.1	-1.2	0.5	2.0	2.3	2.1	4.9	3.0	2.5	-0.8	1.0	-1.3	-4.4
v	2000	8.5	9.2	12.7	14.3	5.0	5.0	2.0	7.8	5.3	1.1	1.1	-0.5	2.1	5.4	11.1	9.5	11.0
	1750	10.2	12.1	14.8	15.0	8.5	8.1	4.2	9.5	6.2	2.8	3.3	3.1	5.9		12.0	12.5	13.2
	1500	12.0	14.4	15.6	16.1	13.2	10.9	7.7	11.5	7.6	6.9	7.3	5.7	5.2	8.3	12.9	13.9	16.1
	1250	13.6	15.6	15.9	16.6	17.0	14.3	12.7	14.0	10.3	9.8	12.2	10.0	9.7	11.0	13.7	14.9	18.6
	1000	13.7	15.7	16.0	17.0	22.0	18.1	21.5	16.3	11.5	10.8	14.2	15.8	14.0	12.9	14.4	15.7	20.5
	800	13.6	15.5	15.9	17.4	23.5	20.9	27.0	18.7	12.8	12.0	14.2	16.5	15.2	13.4	14.7	16.0	21.9
	700	13.4	15.4	15.6	17.5	23.5	22.5	27.7	21.5	14.5	12.8	13.8	16.3	15.0	13.6	14.9	16.1	22.5
	600	13.1	15.3	15.2	17.3	23.4	23.7	27.4	23.8	17.0	14.0	13.6	15.8	14.8	13.8	15.0	16.2	23.1
	500	13.0	15.1	14.9	17.0	23.0	24.6	26.7	24.9	20.4	16.0	13.8	14.9	14.6	13.9	15.1	16.2	23.3
	400	12.9	15.0	14.5	16.6	22.3	24.9	25.2	23.3	22.3	18.0	14.2	13.9	14.4	13.9	15.0	16.0	22.8
	300	12.8	14.7	14.0	16.0	21.1	23.5	21.6	21.2	22.1	18.0	14.5	13.6	14.2	13.9	14.8	15.5	20.7
	200	12.5	14.3	13.5	14.9	19.1	20.0	17.7	18.9	18.6	16.6	14.6	13.4	14.0	13.8	14.2	14.5	17.8
	100	11.8	13.8	12.9	12.9	15.2	15.6	13.8	15.7	15.8	14.1	13.7	12.8	13.4	13.5	13.2	12.5	15.0

7.2.a. Air temperature (°C) at standard heights. Values are interpolated and averaged from radiosonde and airplane (L-20) data at or near the indicated CST.

Height (m)	24 August				25 August 1953												
	1235	1435	1635	1835	2035[1]	2235[1]	0035[1]	0235[1]	0435[1]	0635	0835	1035	1235	1435	1635	1835	2035[1]
2000	14.1	13.6	13.1	12.4	13.1	14.0	14.4	15.1	17.6	18.2	19.5	19.3	18.5	16.4	17.2	15.1	15.9
1750	15.6	15.5	15.4	14.9	14.6	15.2	16.4	17.2	18.8	19.3	20.4	20.3	20.6	18.2	18.5	17.0	18.1
1500	16.8	17.1	17.7	17.0	16.6	16.5	17.9	18.6	20.1	20.1	20.7	20.9	21.3	19.7	19.7	19.1	20.1
1250	17.8	19.3	20.1	19.4	18.7	18.4	19.2	20.2	21.3	21.1	21.6	21.3	23.0	21.2	21.4	21.3	22.9
1000	20.2	21.5	22.4	21.7	20.8	20.4	20.5	21.8	22.4	23.3	23.7	23.2	23.9	23.2	24.0	23.6	24.0
800	22.0	23.5	24.2	23.6	22.4	22.0	21.5	21.7	23.1	24.2	25.3	24.7	24.6	25.3	26.2	25.6	25.6
600	23.7	25.7	25.0	25.4	24.0	23.2	22.3	21.5	23.1	22.9	26.5	26.0	25.7	27.0	28.3	27.4	27.1
400	25.7	27.8	27.7	27.3	24.7	23.5	22.9	21.8	20.6	21.0	22.7	24.0	27.7	29.2	30.0	29.2	28.5
200	27.8	29.9	30.0	29.0	25.2	23.9	23.5	22.5	21.6	21.0	22.8	26.0	29.7	31.3	32.0	30.5	27.5
100	28.8	31.0	31.4	29.5	25.4	24.0	23.7	22.9	22.0	21.5	23.7	27.3	30.6	32.4	32.9	30.9	27.0

[1] Radiosonde data only.

7.2.b. Mixing ratio (g water vapor/kg air) at standard heights. Values are interpolated and averaged from radiosonde and airplane (L-20) data at or near the indicated CST.

Height (m)	24 August				25 August 1953												
	1235	1435	1635	1835	2035[1]	2235[1]	0035[1]	0235[1]	0435[1]	0635[2]	0835	1035	1235	1435	1635	1835	2035[1]
2000	9.2	7.8	10.4	10.0	8.5	5.9	5.6	8.1	2.9	—	3.5	5.5	2.5	4.9	5.4	9.3	9.5
1750	9.3	8.7	10.7	10.4	9.4	7.5	5.9	9.2	5.1	—	4.4	6.2	3.5	6.0	7.3	10.4	9.9
1500	9.8	10.2	11.2	10.8	9.7	9.0	7.9	9.8	7.4	5.3	5.2	6.0	4.3	7.0	9.0	10.8	10.4
1250	10.4	11.3	11.5	11.0	10.0	9.6	10.4	11.7	9.6	8.0	7.4	7.1	5.7	8.5	10.6	11.0	10.8
1000	11.5	11.5	11.6	10.9	10.4	10.0	11.2	13.5	11.6	9.5	9.5	9.1	8.0	12.0	11.4	11.3	11.2
800	12.0	11.2	11.5	10.8	10.6	10.4	11.4	13.8	12.5	11.0	10.5	9.9	11.0	12.6	11.2	11.3	11.5
600	12.2	11.8	11.1	10.6	11.0	10.7	11.6	13.9	13.0	12.5	11.6	10.7	12.5	12.5	10.8	11.2	11.9
400	12.1	11.5	10.6	10.6	11.9	11.1	11.9	13.6	12.0	12.9	13.2	12.9	13.6	12.7	10.5	11.0	12.2
200	12.3	11.2	10.4	10.8	12.1	11.4	12.1	13.3	12.6	13.1	14.2	14.4	13.7	12.6	10.5	11.3	12.4
100	12.3	11.3	10.8	10.8	11.6	11.6	12.1	13.1	12.7	13.8	14.7	14.6	13.6	12.0	10.6	11.2	12.5

[1] Radiosonde data only.   [2] Airplane data only.

7.3.a. Summary of heat budget constituents (mcal cm^{-2} min^{-1}) of the earth-air interface according to the theoretical models by Suomi, Halstead, and Lettau. Net radiation flux R, heat transfer to the soil S, sensible heat transfer to the air Q, and latent heat transfer to the air (heat equivalent of evaporation) E. Values are hourly means centered at indicated CST.

| | 24 August | | | | | | 25 August 1953 | | | | | | | | | | |
	1235	1435	1635	1835	2035	2235	0035	0235	0435	0635	0835	1035	1235	1435	1635	1835	2035
Suomi																	
R_0	−919	−734	−304	74	118	118	120	116	118	33	−375	−750	−870	—	—	—	—
S_0	135	89	−25	−32	−38	−34	−37	−38	−39	−23	51	110	131	—	—	—	—
Q_0	617	538	341	−42	−64	−39	−46	−57	−47	−4	244	508	592	—	—	—	—
E_0	164	106	2	5	−14	−44	−37	−22	−33	−6	80	132	149	—	—	—	—
Halstead																	
R_0	—	—	—	—	—	—	90	80	90	40	−340	−690	−820	−700	−340	30	80
S_0	—	—	—	—	—	—	−10	−20	−18	−15	15	73	118	110	70	25	2
Q_0	—	—	—	—	—	—	−115	−100	−85	−43	285	460	552	490	228	−75	−97
E_0	—	—	—	—	—	—	68	68	30	50	118	207	255	197	98	58	20
Lettau																	
R_0	−875	−724	−325	57	100	95	112	105	110	33	−377	−752	−872	−746	−337	47	93
S_0	207	146	55	−18	−40	−34	−27	−30	−32	−20	60	158	211	161	76	−3	−22
Q_0	545	403	151	−29	−47	−61	−56	−54	−52	−26	184	374	484	360	146	−35	−69
E_0	163	67	56	27	−7	−21	14	16	−9	−14	50	93	87	148	6	12	−28

7.3.b. Representative logarithmic height derivatives of wind speed ($\bar{z}V'$ mm sec⁻¹, from UCLA and JH data), potential temperature ($\bar{z}\theta'$, 10⁻³ °C, from JH and UW data), and water vapor pressure ($\bar{z}e'$, 10⁻³ mb, from JH and UW data); representative values of Karman number k (from $\bar{z}V'$ and UCLA, JH, and MIT stress data), interpolated ground drag τ_0 (dynes cm⁻², from $\bar{z}V'$ and representative k values), and ratio of heat and momentum diffusivities N_Q; representative groundflux ratio F_0 and inverse Bowen ratio B. Values refer to indicated CST and are employed in the computation of the heat budget constituents Q_0 and E_0 (Lettau model; see Table 7.3.a).

| | 24 August | | | | | | 25 August 1953 | | | | | | | | | | |
	1235	1435	1635	1835	2035	2235	0035	0235	0435	0635	0835	1035	1235	1435	1635	1835	2035
$\bar{z}V'$	1611	1667	1597	1055	961	1239	1248	1281	1290	1309	1738	1616	1663	1611	1451	1003	885
$\bar{z}\theta'$	−870	−718	−352	144	270	246	229	207	196	95	−380	−680	−787	−638	−356	177	264
$\bar{z}e'$	−271	−108	−97	−75	23	48	−33	34	19	3	−78¹	−156	−141	−45	−11	−36	89
k	0.39	0.39	0.38	0.37	0.37	0.37	0.37	0.38	0.38	0.38	0.38	0.39	0.39	0.39	0.38	0.37	0.37
τ_0	4.22	4.46	3.98	1.67	1.40	2.36	2.42	2.57	2.60	2.72	4.85	4.23	4.47	4.13	3.28	1.52	1.20
N_Q	1.66	1.46	1.20	0.86	0.84	0.90	0.90	0.92	0.92	0.96	1.20	1.46	1.59	1.53	1.26	0.88	0.78
F_0	2.04	2.08	2.14	1.2²	1.06	0.90	1.33	1.25	1.37	0.46	2.07	2.32	2.16	2.48	2.25	1.14	1.38
B	0.50	0.24	0.44	−0.8²	0.14	0.31	−0.23	0.26	0.16	0.05	0.32	0.37	0.29	0.11	0.05	−0.32	0.54

¹ UW value only.   ² Value disregarded for evaluation of N_Q.

7.4. Richardson number (Ri; units of 10^{-3}) from Mass. Inst. Tech. and Johns Hopkins University data on simultaneous temperature and wind velocity differences, centered at indicated CST and mean height z_m (meters). (Ri') = average height derivative of Richardson number (10^{-3} m^{-1}).

Inst. Set	Height (m)	24 August 1235	1435	1635	1835	2035	2235	25 August 1953 0035	0235	0435	0635	0835	1035	1235	1435	1635	1835	2035
MIT	8.0	−53	−32	−10	—	52	31	32	29	25	19	−12	−38	−46	−39	−13	45	66
MIT	4.0	−48	−32	−17	—	33	18	19	15	14	6	−16	−39	−40	−39	−20	26	46
JH	3.2	−49	−34	−16	18	38	16	23	19	14	6	−16	−26	−40	−33	−19	24	47
JH	1.6	−18	−14	−9	8	14	8	10	6	8	2	−7	−16	−18	−16	−11	9	20
JH	0.8	−10	−7	−4	4	9	6	4	4	4	2	−4	−7	−8	−7	−4	5	10
(Ri')		−10	−7	−3	7	8	5	5	4	4	2	−3	−7	−9	−8	−4	6	11

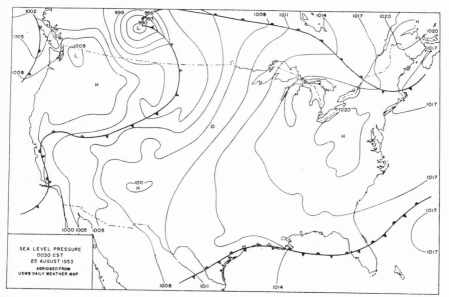

Fig. B.5.1. Continental scale synoptic chart. Sea level pressure distribution for the fifth general observation period.

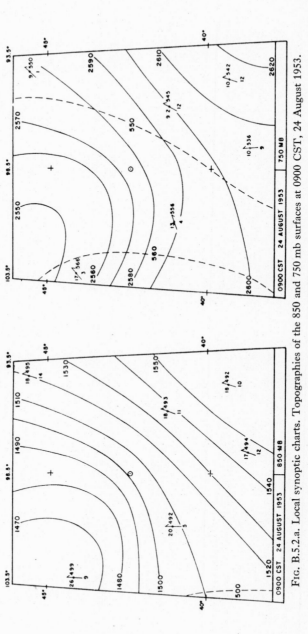

Fig. B.5.2.a. Local synoptic charts. Topographies of the 850 and 750 mb surfaces at 0900 CST, 24 August 1953.

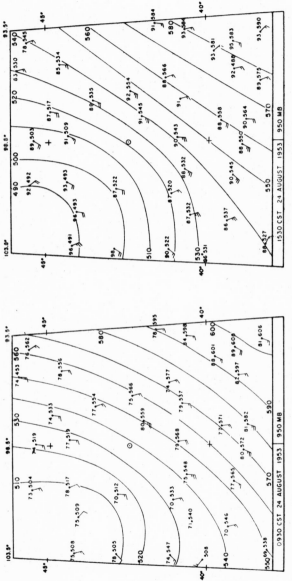

Fig. B.5.3.a. Local synoptic charts. Topography of the 950 mb surface at 0930 and 1530 CST, 24 August 1953.

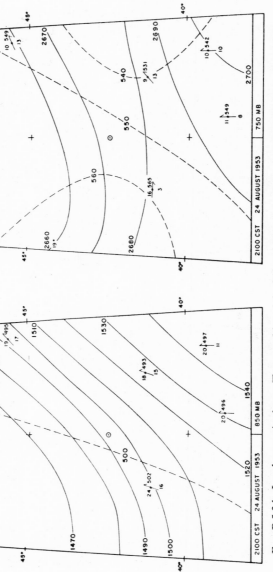

FIG. B.5.2.b. Local synoptic charts. Topographies of the 850 and 750 mb surfaces at 2100 CST, 24 August 1953.

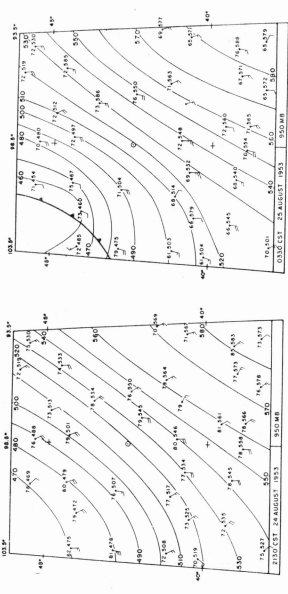

Fig. B.5.3.b. Local synoptic charts. Topography of the 950 mb surface at 2130 CST, 24 August, and 0330 CST, 25 August 1953.

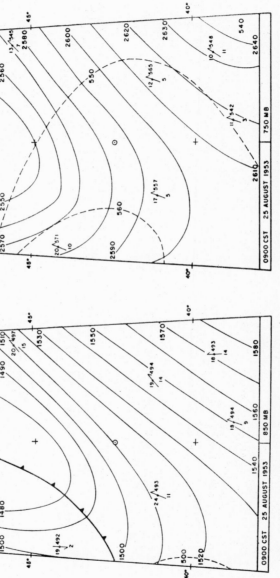

Fig. B.5.2.c. Local synoptic charts. Topographies of the 850 and 750 mb surfaces at 0900 CST, 25 August 1953.

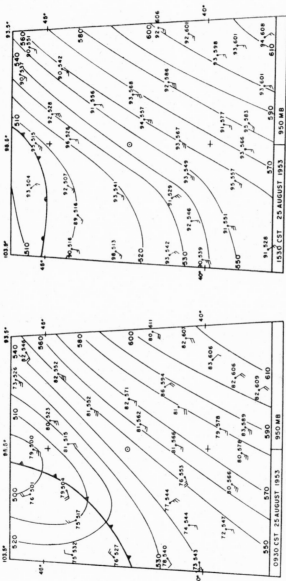

FIG. B.5.3.c. Local synoptic charts. Topography of the 950 mb surface at 0930 and 1530 CST, 25 August 1953.

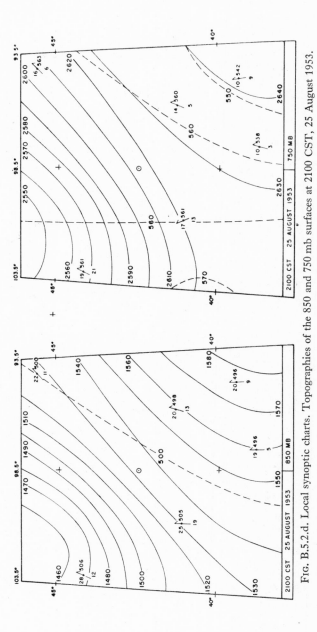

FIG. B.5.2.d. Local synoptic charts. Topographies of the 850 and 750 mb surfaces at 2100 CST, 25 August 1953.

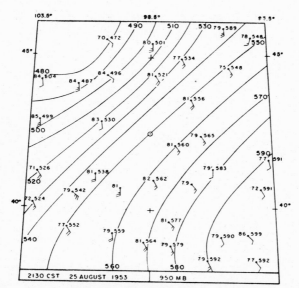

FIG. B.5.3.d. Local synoptic chart. Topography of the 950 mb surface at 2130 CST,
25 August 1953.

K

SIXTH GENERAL OBSERVATION PERIOD

0405 CST 31 August through 0905 CST 1 September 1953

Solar Data for the Field Site near O'Neill, Nebraska

	Sun's elevation angle at apparent noon	Sunrise CST	Apparent noon CST	Sunset CST
31 August	56° 04′	0558	1234	1911
1 September	55° 43′	0559	1234	1909

Summary of Synoptic Conditions

On 27 August a trough of low pressure extended north northeast–south south-west through Western Nebraska. The southern portion of the cold front affecting Nebraska weakened considerably. Winds were southerly at 10 to 20 mph. The skies were overcast to the west and had broken high clouds in the afternoon in the east.

On 28 and 29 August a low-pressure area in central South Dakota and Nebraska drifted southward and deepened. Thunderstorms moved eastward during the night of the 29th. The winds were generally southerly on the 28th, veering to northerly in the western sector on the 29th. Outside the thunderstorm areas the clouds were scattered to broken. By 30 August, North Central Nebraska was on the western periphery of a large high-pressure area centered over West Virginia and dominating the central and eastern parts of the United States. The low-pressure area of the previous day filled. Mostly clear skies prevailed over North Central Nebraska. Winds during the early part of the day were easterly becoming southerly at 5 to 10 mph, then 15 to 20 mph. The sixth general observation period was begun at 0405 CST on 31 August and completed 29 hr later under relatively most favorable conditions.

On 1 September, a cold front approached from the north-northwest and passed through the area during the afternoon of 2 September accompanied by overcast skies and thunderstorms. Initially the winds were southerly and shifted to north-westerly at 10 to 20 mph after the passage of the front. There were scattered clouds on 1 September.

For this period an analysis of the advective terms of the equation of motion was made by Dr. Blackadar of the Department of Meteorology, New York University. Synoptic pilot balloon observations over the central part of the United States were used to construct streamline and isotach charts for 500 m (average of first and second pibal level above the surface) and at 700 mb which is about 2500 m above the surface at O'Neill. The average magnitude of the advection terms was about 20 per cent of the geostrophic deviation term.

Measurements of Kinematic advection (NYU)

u = west component, v = south component, f = Coriolis parameter

$A_x = f^{-1}(u\delta u/\delta x + v\delta u/\delta y)$; $A_y = f^{-1}(u\delta v/\delta x + v\delta v/\delta y)$, (m/sec)

	31 August 0900 CST		2100 CST		1 September 1953 0900 CST	
	A_x	A_y	A_x	A_y	A_x	A_y
2500 m	—	—	0.7	−0.5	0.6	0.0
500 m	0.1	−1.8	0.3	−1.1	1.1	−1.3

1.1.a. Mean geopotential H (dynamic m above 601 = geopotential of test site), West and South components of the geostrophic wind u_g, v_g (m/sec) at indicated pressure (mb) levels. Values are estimated for the O'Neill site from local synoptic charts.

		31 Aug. 0900		31 Aug. 2100		1 Sept. 0900	
mb	H	u_g	v_g	u_g	v_g	u_g	v_g
750	2008	3.8	3.6	8.0	4.3	8.3	9.2
800	1451	3.7	3.7	11.8	5.8	9.8	10.2
850	929	5.6	5.2	8.9	6.5	10.2	9.8
900	430	8.0	7.7	10.0	8.7	10.7	10.8
950	−50	7.7	7.9	11.8	9.7	12.0	11.5

1.1.b. Direction (deg from North) and speed (m/sec) of the 950 mb geostrophic wind. Values are estimated for the O'Neill site from local synoptic charts.

31 August							1 September 1953			
0330	0630	0930	1230	1530	1830	2130	0030	0330	0630	0930
226	224	224	227	227	228	231	229	228	226	226
11.8	11.8	11.1	12.5	14.3	14.3	15.4	15.4	15.4	16.7	16.7

1.2. Direction (deg from North) of the mean surface wind from standard vane recordings at 1-min intervals (Mass. Inst. Tech., 16 m level). Hourly and 15-min averages centered at indicated CST.

	31 August										1 September 1953					
	0435[1]	0635	0835	1035	1235	1435	1635	1835	2035	2235[2]	0035	0235	0435	0635	0835
60-min mean:	187	183	183	180	180	183	177	180	173	172	185	181	189	190	194
15-min mean:	186	181	180	177	183	183	174	180	173	172	185	181	189	192	197

[1] Period 0410 to 0505 CST.   [2] Data missing from 2246 to 2251 CST.

1.3. Standard shelter temperature (°F), relative humidity (%); station pressure (inches) and air density (mg cm^{-3}); amount (tenths) and types of clouds.

Month	Day	CST	Temp.	RH	Pressure	Density	Clouds	Remarks
Aug.	31	0430	74	63	27.820	1.10	1 Ci	A few scattered small clouds overhead
		0630	71	77	.825	1.10	1 ScAc	Clear overhead. ScAc to N moving to NE
		0830	78	64	.815	1.09	0 CuAc	Cu to N
		1030	87	49	.820	1.07	1 Ac	Tall Cu visible to N
		1230	91	38	.820	1.06	0 —	Small Cu to S
		1430	94	38	.780	1.06	1 Cu	Small Cu to S
		1630	94	39	.760	1.06	0 —	Small Cu to S. Dissipating Cb far to N and NW
		1830	87	72	.775	1.06	0 —	
		2030	81	55	.795	1.08	1 Cb	Cb far to NW. Clear overhead
		2230	79	57	.805	1.08	1 Cb	Lightning on horizon to N and NW. Clear
Sept.	1	0030	76	58	.800	1.09	0 —	
		0230	74	66	.805	1.10	0 —	
		0430	73	67	.820	1.10	1 Ci	
		0630	72	65	.840	1.10	2 AcCi	Clear overhead. Ci to S, Ac to W and N
		0830	79	58	.840	1.09	2 CbAc	Ac to S, W, and N
		1030	89	44	.860	1.07	5 Ac	Cloudy

2.1.a. Soil temperature (°C) from thermistors (University of Texas) and soil thermocouples (University of California and Johns Hopkins University). Values are readings at indicated CST.

Inst. Set	Depth (cm)	31 August										1 September 1953				
		0435	0635	0835	1035	1235	1435	1635	1835	2035	2235	0035	0235	0435	0635	0835
UT	0.5	23.84	23.22	28.80	40.74	48.56	46.65	40.43	32.85	28.57	26.37	25.05	—	22.96	22.70	—
UCLA	1.3	23.00	22.11	27.89	38.44	47.50	47.61	40.89	32.11	27.56	25.89	25.39	26.78	22.33	22.11	28.22
UT	1.5	24.68	23.83	27.47	36.03	43.09	43.69	39.81	33.68	29.61	27.42	26.13	—	23.83	23.30	—
UT	2.5	25.25	24.32	26.82	33.58	39.74	41.34	39.05	34.00	30.26	27.99	26.57	—	24.50	23.87	—
JH	2.5	25.54	24.84	25.77	29.42	33.25	35.25	34.84	32.63	30.07	28.42	27.09	26.09	25.30	24.64	—
UT	3.5	25.67	24.74	26.35	31.69	37.20	38.99	37.91	34.02	30.69	28.51	27.17	—	25.05	24.30	—
UT	4.5	25.95	24.98	26.10	30.54	35.59	37.83	37.20	34.00	30.90	28.80	27.49	—	25.32	25.60	—
JH	5.0	26.00	25.30	25.35	27.36	30.32	32.63	33.20	32.05	30.20	28.74	27.50	26.60	25.83	25.16	—
UT	5.5	25.88	25.04	25.83	29.43	33.73	36.12	36.24	33.66	31.04	29.11	27.64	—	25.59	24.74	—
UCLA	10.0	25.89	25.00	24.72	26.50	29.06	31.22	31.67	31.39	29.78	28.89	27.78	23.17	25.94	25.28	25.00
JH	10.0	26.42	25.84	25.42	25.98	27.62	29.52	30.62	30.62	29.91	28.84	27.84	27.06	26.40	25.80	—
JH	20.0	26.32	25.97	25.56	25.39	25.57	26.11	26.88	27.41	27.68	27.57	27.22	26.87	26.53	26.12	—
UCLA	25.0	25.83	25.06	24.67	24.83	25.11	24.17	25.56	26.11	26.17	26.67	26.67	26.22	26.11	25.83	25.28
JH	40.0	24.50	24.48	24.36	24.34	24.27	24.24	24.26	24.32	24.47	24.64	24.73	24.78	24.84	24.78	—
JH	80.0	21.62	21.64	21.62	21.67	21.68	21.66	21.69	21.72	21.77	21.76	21.78	21.80	21.90	21.89	—

2.1.b. Change of soil temperature (°C hr⁻¹) averaged over indicated layers from soil temperature integrators (University of Wisconsin). Values are differences between readings at the end and beginning of 1-hr intervals centered at indicated CST.

Depth (cm)	31 August 0435	0635	0835	1035	1235	1435	1635	1835	2035	2235	0035	1 September 1953 0235	0435	0635	0835
0–5	−0.48	0.13	1.84	2.43	1.64	1.06	−1.42	−1.81	−0.97	−0.66	−0.52	−0.44	−0.37	0.23	1.44
5–15	−0.36	−0.21	0.32	0.80	1.07	0.73	0.04	−0.47	−0.66	−0.56	−0.40	−0.39	−0.33	−0.20	0.24
15–50	0.07	0.10	0·09	0.04	0.09	0.13	0.13	0.16	0.05	0.04	0.05	0.06	0.08	0.11	0.08

2.2.a. Soil thermal conductivity (mcal cm⁻¹ sec⁻¹ deg⁻¹) computed from soil thermistor response to defined heating pulses (University of Texas, Albrecht heat flux meter No. 2). Values are derived from 60-sec trials beginning at indicated CST.

Depth (cm)	31 August 0440	0635	0835	1035	1235	1435	1635	1835	2035	2235	0035	1 September 1953 0235	0435	0635	0835
0.5	0.60	0.60	0.61	0.61	0.62	0.60	0.60	0.61	0.62	0.62	0.62	0.62	0.61	0.61	0.62
1.5	0.61	0.62	0.61	0.62	0.63	0.64	0.64	0.65	0.66	0.67	0.66	0.66	0.74	0.73	0.76
2.5	0.86	0.88	0.90	0.90	0.90	0.90	0.92	0.93	0.92	0.91	0.87	0.89	0.90	0.90	0.90
3.5	0.77	0.77	0.75	0.79	0.80	0.73	0.73	0.72	0.78	0.83	0.86	0.90	0.80	0.79	0.77
4.5	0.84	0.84	0.83	0.87	0.86	0.87	0.86	0.89	0.87	0.87	0.86	0.86	0.84	0.76	0.72
5.5	1.12	1.04	1.03	0.98	1.02	1.02	1.01	1.01	1.04	1.04	1.06	1.03	1.03	1.01	1.00

2.2.b. Soil moisture (% wet weight) and density (g cm⁻³) from soil samples at the Johns Hopkins University site. Indicated CST refers to the approximate time of soil sample extraction.

Depth (cm)	Soil Moisture 31 August 1953 0700	Soil Density 0700
0 to 6	2.0	1.42
2 to 5	2.5	—
10	3.2	—
10 to 16	3.1	1.60
17 to 23	—	1.68
20	2.7	1.65
20 to 26	2.8	—
40	2.0	—

2.2.c. Soil heat capacity (cal cm⁻³ deg⁻¹) from soil samples at the University of Wisconsin site (calorimetric determination). Indicated CST refers to the approximate time of soil sample extraction (0-10 cm layer).

31 August 1953 1200	1600
0.30	0.40

2.4. Vertical flux of heat (mcal cm^{-2} min^{-1}) from soil temperature integrators (University of Wisconsin), Albrecht heat flux meter No. 2 (University of Texas-Al), Gier and Dunkle heat flow meters (University of California; University of Texas-GD; Johns Hopkins University-GD), and numerical integration of soil temperature profile changes (Johns Hopkins University). UW and JH values are 60-min averages, UCLA values are 15-min averages, and UT and JH-GD values are approximately 2-min averages. All averages are centered at indicated CST.

Inst. Set	Depth (cm)	31 August 0435	0635	0835	1035	1235	1435	1635	1835	2035	2235	1 September 1953 0035	0235	0435	0635	0835
UW	0.0	−52	−31	50	107	127	106	8	−40	−52	−61	−52	−50	−50	−32	36
UT-Al	0.0¹	—	−36	93	318	282	172	25	−60	−64	−65	−74	−59	−50	−33	128
JH	0.0¹	−20	−13	1	67	103	90	50	3	18	−22	—	—	—	—	—
UCLA	0.2²	−40	−27	80	203	290	166	37	−52	−52	−47	−44	−46	−41	−22	85
UT-GD	0.2²	−34	−25	85	178	189	125	31	−38	−44	−37	−38	—	−37	−22	97
UCLA	1.3	−19	−14	27	87	120	105	50	−12	−21	−22	−21	−25	−21	−12	27
UT-Al	2.0	—	−23	31	118	162	116	38	−16	−33	−29	−22	−27	−33	−28	32
JH-GD	2.5	−13	−13	10	53	83	80	50	13	−7	−12	−13	−13	−13	−13	8
UW	5.0	−38	−36	−4	35	79	75	35	13	−23	−42	−37	−38	−39	−39	−6
UCLA	10.0	−11	−12	4	27	64	70	60	34	10	−1	−7	−10	−13	−13	−5
UW	15.0	−18	−24	−22	−10	18	34	32	40	14	−10	−14	−16	−20	−28	−20

¹ Values are extrapolated to surface.
² Approximative depth: the upper plates of the flow meters were "just covered with soil".

3.1. Summary of data on radiation (mcal cm^{-2} min^{-1}). Short-wave radiation from two Eppley pyrheliometers (Johns Hopkins University and GRD); net radiation from two Gier and Dunkle radiometers (Johns Hopkins University and University of Texas) and the Suomi net radiometer (University of Wisconsin); total radiation from the Gier and Dunkle radiometer (University of Texas). Values are hourly averages centered at indicated CST.

	Inst. Set	31 August 0435	0635	0835	1035	1235	1435	1635	1835	2035	2235	1 September 1953 0035	0235	0435	0635	0835
	JH	—	—	—	1150	1350	1180	710	100	0	0	0	0	0	80	670
(Short-Wave)	GRD	0	90	645	1102	1272	1082	640	97	0	0	0	0	0	90	640
	GRD¹	0	80	650	1110	1280	1080	640	90	0	0	0	0	0	80	290²
	JH	−70	−30	312	660	800	690	330	−60	−90	−80	−80	−80	−70	−40	300
(Net)	UT	−89	10	429	842	984	759	299	−105	−119	−121	−116	—	−89	29	408
	UW	−81	−56	319	650	767	636	252	−88	−110	−107	−103	−100	−100	−39	304
(Total)	UT	536	623	1294	1881	2098	1832	1244	621	543	533	528	—	541	652	1308

¹ 10-min average centered at indicated CST.   ² Subject to error because of clouds.

3.2. Boundary shear-stress (dynes cm^{-2}) from drag recorder (University of California) and Sheppard-type drag plate (Johns Hopkins University); direction of boundary shear-stress (deg from North) from drag recorder (University of California). Values are 10-min means centered at indicated CST.

Inst. Set	31 August 0435	0635	0835	1035	1235	1435	1635	1835	2035	2235	1 September 1953 0035	0235	0435	0635	0835
UCLA	1.26¹	1.52	—	—	2.72²	—	—	—	1.13	1.30	1.28	1.14	1.55	—	2.95
JH	1.5	1.7	2.7	2.6	2.7	3.8	3.5	1.7	1.1	1.4	1.3	1.0	1.3	1.7	2.8
UCLA	180	180	—	—	173²	—	—	—	191	191	196	194	203	—	206

¹ For time interval 0430 to 0444.
² UCLA data from beginning through this run were evaluated by reading charts at 5-sec intervals. Planimeter was used for all following data.

3.3. Characteristics of low level smoke-puff drift (Johns Hopkins University); direction of drift (deg from North); time t_{25} (sec) required to cross 25 m circle; lateral width S (deg) at 25 m and time t_D (sec) required to reach threshold of visibility. Values are ensemble averages for 10 smoke puffs fired at approximately 1-min intervals beginning at indicated CST.

	31 August										1 September 1953				
	0400	0600	0800	1000	1200	1400	1600	1800	2000	2200	0000	0200	0400	0600	0800
dd	202	193	195	193	190	199	180	184	187	188	192	191	196	194	203
t_{25}	5.0	5.7	4.4	4.3	3.7	3.8	4.1	4.0	5.3	5.0	5.3	6.5	5.0	4.9	4.2
S	12.2	17.1	12.6	10.7	10.7	11.7	10.4	14.2	13.5	16.0	12.9	12.3	15.4	11.2	11.1
t_D	—	30	14	13	13	16	13	15	—	—	—	—	—	23	16

3.4. Characteristics of surface pressure variations from micro-barograms (GRD, Paulin-type aneroid system); trend (WBAN Synoptic Code number); qualitative index of micro-variations ("a" = calm to "d" = very unruly); trace ratio (trace length relative to trend length); trend ratio (trend length relative to chart length); period (min), amplitude (10^{-2} mb) and number of perceptible waves. Values refer to 2-hr intervals centered at indicated CST.

	31 August										1 September 1953			
	0535	0735	0935	1135	1335	1535	1735	1935	2135	2335	0135	0335	0535	0735
Trend	2	9	0	8	8	6	7	3	1	2	2	4	3	2
Index	b	b-c	c	c-d	d	d	c-b	b-a	a-b	a-c	a	b	b	b-c
Trace ratio	1.25	1.5	1.5	1.6	1.8	2.0	1.4	1.1	1.1	1.2	1.1	1.2	1.2	1.4
Trend ratio	1.0	1.1	1.0	1.1	1.3	1.0	1.0	1.2	1.1	1.0	1.1	1.0	1.2	1.0
Period	40	15	50	15	50	5	25	25	45	35	40	30	20	40
Ampl.	10	4.5	4	3	5	4	5	3	3	7	4	7	3.5	5
Number	1	4	1	4	2	2	2	1	2	1	1	1	3	2
Period	20	—	25	—	5	40	—	—	—	45	—	40	—	—
Ampl.	4	—	4	—	4	3.5	—	—	—	3	—	4	—	—
Number	1	—	2	—	5	2	—	—	—	1	—	1	—	—

4.1.a. Hourly mean wind speed (cm/sec) from standard three-cup anemometers (Mass. Inst. Tech.), modified Sheppard-type anemometers (University of California), ping-pong ball anemometers (Iowa State College) and modified SCS cup anemometers (Johns Hopkins University); centered at indicated CST.

Inst. Set	Height (m)	31 August										1 September 1953				
		0435	0635	0835	1035	1235	1435	1635	1835	2035	2235	0035	0235	0435	0635	0835
MIT	16.0	770	787	927	881	970	1145	1105	896	759	796	769	724	835	786	959
MIT	8.0	655	690	856	818	903	1052	1008	802	650	694	668	617	729	694	883
UCLA	8.0	684	727	895	876	919	1090	1072	855	684	724	704	666	748	726	924
ISC	7.0	641	692	825	816	901	1044	1012	784	635	681	637	611	701	674	856
JH	6.4	636	672	—	—	—	1004	999	789	611	672	657	590	683	676	854
UCLA	4.15	602	648	808	793	836	974	964	757	591	636	617	580	660	643	839
MIT	4.0	578	622	787	756	833	965	919	718	571	620	595	544	649	625	809
ISC	4.0	563	617	748	746	825	953	922	702	559	605	564	537	621	603	772
JH	3.2	561	603	756	746	782	924	912	716	541	599	590	526	609	609	782
MIT	2.0	502	545	704	681	749	858	824	632	497	546	518	475	567	552	721
UCLA	2.0	523	564	710	698	740	866	849	660	510	556	534	496	570	558	738
JH	1.6	495	535	676	668	706	832	815	636	473	530	520	458	537	533	697
UCLA	1.0	445	484	612	606	644	748	732	566	434	476	456	424	488	478	636
ISC	1.0	424	471	583	589	653	749	715	542	425	461	431	408	469	454	600
JH	0.8	431	468	588	586	621	731	718	555	413	466	452	399	470	466	605
UCLA	0.5	382	416	528	524	560	649	—	486	374	408	392	366	420	410	551
JH	0.4	358	389	497	497	526	619	609	470	346	391	376	334	393	389	512

4.1.b. 15-min mean wind speed (cm/sec) from standard three-cup anemometers (Mass. Inst. Tech.), modified Sheppard-type anemometers (University of California) and ping-pong ball anemometers (Iowa State College); centered at indicated CST.

Inst. Set	Height (m)	31 August										1 September 1953				
		0435	0635	0835	1035	1235	1435	1635	1835	2035	2235	0035	0235	0435	0635	0835
MIT	16.0	733	770	909	929	963	1155	1128	909	764	784	757	716	824	770	973
MIT	8.0	638	676	848	855	902	1051	1024	814	655	682	659	608	723	676	895
UCLA	8.0	678	708	881	918	973	1059	1122	855	661	730	693	645	732	702	926
ISC	7.0	630	684	825	834	901	1014	1028	738	652	683	631	608	695	659	852
UCLA	4.15	594	630	789	826	882	950	1008	760	571	642	607	562	650	622	845
MIT	4.0	564	608	780	784	831	960	929	730	584	605	584	537	642	608	821
ISC	4.0	547	611	750	768	825	929	932	706	574	606	564	537	615	589	768
MIT	2.0	493	527	696	709	747	858	834	642	513	534	510	470	561	534	726
UCLA	2.0	512	551	694	731	782	840	864	660	494	556	520	479	555	536	742
UCLA	1.0	436	472	592	633	689	724	782	564	420	476	444	410	474	459	642
ISC	1.0	412	461	583	606	650	733	720	547	434	462	440	405	461	446	595
UCLA	0.5	377	406	515	546	592	630	665	487	359	410	380	353	409	395	556

4.2. Mean air temperature (°C) from aspirated thermocouples (Mass. Inst. Tech., 15-min means; University of California, average of six readings taken every 3 min), shielded thermocouples (Johns Hopkins University, average of 20 readings at each level during a 5-min interval) and shielded thermistors (University of Texas, 10-sec means); centered at indicated CST.

Inst. Set	Height (m)	31 August 0435	0635	0835	1035	1235	1435	1635	1835	2035	2235	1 September 1953 0035	0235	0435	0635	0835
MIT	16.0	23.28	22.24	25.50	28.31	31.32	32.62	32.36	30.71	27.80	26.52	25.30	23.87	23.15	22.93	26.14
MIT	8.0	23.18	22.23	25.63	28.61	31.56	32.95	32.59	30.69	27.62	26.37	25.14	23.70	23.04	22.87	26.30
UCLA	8.0	22.83	21.28	23.39	27.78	31.39	32.33	32.11	30.61	27.06	25.94	25.00	23.50	22.78	22.50	25.89
JH	6.4	23.18	22.02	25.05	28.53	31.23	32.00	32.58	30.45	27.53	26.12	25.25	23.34	22.99	22.67	26.27
MIT	4.0	23.10	22.21	25.81	29.01	32.00	33.37	32.83	30.66	27.46	26.24	24.97	23.55	22.92	22.86	26.56
UCLA	4.0	22.78	21.22	24.67	28.61	31.61	33.00	32.44	30.61	26.83	25.83	24.89	23.33	22.56	22.28	26.17
JH	3.2	23.07	22.04	25.39	29.34	31.86	32.77	32.98	30.37	27.36	25.97	25.13	23.16	22.88	22.64	26.65
MIT	2.0	23.00	22.20	26.20	29.80	32.90	34.10	33.30	30.60	27.30	26.10	24.80	23.40	22.80	22.80	27.00
UCLA	2.0	22.78	21.44	24.94	28.39	32.33	33.39	32.56	30.56	26.72	25.67	24.72	23.11	22.72	22.56	26.39
JH	1.6	22.92	22.00	25.67	29.75	32.44	33.61	33.28	30.33	27.17	25.81	24.98	22.99	22.74	22.60	27.06
UCLA	1.0	22.39	21.06	25.56	29.50	33.67	34.44	33.22	30.56	26.50	25.50	24.33	22.94	22.22	22.22	26.67
JH	0.8	22.83	21.98	26.28	30.58	33.43	34.06	33.70	30.25	27.00	25.63	24.86	22.82	22.61	22.57	27.60
UT	0.8	22.8	21.95	26.25	30.8	33.65	34.85	33.9	30.7	26.75	25.4	24.55	23.0	22.65	22.9	27.7
UCLA	0.5	22.33	18.00	22.67	30.00	35.00	36.22	34.06	30.44	26.22	25.00	24.22	22.17	22.00	22.00	26.22
UT	0.5	22.65	22.2	26.45	30.95	34.3	35.7	34.05	30.75	26.95	25.5	24.4	22.8	22.55	22.9	27.8
JH	0.4	22.73	21.97	26.38	31.14	34.41	34.73	34.19	30.19	26.88	25.45	24.71	22.70	22.42	22.53	27.98
UT	0.3	22.5	22.1	26.95	32.55	36.7	35.85	34.0	30.85	26.95	25.4	24.3	22.7	22.35	23.0	28.4
JH	0.2	22.62	21.94	27.14	32.01	35.25	35.30	34.50	30.11	26.75	25.32	24.46	22.56	22.26	22.48	28.30
JH	0.1	22.48	21.90	27.64	32.70	36.24	36.15	34.79	30.03	26.62	25.17	24.32	22.36	22.17	22.42	28.68
UT	0.1	22.5	22.0	28.5	33.55	36.1	37.75	34.95	30.8	26.6	25.3	24.25	22.6	22.25	23.2	29.05

4.3.a. Mean water vapor pressure (mb) from dew-point apparatus (Johns Hopkins University). Simultaneous air sampling at given intake levels. Values are 5-min averages centered at indicated CST.

Height (m)	31 August										1 September 1953				
	0435	0635	0835	1035[1]	1235	1435	1635[2]	1835	2035	2235	0035	0235	0435	0635	0835
6.4	17.58	19.09	21.54	21.16	19.01	19.03	18.24	18.13	18.41	17.78	17.56	17.84	17.26	17.65	18.50
3.2	17.89	18.59	20.62	21.02	19.10	19.22	18.46	17.90	18.49	17.78	17.66	17.61	17.37	17.65	18.74
1.6	17.83	18.87	21.54	21.15	18.99	19.26	18.48	18.13	18.54	17.82	17.65	17.73	17.43	17.65	18.87
0.8	17.91	18.54	21.40	21.08	19.04	19.22	18.52	18.25	18.46	17.78	17.65	17.65	17.44	17.65	18.68
0.4	17.90	19.28	21.01	20.94	19.13	19.21	18.44	18.25	18.63	17.84	17.68	17.75	17.36	17.68	18.71
0.2	17.81	18.65	20.62	20.82	18.80	19.30	18.70	18.59	18.47	17.77	17.70	17.78	17.37	17.67	18.61
0.1	17.92	18.65	22.34	21.20	19.08	19.30	18.60	18.34	18.47	17.84	17.89	17.78	17.40	17.65	18.61

[1]Average of 0935 and 1135 data.   [2]Average of 1535 and 1735 data.

4.3.b. Mean vertical difference (between 82 and 39 cm) of dry-bulb temperature $(10^{-3}\,°C)$ and water vapor pressure $(10^{-3}\,mb)$ from double psychrometer lift-apparatus (University of Wisconsin). Values are hourly means (based on one sample every 10 min) centered at indicated CST.

	31 August										1 September 1953				
	0435	0635	0835	1035	1235	1435	1635	1835	2035	2235	0035	0235	0435	0635	0835
$10^{-3}\,°C$	86	−30	−416	−759	−834	−740	−476	−20	102	85	109	85	83	−16	−473
$10^{-3}\,mb$	−54	−44	−76	−221	−58	−61	−212	−144	−112	−142	−71	−101	−83	−193	−163

5.1. Standard deviation of temperature fluctuations $(10^{-2}\,°C)$ from fast-response thermocouples (Mass. Inst. Tech., one sample per sec during 11-min periods) and bead thermistors (Iowa State College, 10 samples per sec during 10-min periods). Periods are centered at indicated CST.

Inst. Set	Height (m)	31 August										1 September 1953				
		0435	0635	0835	1035	1235	1435	1635	1835	2035	2235	0035	0235	0435	0635	0835
MIT	12.0	13	7	22	28	—	—	—	10	12	9	11	10	10	9	27[1]
ISC	8.0	24	11	67	112	129	118	106	31	45	30	61	44	28	13	70
MIT	6.0	14	7	36	53	—	—	—	11	15	11	16	15	13	10	44[1]
ISC	4.0	23	11	70	121	136	121	111	31	43	31	62	42	29	12	72
MIT	3.0	14	7	44	72	—	—	—	13	19	17	19	17	17	16	49[1]
ISC	2.0	23	12	70	121	138	124	101	26	42	30	53	42	30	15	72
MIT	1.5	13	7	41	63	—	—	—	14	20	15	21	14	14	11	45[1]
ISC	1.0	23	12	70	121	142	123	96	27	40	30	58	41	29	16	71
ISC	0.5	22	13	75	117	146	120	106	27	42	28	—	41	23	15	70
ISC	0.25	22	14	79	117	150	120	106	27	44	30	—	41	24	17	70

[1] Period centered at 0845.

5.2.a. Statistics of fluctuations quantities from 1-sec samplings of fast-response probes (Mass. Inst. Tech.). Total air speed V (cm/sec); standard deviation of horizontal (parallel and perpendicular to 10-min mean wind) and vertical eddy components $S(u)$, $S(v)$, and $S(w)$ (cm/sec); gustiness ratios $G(x)$, $G(y)$, and $G(z)$; mean cross products of eddy components $\overline{uv}$, $\overline{vw}$, and $\overline{uw}$ (cm² sec⁻²); horizontal Reynolds' stress (parallel to 10-min mean wind) τ (dynes cm⁻²); linear correlation coefficients between eddy components and air temperature $(u;v)$, $(v;w)$, $(u;w)$, $(u;T)$, $(v;T)$, and $(w;T)$; mean cross product of vertical eddy component and air temperature multiplied by density and specific heat of air Q (mcal cm⁻² min⁻¹). Values are 10-min means or totals centered at indicated CST.

Date	CST	Height	V	$S(u)$	$S(v)$	$S(w)$	$G(x)$	$G(y)$	$G(z)$	$\overline{uv}$	$\overline{vw}$	$\overline{uw}$	τ	$(u;v)$	$(v;w)$	$(u;w)$	$(u;T)$	$(v;T)$	$(w;T)$	Q
1953 31 Aug.	0435	12.0	687	74	45	36	.11	.07	.05	−160	−40	−680	0.8	−0.05	−0.03	−0.26	0.42	0.00	−0.21	−18
		6.0	598	75	53	40	.13	.09	.07	−140	−60	−790	0.9	−0.04	−0.03	−0.26	0.38	0.00	−0.18	−18
		3.0	530	81	49	32	.15	.09	.06	−60	30	−780	0.9	−0.02	0.02	−0.30	0.71	0.00	−0.22	−18
		1.5	449	78	50	35	.17	.11	.08	−230	10	−1030	1.1	−0.06	0.01	−0.38	0.59	0.00	−0.22	−18
	0635	12.0	716	92	56	41	.13	.08	.06	580	−80	−1050	1.1	0.11	−0.04	−0.28	0.62	0.00	0.00	0
		6.0	649	99	62	41	.15	.10	.06	30	−80	−1110	1.1	0.01	−0.03	−0.27	0.58	0.00	0.00	0
		3.0	577	101	57	34	.18	.10	.06	−170	−10	−690	0.8	−0.03	−0.01	−0.20	0.57	0.00	0.00	0
		1.5	479	95	65	39	.20	.14	.08	100	−150	−1180	1.3	0.02	−0.06	−0.32	0.60	0.00	0.00	0
	0835	12.0	878	177	100	62	.20	.11	.07	3610	−390	−3940	4.3	0.20	−0.06	−0.36	−0.54	−0.09	0.37	78
		6.0	808	170	103	55	.21	.13	.07	1380	−320	−1770	1.9	0.08	−0.06	−0.19	−0.60	−0.16	0.25	78
		3.0	740	160	109	52	.22	.15	.07	−2170	90	−2140	2.3	−0.12	0.02	−0.26	−0.63	0.04	0.17	60
		1.5	641	147	97	57	.23	.15	.09	−330	−30	−3020	3.3	−0.02	−0.01	−0.36	−0.53	0.03	0.13	48
	1035	12.0	879	143	181	55	.16	.21	.06	2480	−840	−2340	2.5	0.10	−0.08	−0.30	−0.20	−0.18	0.26	60
		6.0	810	145	144	52	.18	.18	.06	2950	−230	−1930	2.1	0.14	−0.03	−0.26	−0.40	−0.24	0.22	96
		3.0	735	143	146	48	.19	.20	.07	280	−840	−1970	2.1	0.01	−0.12	−0.29	−0.49	−0.06	0.23	126
		1.5	646	138	157	58	.21	.24	.09	−2340	650	−3160	3.4	−0.11	0.07	−0.39	−0.40	−0.02	0.16	96
	1835	12.0	869	115	86	50	.13	.10	.06	1180	−350	−1420	1.5	0.12	−0.08	−0.25	0.26	0.12	−0.20	−18
		6.0	770	114	71	43	.15	.09	.06	900	100	−910	1.0	0.11	0.03	−0.19	0.32	0.13	0.00	0
		3.0	686	133	74	40	.19	.11	.06	180	50	−1430	1.5	0.02	0.02	−0.27	0.35	0.10	0.00	0
		1.5	580	132	75	57	.23	.13	.10	830	−40	−2800	3.0	0.08	−0.01	−0.37	0.38	0.00	−0.13	−18

Date	CST	Height	V	$S(u)$	$S(v)$	$S(w)$	$G(x)$	$G(y)$	$G(z)$	$\overline{uv}$	$\overline{vw}$	$\overline{uw}$	τ	$(u;v)$	$(v;w)$	$(u;w)$	$(u;T)$	$(v;T)$	$(w;T)$	Q
	2035	12.0	702	88	68	39	.13	.10	.06	−480	−20	−850	0.9	−0.08	−0.01	−0.25	0.47	0.12	0.00	0
		6.0	617	95	37	39	.15	.06	.06	−680	60	−860	0.9	−0.19	0.04	−0.23	0.56	0.00	−0.17	−18
		3.0	549	104	45	33	.19	.08	.06	−1380	70	−870	0.9	−0.29	0.05	−0.25	0.66	−0.23	−0.16	−18
		1.5	470	104	59	40	.22	.13	.09	−370	−10	−1640	1.8	−0.06	0.00	−0.39	0.67	0.00	−0.13	−18
	2235	12.0	734	86	73	42	.12	.10	.06	400	−20	−790	0.9	0.06	−0.01	−0.22	0.52	0.00	−0.26	−18
		6.0	647	93	44	42	.14	.07	.07	−100	80	−820	0.9	−0.02	0.04	−0.21	0.49	0.00	−0.22	−18
		3.0	574	105	54	35	.18	.09	.06	60	70	−740	0.8	0.01	0.04	−0.20	0.67	−0.12	−0.17	−18
		1.5	491	104	61	45	.21	.12	.09	−70	90	−1900	2.1	−0.01	0.03	−0.41	0.58	−0.11	−0.15	−18
1953 1 Sept.	0035	12.0	707	92	51	39	.13	.07	.06	300	−70	−1040	1.1	0.06	−0.04	−0.29	0.49	0.00	−0.23	−18
		6.0	626	91	50	35	.15	.08	.06	−210	40	−1060	1.2	−0.05	0.02	−0.33	0.62	−0.13	−0.18	−18
		3.0	548	96	48	35	.18	.09	.06	110	−70	−1020	1.1	0.02	−0.06	−0.31	0.60	−0.11	−0.15	−18
		1.5	465	93	61	40	.20	.13	.09	−330	−106	−1162	1.3	−0.06	−0.04	−0.31	0.67	−0.08	−0.12	−18
	0235	12.0	666	88	67	37	.13	.10	.06	−40	50	−630	0.7	−0.01	0.02	−0.19	0.57	0.00	0.00	0
		6.0	573	93	51	35	.16	.09	.06	210	0	−880	1.0	0.04	0.00	−0.27	0.65	0.00	−0.19	−18
		3.0	503	95	52	32	.19	.10	.06	−640	−20	−720	0.8	−0.13	−0.01	−0.24	0.62	−0.11	−0.18	−18
		1.5	421	84	45	36	.20	.11	.09	80	−190	−1060	1.2	0.02	−0.12	−0.35	0.51	0.00	−0.20	−18
	0435	12.0	774	104	51	45	.13	.07	.06	650	−150	−1370	1.5	0.12	−0.07	−0.29	0.58	0.00	−0.22	−18
		6.0	688	99	55	47	.14	.08	.07	−310	−180	−1580	1.8	−0.06	−0.07	−0.34	0.62	0.00	−0.33	−30
		3.0	600	106	57	38	.18	.10	.06	−270	50	−700	0.8	0.05	0.02	−0.17	0.55	0.00	−0.15	0
		1.5	508	93	66	46	.18	.13	.09	0	−150	−1440	1.6	0.00	−0.05	−0.34	0.54	0.11	0.00	0
	0635	12.0	726	95	41	40	.13	.06	.06	−220	−150	−1240	1.4	−0.06	−0.09	−0.33	0.47	0.00	−0.28	−18
		6.0	644	88	42	41	.14	.07	.06	10	−20	−930	1.0	0.00	−0.01	−0.26	0.45	0.00	0.00	0
		3.0	570	92	50	34	.16	.09	.06	−50	−90	−780	0.9	−0.01	−0.05	−0.25	0.20	0.00	0.00	0
		1.5	482	92	61	44	.19	.13	.09	−280	−50	−1480	1.6	−0.05	−0.02	−0.37	0.40	0.00	0.00	0
	0845	12.0	929	141	143	59	.15	.15	.06	250	520	−2230	2.4	0.01	0.06	−0.27	−0.37	−0.21	0.13	30
		6.0	862	145	119	49	.17	.14	.06	730	−80	−1800	2.0	0.04	−0.01	−0.25	−0.55	−0.17	0.23	78
		3.0	776	157	104	51	.20	.13	.07	−270	−220	−2440	2.7	−0.02	−0.04	−0.30	−0.60	−0.08	0.16	60
		1.5	675	151	127	58	.22	.19	.09	1480	−200	−3040	3.3	0.08	−0.03	−0.35	−0.50	0.00	0.19	78

5.2.b. Standard deviation $S(u)$, $S(w)$ of eddy components (in the direction of the estimated mean wind, u, and the vertical; cm/sec) and gustiness ratios $G(x)$, $G(z)$, from rotating pressure tube anemometer (Texas A & M College); one sample per sec during 5-min periods centered at indicated CST.

Date (1953)	CST	Height (m)	u	$S(u)$	$S(w)$	$G(x)$	$G(z)$
31 August	0433	3.1	594	93	32	0.16	.054
	0632	3.1	564	85	31	0.15	.055
	0832	3.1	567	124	41	0.22	.072
	1404	3.1	1069	145	42	0.14	.040
1 September	0258	3.1	479	57	15	0.12	.031
	0432	3.1	516	60	13	0.12	.025
	0632	3.1	505	57	15	0.11	.030
	0832	3.1	644	69	22	0.11	.034

6.1.a. Loeser technique of daytime wind profile measurements (GRD). Mean height Z (m); duration t (sec) of evaluated drift; mean West, South, and upward components u, v, w (m/sec) of drift of individual smoke puffs. Values are t-sec averages centered at indicated CST $+ t/2$ sec.

31 August 1953

CST	Z	t	u	v	w	CST	Z	t	u	v	w	CST	Z	t	u	v	w
0630	1290	72	2.4	5.4	0.4	0635	1324	120	2.3	5.3	0.3	0640	1156	108	3.6	6.8	0.2
	1084	120	4.1	6.9	0.3		1120	120	3.5	6.9	0.3		348	84	8.9	14.2	0.3
	914	120	5.6	7.6	0.2		953	120	5.1	7.6	0.2						
	771	114	7.0	9.0	0.3		804	120	6.5	8.2	0.2						
	643	90	10.0	9.6	0.3		666	90	9.1	9.3	0.0						
	554	78	8.9	12.0	0.2		561	84	9.3	10.3	0.1						
	452	72	8.1	14.0	0.1		469	78	8.0	13.2	0.2						
							400	72	7.9	14.1	0.2						
							331	72	7.9	14.6	0.3						
							289	66	9.4	14.8	0.4						
							256	60	10.5	15.1	0.4						
							208	66	9.5	14.1	0.3						
0830	1264	120	1.9	6.2	0.3	0835	1342	120	0.1	5.8	0.2	0840	1330	120	0.4	6.0	0.3
	1034	120	3.9	7.0	0.1		1125	120	3.5	6.4	0.2		1130	120	3.4	6.1	0.4
	834	120	5.1	9.4	0.1		911	120	3.9	9.7	0.0		949	120	3.8	9.0	0.4
	674	120	5.6	8.2	0.2		736	120	5.1	8.5	0.1		799	120	4.8	10.0	0.3
	567	120	5.9	9.7	0.1		604	114	5.9	9.2	−0.3		667	120	5.6	8.5	0.2
	480	120	6.0	12.0	0.2		492	114	6.3	12.1	−0.2						
	398	114	6.3	13.3	0.3		372	114	6.4	14.0	−0.2						
	329	102	6.5	14.1	0.2		279	78	6.1	13.1	−0.8						
	239	72	3.8	12.2	0.9		215	66	4.5	12.1	−0.5						
	120	48	1.7	10.8	0.6		152	30	3.1	9.8	−0.9						
	84	24	1.3	11.8	0.2		120	30	2.5	11.0	−0.3						
1030	1299	120	1.5	7.8	0.5	1035	1372	120	1.7	7.8	0.6	1040	1348	120	1.9	8.2	0.5
	1102	120	2.2	7.1	0.4		1160	120	2.0	7.6	0.8		1151	114	2.1	7.0	0.5
	984	120	2.8	8.0	0.7		960	114	3.0	8.0	0.5		987	120	2.8	8.1	0.4
	790	120	3.3	8.4	0.6		825	114	3.6	8.1	0.6		853	120	3.6	7.9	0.5
	710	120	3.7	8.4	0.6		691	108	3.8	8.2	0.4		732	120	3.4	8.1	0.6
	597	114	3.5	8.7	0.4		476	108	2.8	9.4	−0.1		614	120	3.7	9.1	0.8
	493	114	2.9	10.1	0.1		455	102	2.8	8.5	1.0		521	120	2.8	9.3	0.8
	435	114	1.9	9.7	0.4		392	102	1.9	8.6	1.7		401	102	1.7	9.5	0.0

CST	Z	t	u	v	w
	372	108	2.2	10.0	0.6
	319	108	2.5	10.1	0.2
	257	36	3.2	10.2	0.2
	240	36	3.4	9.4	0.6
1230	1348	120	3.1	8.5	−0.1
	1139	114	2.9	8.6	0.0
	995	120	2.7	9.7	0.2
	834	120	3.1	9.9	−0.2
	684	114	3.3	10.2	−0.8
	607	114	2.8	10.1	−0.4
	495	114	2.3	10.3	−1.1
1430	1379	120	4.0	10.9	2.5
	1155	120	5.0	12.7	1.9
	923	72	5.8	14.1	2.4
	810	102	5.3	13.5	1.9
	629	72	3.9	12.0	1.6
	538	60	3.1	13.5	1.9
	433	48	0.8	12.8	2.4
	402	60	2.4	12.0	2.9
	259	60	1.1	13.8	1.2
	224	66	0.9	14.0	1.4
	113	12	−0.6	12.1	0.7
	81	12	0.8	10.9	0.6
1630	1164	120	5.3	11.8	−0.6
	968	120	4.5	12.3	−0.4
	836	114	2.4	13.5	−0.2
	698	90	0.2	14.1	0.0
	563	108	−0.9	14.3	−0.2
	499	108	−0.7	14.4	0.4
	369	42	0.3	14.8	0.2
	298	60	1.4	15.2	0.4
	228	48	2.3	13.2	0.7
	190	48	2.7	13.6	1.2
	150	42	2.1	14.2	1.0
	97	18	2.1	14.0	1.2
1830	1252	120	5.5	13.8	0.1
	1050	114	5.1	13.5	−0.1
	888	108	4.7	13.8	0.0
	754	108	4.5	14.0	0.2
	612	102	3.1	14.5	−0.1
	528	102	3.4	14.6	0.0
	418	78	3.0	14.1	−0.4
	356	72	2.5	14.0	−0.1
	263	36	2.0	13.8	0.4
	204	12	0.6	11.6	0.9
	169	12	0.0	11.4	−0.2

1 September 1953

CST	Z	t	u	v	w
0630	1285	102	6.9	6.2	−0.1
	1088	108	8.4	6.6	0.2
	922	102	10.3	8.0	0.0
	782	102	11.8	8.7	0.1
	665	96	12.8	8.3	0.4
	455	78	15.7	10.5	0.3
	368	72	15.4	14.0	0.1
	312	24	13.8	15.5	0.1

CST	Z	t	u	v	w
140	60	−0.2	10.4	−1.1	
1235	1269	120	2.7	9.3	−0.4
	1049	114	4.1	10.3	−0.2
	827	108	3.4	10.8	−0.7
	602	108	2.0	11.4	−2.0
	496	102	1.6	12.1	−1.5
	279	84	1.4	11.1	−1.2
	225	18	1.9	10.3	−1.1
	189	18	5.9	8.1	2.1
	156	18	5.3	9.9	1.8
	52	36	0.9	8.8	−1.6
1435	1326	120	5.3	11.1	−0.1
	1123	114	4.0	10.4	−0.3
	969	102	3.9	9.6	−0.4
	820	108	2.9	10.8	−0.7
	763	102	3.3	12.6	0.3
	669	102	3.2	12.6	0.0
	580	96	2.6	13.0	−0.1
	492	78	2.6	12.6	−0.6
	479	42	1.9	13.3	−0.1
	460	30	1.9	12.7	2.1
	413	42	3.1	11.2	2.1
	362	42	4.5	10.9	1.4
1635	1261	120	4.0	10.7	−0.2
	986	120	3.6	11.1	−1.0
	686	114	2.4	12.8	−0.6
	578	108	2.1	13.0	−0.3
	437	108	2.4	12.9	−0.9
	378	108	2.7	12.8	−0.4
	262	36	1.9	13.5	0.9
	209	36	1.1	14.0	0.7
	147	24	0.5	14.0	0.2
	101	18	−0.5	13.7	−0.1
1835	1350	120	5.4	12.6	0.1
	1141	120	5.0	13.6	0.2
	949	120	4.8	14.2	0.0
	790	120	3.8	15.3	−0.1
	670	114	3.7	15.2	0.0
	575	114	3.6	15.0	0.1
	482	114	3.2	15.1	0.2
	379	66	3.6	14.9	−0.1
	314	48	3.3	14.4	0.2
	252	18	1.9	14.3	0.3
	213	30	1.7	13.1	0.4
	155	12	2.5	13.1	1.0
0635	1292	102	6.5	5.7	0.3
	1093	108	8.6	6.7	0.4
	930	102	10.6	8.2	0.3
	785	102	11.7	8.2	0.3
	665	96	13.1	8.1	0.2
	569	84	14.2	9.1	0.1
	471	72	16.1	10.5	0.2
	392	72	15.1	13.4	0.2

CST	Z	t	u	v	w
	154	90	1.2	9.5	−0.8
	81	36	0.5	9.4	−0.2
	33	30	1.1	9.9	−0.5
1240	1563	120	1.2	5.6	−0.1
	1378	120	3.9	7.9	−0.1
	1118	84	2.7	8.3	−1.5
	1085	84	3.5	9.1	0.1
	987	78	1.7	8.6	0.7
	923	120	2.3	8.0	0.2
	818	90	4.0	9.3	1.0
	681	96	2.8	9.3	1.1
	649	96	2.7	9.7	1.2
	572	90	2.9	10.5	1.0
	546	120	2.8	11.3	1.1
1440	1150	120	3.6	11.0	−1.2
	1024	114	2.9	10.5	−0.7
	779	108	1.6	11.7	−2.0
	674	108	2.1	13.8	−1.2
	592	108	2.5	14.4	−0.5
	503	102	2.6	13.7	−0.7
	428	102	2.3	14.2	−0.2
1640	1316	120	4.0	12.7	0.0
	1084	120	2.3	13.7	−0.4
	897	120	2.6	14.2	−0.5
	804	78	1.8	12.4	0.5
	594	114	1.3	11.7	0.5
	504	114	1.8	11.4	0.8
	376	90	1.8	11.4	−0.1
	328	84	1.2	12.3	0.3
	274	36	0.0	12.0	0.8
	225	42	−0.4	9.6	1.1
	211	42	0.6	10.2	1.9
1840	1197	120	5.4	14.1	−0.1
	1023	120	5.3	14.5	0.0
	856	120	4.4	14.6	0.1
	722	120	4.2	14.4	0.1
	617	120	4.0	14.2	0.2
	507	102	3.1	14.5	0.1
	432	120	2.7	14.6	0.2
	382	120	2.7	14.8	0.6
	290	54	2.0	14.6	0.3
	244	42	1.6	14.6	0.4
	197	24	1.8	13.9	0.6
	158	12	1.8	13.0	−0.2
0640	1291	108	6.6	5.2	0.4
	941	96	10.5	8.1	0.3
	757	96	12.0	7.4	0.3
	464	72	16.0	11.0	0.1
	355	60	14.7	14.8	0.0
	251	36	10.1	15.6	−0.1

CST	Z	t	u	v	w	CST	Z	t	u	v	w	CST	Z	t	u	v	w
							320	66	13.5	15.8	0.2						
							266	30	10.5	15.3	0.0						
							220	30	8.7	15.1	−0.5						
0830	1268	120	5.5	8.8	0.0	0835	1494	120	4.3	6.6	0.3	0840	1693	54	3.2	6.0	0.4
	1122	120	6.6	8.6	0.3		1262	114	5.3	8.5	0.1		1480	120	4.4	7.2	0.2
	944	120	7.7	7.3	0.3		865	108	8.5	5.9	0.6		1306	120	5.4	8.4	0.2
	534	42	11.2	9.4	−0.3								1113	120	7.6	7.2	0.2
													879	54	8.5	6.1	0.0
													774	36	9.4	6.8	0.0
													676	18	9.3	6.8	−0.2

6.1.b. Loeser technique of night-time wind profile measurements (GRD). Median values of West and South components u, v (m/sec) of drift; number N of balloons of a pibal swarm which cross the indicated levels. Basic data are overlapping 24-sec mean displacements toward the east and north of each of the N balloons at 12-sec intervals during a 4-min period centered at indicated CST.

Height (m)	31 August 2035			2235			1 September 1953 0035			0235			0435		
	u	v	N	u	v	N	u	v	N	u	v	N	u	v	N
1600	—	—	—	—	—	—	6.3	4.9	1	—	—	—	—	—	—
1400	—	—	—	7.7	8.8	1	10.5	8.8	2	7.4	5.6	1	7.7	4.5	1
1200	7.0	13.5	2	7.9	11.8	2	12.0	12.4	3	11.0	8.1	3	10.0	5.7	2
1000	7.0	15.3	3	8.7	14.5	4	11.8	14.5	4	12.8	11.0	4	11.4	7.7	5
800	6.8	16.9	4	7.9	17.0	4	11.7	16.8	4	14.5	13.1	6	13.8	10.7	8
700	5.9	16.9	3	8.3	18.0	5	12.4	17.4	5	15.0	14.8	6	15.7	11.5	7
600	6.1	18.0	5	7.5	19.2	5	12.7	18.8	3	15.1	16.0	5	16.7	12.1	7
500	5.4	17.6	5	7.5	20.1	4	11.9	20.2	6	11.5	17.3	7	17.0	13.7	7
400	4.5	17.9	5	7.2	20.8	6	11.6	21.4	6	14.9	18.2	6	16.5	16.0	6
300	3.4	18.2	5	5.8	21.1	5	10.5	20.7	5	10.5	18.0	6	12.5	17.5	5
200	2.1	17.2	5	3.4	18.9	4	6.5	17.0	4	6.6	15.5	4	8.0	16.4	4
100	0.0	13.7	4	1.5	13.9	1	3.8	12.3	2	4.5	11.8	3	4.3	12.4	2

6.2. Rawinsonde (GMD-1A) wind speed (m/sec) and direction (deg from North) from 1-min mean drift at 30-sec intervals, for first 7 min of ascent started at indicated CST.

31 August 1953

0435 m	m/sec	deg	0635 m	m/sec	deg	0835 m	m/sec	deg	1035 m	m/sec	deg	1235 m	m/sec	deg
2137	2.8	180	2254	5.3	168	1714	5.4	154	1968	5.7	167	1754	7.5	186
1867	8.2	204	1988	4.4	205	1489	5.7	171	1699	8.6	171	1523	7.8	189
1710	6.8	218	1854	4.4	204	1371	6.5	181	1551	8.2	180	1418	8.5	197
1558	7.8	213	1698	5.3	181	1260	6.8	189	1407	8.7	194	1298	9.3	198
1402	7.6	207	1544	5.4	185	1146	7.4	204	1261	7.9	193	1183	8.2	194
1247	7.9	213	1388	6.2	192	1030	7.1	208	1114	6.9	194	1060	7.7	190
1092	10.0	212	1233	6.8	207	917	10.5	203	972	7.3	202	923	8.4	193
940	12.2	213	1077	7.8	212	787	12.4	204	834	9.0	201	789	9.7	194
790	14.0	218	917	8.2	219	658	10.8	210	698	9.7	201	650	9.4	197
640	16.4	219	751	11.1	222	526	12.3	210	560	9.6	199	514	9.2	194
488	19.8	214	588	15.0	216	398	14.4	206	423	9.0	193	377	8.7	187
338	20.3	209	425	18.0	210	266	13.5	202	286	8.4	183	251	8.9	187
178	17.0	203	243	18.3	205	135	10.7	195	143	10.5	176	125	10.3	185

31 August 1953

1435			1635			1835			2035			2235		
m	m/sec	deg	m	m/sec	deg	m	m/sec	deg	m	m/sec	deg	m	m/sec	deg
1955	5.2	195	2088	3.9	226	2247	3.0	195	1873	3.9	208	2296	2.4	188
1697	6.7	198	1882	3.4	234	1999	1.5	247	1637	10.0	220	1991	4.5	219
1536	8.4	203	1780	4.8	220	1874	2.2	234	1497	13.3	216	1822	5.3	214
1372	11.1	205	1634	8.9	214	1748	6.3	213	1358	14.8	210	1658	4.8	227
1209	13.6	197	1465	12.9	208	1633	11.2	207	1222	14.1	207	1491	8.2	227
1047	13.3	191	1294	13.2	204	1440	16.3	204	1084	14.6	206	1325	14.2	220
899	12.7	192	1124	12.8	203	1246	17.1	204	947	16.2	204	1155	15.6	213
772	14.4	197	954	13.6	194	1052	17.6	201	805	17.3	204	990	16.7	206
649	16.3	197	796	12.8	194	864	17.3	197	669	19.1	198	825	20.3	200
521	17.2	193	639	11.8	188	703	15.6	196	532	19.6	195	660	21.4	203
398	16.2	191	480	12.8	190	541	15.4	196	394	19.0	194	495	23.1	200
269	13.8	190	325	14.4	186	380	14.8	192	258	16.4	190	326	21.4	197
133	11.7	183	169	14.5	183	221	15.3	187	127	12.2	184	162	15.1	190

1 September 1953

0035			0238			0435			0635			0835		
m	m/sec	deg	m	m/sec	deg	m	m/sec	deg	m	m/sec	deg	m	m/sec	deg
1952	5.0	219	2394	1.9	227	1997	1.7	254	1930	3.3	171	1800	4.4	206
1721	6.6	220	2037	4.4	234	1745	4.2	247	1691	6.2	214	1572	9.3	214
1580	7.4	229	1861	4.0	254	1607	6.9	238	1571	7.1	217	1460	9.6	216
1450	7.2	237	1685	4.0	249	1462	6.5	241	1451	7.1	218	1348	9.5	216
1330	11.5	230	1509	6.7	237	1318	8.6	239	1331	8.4	224	1239	9.9	216
1180	13.7	232	1330	9.2	232	1170	12.2	239	1212	8.9	231	1125	10.2	215
1040	20.2	220	1150	11.2	232	1022	12.7	238	1097	8.7	234	1012	10.8	218
900	25.9	216	981	15.6	233	880	14.2	234	940	11.4	232	874	11.7	226
740	25.4	215	811	18.2	230	744	19.1	233	786	15.1	233	746	12.6	242
600	24.4	213	642	19.4	224	608	23.2	231	633	16.9	235	608	13.0	231
460	23.7	210	472	16.3	222	470	24.9	228	480	19.4	235	470	12.4	230
300	23.1	207	305	21.0	262	332	21.9	221	327	19.9	227	335	10.9	222
160	17.1	202	151	15.6	204	197	18.0	206	163	15.4	212	185	10.9	206

6.3. Double theodolite pibal wind speed (m/sec) and direction (deg from North) from 1-min mean drift at 30-sec intervals, for first 7 min of ascent started at indicated CST.

31 August 1953

0830			1030			1230			1630			1730		
m	m/sec	deg	m	m/sec	deg	m	m/sec	deg	m	m/sec	deg	m	m/sec	deg
1250	6.7	173	1456	6.4	185	1718	6.5	187	1478	12.9	202	1454	12.4	201
1171	6.0	193	1388	7.3	190	1638	6.2	189	1300	12.5	197	1327	14.0	201
1105	6.7	213	1304	7.9	187	1552	7.2	196	1194	14.2	195	1227	12.3	201
1021	7.8	205	1228	6.5	186	1468	8.1	200	1068	13.3	195	1119	12.2	199
940	8.4	202	1160	7.0	191	1378	8.8	200	965	10.7	195	1026	12.7	194
874	9.5	200	1078	7.9	194	1277	9.8	196	872	9.9	192	914	12.9	191
798	9.9	204	984	8.0	193	1150	9.8	194	775	12.1	188	821	13.1	189
723	9.0	210	870	8.1	196	1063	9.5	195	664	13.2	186	729	13.4	188
656	10.2	209	782	8.0	201	927	10.1	191	596	12.0	185	653	12.6	186
558	12.2	206	692	7.1	200	796	10.5	188	510	13.0	185	579	12.6	185
470	14.0	203	620	9.5	202	617	10.8	191	424	15.8	182	464	13.3	183
356	14.4	201	488	11.5	200	448	10.6	190	294	16.5	180	358	12.5	183
256	12.0	198	342	9.2	192	268	9.9	188	194	13.0	178	271	14.2	180
134	10.3	192	172	8.6	184	118	8.6	191	102	11.5	174	132	13.8	180

31 August									1 September 1953					
1930			2030			2230			0045			0530		
m	m/sec	deg	m	m/sec	deg	m	m/sec	deg	m	m/sec	deg	m	m/sec	deg
1204	15.6	206	1103	14.7	204	1006	15.9	210	727	10.4	221	734	14.0	231
1114	14.9	204	1034	14.9	203	954	14.0	210	737	23.2	214	672	16.4	229
1057	14.2	201	955	17.2	201	898	15.8	208	610	30.4	212	629	15.4	230
963	15.7	201	875	17.1	200	832	19.4	206	554	14.8	215	572	15.0	232
882	15.0	199	802	15.0	200	759	18.9	204	538	19.2	213	531	15.2	233
798	15.0	197	732	17.4	198	702	17.8	204	502	20.1	213	492	18.0	230
698	15.6	196	646	19.1	196	630	19.5	203	468	19.8	210	449	17.0	231
629	16.2	195	575	17.6	195	566	20.5	202	424	21.8	208	416	18.4	228
545	16.6	194	506	18.5	194	501	20.0	196	369	26.8	206	360	21.0	223
468	17.2	193	430	18.6	193	450	21.4	198	298	22.8	207	308	20.6	220
389	17.6	191	360	18.0	192	373	22.1	197	278	19.2	204	261	20.4	213
311	17.8	190	284	18.2	189	311	20.4	194	212	16.0	201	192	17.6	205
232	16.0	188	208	16.8	187	218	19.0	189	189	14.6	196	140	15.4	199
140	13.7	185	122	14.1	183	104	14.1	184	68	14.5	181	77	11.8	196

6.4. Radiosonde pressure (mb), temperature (°C), and relative humidity (%) at significant levels of ascent started at indicated CST. (M = "motorboating", i.e., a humidity value below the minimum value that the radiosonde can measure at that temperature.)

	31 August										1 September 1953				
	0435	0635	0835	1035	1235	1435	1635	1835	2035	2235	0035	0238	0435	0635	0835
mb	942	942	942	942	942	941	940	941	941	941	942	941	942	942	943
°C	23.0	22.2	26.8	30.8	33.5	34.5	34.0	31.0	27.0	25.6	24.6	23.4	22.4	23.5	28.2
%	67	73	60	49	39	38	37	43	52	58	61	64	67	62	52
mb	900	912	921	880	801	853	933	774	930	908	909	897	854	897	901
°C	24.1	24.3	23.7	23.1	18.0	23.5	31.4	16.6	28.3	26.5	26.4	25.1	24.3	26.1	24.0
%	61	75	65	67	65	67	40	70	47	50	55	58	52	54	58
mb	838	850	910	872	798	770	776	756	791	774	779	798	755	735	892
°C	22.1	23.1	25.4	23.6	19.1	17.0	17.0	17.1	16.7	16.8	17.1	18.7	17.1	13.8	26.0
%	56	66	59	61	43	62	69	48	59	65	63	65	65	65	54
mb	806	768	876	774	725	760	756	699	702	744	684	714	740	712	872
°C	20.6	17.4	24.8	19.2	15.6	17.8	17.5	12.7	13.5	15.7	11.7	12.6	16.7	13.8	25.3
%	60	80	52	29	30	43	43	45	20	42	23	42	43	41	55
mb	672	740	788	744	680	732	693	685	679	673	586	682	679	664	730
°C	8.0	14.5	19.4	16.8	11.5	16.2	13.0	11.9	11.4	10.5	2.5	11.7	12.6	10.5	13.0
%	94	87	55	43	26	43	49	23	20	20	35	24	22	23	68
mb	655	676	768	651	594	707	689	614	592	609	565	605	631	647	697
°C	6.5	8.7	17.5	8.9	3.3	14.0	13.2	5.6	2.6	5.2	1.2	3.6	7.7	8.6	11.6
%	88	74	68	26	35	37	21	23	25	28	25	26	22	26	50
mb	648	653	738	606	—	694	600	—	579	546	546	542	602	636	674
°C	6.6	7.9	16.0	4.2	—	14.0	4.8	—	1.6	−1.4	−0.9	−2.7	4.9	7.0	10.1
%	75	56	43	40	—	23	30	—	36	24	—	58	37	43	53

L

	31 August										1 September 1953				
	0435	0635	0835	1035	1235	1435	1635	1835	2035	2235	0035	0238	0435	0635	0835
mb	633	618	650	559	—	626	—	—	568	—	—	516	—	605	600
°C	5.3	4.0	8.5	−0.5	—	6.8	—	—	1.3	—	—	−5.1	—	4.1	4.6
%	57	61	33	25	—	30	—	—	22	—	—	46	—	48	48
mb	586	591	630	534	—	595	—	—	554	—	—	—	—	—	—
°C	0.8	1.1	5.8	−3.4	—	4.0	—	—	−0.1	—	—	—	—	—	—
%	52	44	45	M	—	32	—	—	26	—	—	—	—	—	—
mb	575	544	620	—	—	—	—	—	—	—	—	—	—	—	—
°C	−0.3	−4.0	5.2	—	—	—	—	—	—	—	—	—	—	—	—
%	40	33	32	—	—	—	—	—	—	—	—	—	—	—	—
mb	542	534	588	—	—	—	—	—	—	—	—	—	—	—	—
°C	−4.7	−4.5	1.7	—	—	—	—	—	—	—	—	—	—	—	—
%	45	38	26												

6.5. Air temperature T (°C) and mixing ratio W (g water vapor/kg air) at altitude Z (m) from aerograph (L-20) data. CST of start, top level, and end of flight is indicated.

31 August 1953

(0623-0637-0647)			(0812-0830-0854)			(1017-1035-1044)			(1261-1230-1240)		
Z	T	W	Z	T	W	Z	T	W	Z	T	W
25	23.2	5.6	16	25.6	15.1	25	28.8	8.4	33	30.2	16.0
65	23.1	14.1	33	24.8	14.3	48	28.7	15.1	65	29.8	13.5
95	23.5	14.5	48	24.7	14.2	80	27.7	14.2	180	28.3	12.4
165	23.7	13.9	95	23.8	13.7	165	26.7	14.3	330	27.3	12.5
330	25.0	13.8	165	23.7	14.2	330	25.3	14.3	650	24.4	13.4
650	24.4	12.7	240	23.3	14.0	650	24.6	13.1	990	21.3	12.9
990	23.8	12.3	330	25.1	14.1	990	23.1	9.8	1290	19.4	10.9
1290	21.9	12.5	480	24.3	13.1	1290	21.3	7.1	1640	19.5	6.2
1640	19.4	12.3	650	23.6	12.5	1640	20.7	8.4	1290	19.0	4.0
1290	21.4	12.4	990	22.6	12.4	1640	20.4	5.7	990	21.2	13.7
650	23.8	11.8	1140	22.0	11.2	1290	22.4	7.0	650	25.7	12.7
330	23.8	12.9	1290	20.6	10.9	990	23.1	8.7	330	27.7	13.0
165	23.7	13.1	1470	20.4	11.1	650	24.1	14.5	65	29.7	13.1
135	22.8	13.4	1640	19.1	10.8	480	24.4	14.9	16	30.6	13.1
95	22.7	13.7	1800	17.4	11.5	240	26.7	15.7			
65	22.7	13.8	1370	20.6	12.4	95	28.2	15.5			
33	23.1	14.1	1290	21.3	10.9	65	28.6	15.5			
			990	22.2	12.4	33	29.2	15.5			
			650	24.6	13.0	16	28.6	14.6			
			480	25.5	13.5						
			330	24.8	13.6						
			165	25.1	14.5						
			95	25.8	15.0						
			33	26.7	15.0						

31 August (1419-1434-1444)			(1615-1630-1641)			(1815-1830-1840)			1 September 1953 (0629-0643-0653)			(0817-0831-0841)		
Z	T	W	Z	T	W	Z	T	W	Z	T	W	Z	T	W
16	31.2	12.7	33	32.2	13.5	16	31.2	11.7	26	23.6	12.6	26	25.7	13.4
95	30.8	12.5	80	30.8	11.9	48	30.7	12.0	105	23.4	12.5	70	25.1	13.6
165	29.8	12.5	165	30.2	11.8	95	30.6	12.1	165	23.7	12.9	105	24.8	12.8
330	28.7	13.0	330	29.1	13.1	165	29.8	11.9	330	24.7	13.1	165	24.0	12.4
670	25.8	13.6	650	25.9	12.4	240	29.3	12.5	660	25.5	12.8	330	23.7	12.7
990	22.7	13.2	990	22.8	12.4	330	28.7	11.6	990	22.7	9.9	660	24.4	12.6
1290	19.6	12.8	1290	19.8	12.7	650	25.7	11.8	1290	20.8	11.5	990	21.7	11.8
1640	18.0	10.1	1640	17.3	11.1	990	22.7	13.2	1620	17.9	11.3	1290	19.5	12.1
1290	19.5	13.2	1290	19.6	12.7	1290	20.0	12.7	1290	20.7	11.8	1620	17.1	12.1
990	22.6	13.9	990	22.7	13.6	1640	17.5	10.6	990	22.2	12.5	1290	19.4	13.6
650	25.6	13.9	650	21.1	9.8	1290	19.7	12.9	660	25.0	13.1	990	22.4	13.9
330	28.7	13.9	330	29.1	13.0	990	22.8	12.8	590	24.7	11.5	660	24.4	12.6
165	30.1	13.6	80	31.3	12.5	650	25.6	12.7	165	23.7	12.1	330	24.2	12.6
95	30.6	13.7	48	30.8	11.8	330	28.7	12.5	105	23.7	12.4	165	24.3	12.8
			16	31.9	12.5	95	30.5	12.6	70	24.3	13.1	105	25.8	13.6
						48	30.8	12.7	17	23.2	12.4	26	26.2	13.9
						16	30.7	12.4						

7.1. Representative values of West and South components of the wind u, v (m/sec) at standard heights. Values are estimated from the combination of smoke puff or pibal swarm, rawinsonde and double theodolite pibal data at or near the indicated CST.

	Height (m)	31 August										1 September 1953				
		0435	0635	0835	1035	1235	1435	1635	1835	2035	2235	0035	0235	0435	0635	0835
u	2000	1.3	−2.0	−2.2	−1.6	0.1	2.6	3.0	1.9	0.6	1.9	2.5	3.2	1.0	−0.5	2.1
	1750	2.8	−0.7	−2.2	−1.1	1.0	3.1	3.8	3.6	3.6	3.7	4.3	4.2	3.4	1.8	3.2
	1500	3.9	0.8	−1.5	0.3	2.0	3.6	4.4	6.0	6.8	6.0	7.0	6.4	6.0	4.3	4.7
	1250	5.0	2.7	1.3	1.7	2.8	4.0	4.5	6.2	7.2	8.3	11.1	9.6	9.2	7.0	5.9
	1000	6.5	4.7	3.6	2.7	2.8	4.0	3.6	5.5	7.1	8.4	13.5	13.1	11.5	9.1	7.4
	800	8.5	6.6	5.0	3.5	2.8	3.8	2.9	4.7	6.6	8.3	13.7	14.5	13.7	11.6	8.9
	700	9.7	8.6	5.5	3.6	2.7	3.7	2.6	4.3	6.1	8.1	13.4	14.9	15.6	13.2	9.8
	600	10.5	9.0	5.9	3.5	2.5	3.5	2.2	4.0	5.7	8.0	13.0	15.1	16.8	14.3	10.5
	500	10.9	8.7	6.1	3.0	2.3	3.1	1.8	3.6	5.1	7.7	12.2	15.0	17.3	15.7	11.8
	400	10.8	8.7	6.2	2.3	1.9	2.8	1.5	3.0	4.5	7.2	11.5	14.2	16.5	15.4	10.0
	300	9.2	9.2	5.5	1.6	1.5	2.3	1.2	2.5	3.4	5.8	10.3	11.5	13.1	12.7	7.2
	200	7.4	8.5	3.8	0.8	1.3	1.5	0.9	1.7	2.0	3.5	6.9	7.5	8.0	8.3	4.9
	100	5.5	5.9	2.2	0.0	1.1	0.7	0.5	1.0	0.5	1.4	3.8	4.5	4.2	4.5	3.1
v	2000	5.9	4.0	4.2	6.3	6.6	3.7	2.8	1.0	1.3	2.7	3.7	1.1	0.5	3.2	5.5
	1750	6.2	4.8	4.6	6.8	7.1	5.7	5.7	5.0	4.5	3.5	4.3	1.9	1.9	4.0	6.4
	1500	6.6	5.4	5.5	7.5	8.7	8.6	9.5	11.5	10.4	6.7	6.2	4.2	3.5	5.0	7.5
	1250	7.5	6.0	6.4	7.7	8.6	11.5	11.8	14.3	13.3	11.3	10.7	7.3	5.3	5.9	8.3
	1000	9.3	7.0	7.7	7.7	9.2	12.6	12.7	14.7	15.3	14.7	15.1	10.7	7.5	7.3	7.9
	800	11.4	8.1	9.6	8.1	9.8	13.3	13.0	14.9	16.8	17.5	18.3	12.9	10.5	8.6	7.5
	700	12.7	9.2	9.2	8.5	10.1	13.6	13.2	15.0	17.6	18.7	19.4	14.5	12.0	9.3	8.0
	600	14.3	11.0	10.2	8.8	10.4	13.8	13.3	15.0	18.4	19.5	20.2	15.7	13.3	10.0	8.6
	500	15.9	13.2	11.5	9.0	10.7	13.9	13.4	14.9	18.6	20.4	21.1	16.9	14.9	10.8	9.1
	400	17.5	14.8	13.5	9.3	10.8	13.7	13.4	14.7	18.5	21.0	21.6	17.8	16.3	12.3	9.5
	300	17.4	16.3	13.2	9.5	10.7	13.4	13.5	14.4	18.2	21.1	20.7	17.7	17.1	14.8	10.0
	200	16.5	16.3	11.5	9.7	10.2	12.9	13.4	14.0	16.5	18.5	17.0	16.0	16.2	14.9	10.5
	100	15.1	14.8	10.5	10.0	9.6	11.8	13.1	13.6	13.2	14.1	13.0	11.9	13.7	12.0	11.1

7.2.a. Air temperature (°C) at standard heights. Values are interpolated and averaged from radiosonde and airplane (L-20) data at or near the indicated CST.

Height (m)	31 August 0435[1]	0635	0835	1035	1235	1435	1635	1835	1 September 1953 2035[1]	2235[1]	0035[1]	0235[1]	0435[1]	0635	0835
2000	16.3	16.2	16.4	18.3	18.5	16.5	16.3	16.5	15.3	16.1	15.3	15.7	17.1	15.0	14.9
1750	18.1	18.2	18.0	19.6	18.8	17.3	16.8	16.8	16.2	16.4	16.9	17.2	18.7	16.9	16.7
1500	20.0	20.0	19.9	20.8	19.3	19.0	18.6	18.6	17.4	18.7	18.5	18.8	20.4	18.9	18.5
1250	21.4	21.6	21.4	21.4	19.8	20.7	20.7	20.5	19.4	20.4	20.3	20.3	22.0	20.9	20.2
1000	22.4	23.1	23.3	22.8	22.0	22.6	23.2	22.6	21.4	22.1	22.0	21.8	23.7	22.3	22.2
800	23.0	23.6	23.7	23.7	23.9	24.6	24.8	24.3	23.0	23.5	23.4	23.1	24.1	24.0	23.8
600	23.6	24.1	24.6	24.2	26.0	26.5	26.4	26.1	24.6	24.9	24.7	24.3	23.7	25.1	24.8
400	24.0	24.3	25.0	25.3	27.6	28.5	28.4	27.9	26.2	26.2	26.1	24.9	23.2	24.9	24.1
200	23.5	23.5	24.4	27.0	29.4	30.7	30.3	29.5	27.8	26.1	25.6	24.1	22.8	24.1	24.8
100	23.2	23.0	25.0	28.0	30.4	31.8	31.1	30.4	27.9	25.8	25.1	23.8	22.6	23.8	25.8

[1] Radiosonde data only.

7.2.b. Mixing ratio (g water vapor/kg air) at standard heights. Values are interpolated and averaged from radiosonde and airplane (L-20) data at or near the indicated CST.

Height (m)	31 August 0435[1]	0635	0835	1035	1235	1435	1635	1835	1 September 1953 2035[1]	2235[1]	0035[1]	0235[1]	0435[1]	0635	0835
2000	10.3	12.2	10.0	4.9	5.7	7.8	8.1	8.7	6.5	7.7	7.7	8.3	10.4	10.2	10.6
1750	10.6	12.6	11.3	5.0	6.5	9.6	10.8	10.5	8.0	10.2	9.4	9.7	10.9	10.6	11.0
1500	11.0	12.7	11.0	6.5	8.1	11.4	11.6	11.4	9.3	10.8	10.3	11.2	11.1	11.2	11.9
1250	11.3	12.8	11.0	8.0	12.1	13.1	12.2	12.3	10.0	11.2	11.0	11.7	11.3	11.5	12.4
1000	11.8	12.8	12.0	9.8	12.6	13.8	12.6	12.3	10.6	11.7	11.7	12.3	11.5	11.5	12.7
800	12.3	13.0	12.3	12.1	12.8	14.0	12.0	12.3	11.1	12.1	12.3	12.7	11.7	12.2	12.7
600	12.9	13.4	12.7	13.9	12.8	14.0	11.7	12.3	11.6	12.4	12.8	13.1	11.8	12.4	12.8
400	13.2	14.0	13.5	14.5	12.9	13.8	12.5	12.3	12.1	12.8	13.4	13.3	12.0	12.6	12.6
200	13.0	13.8	14.0	14.8	13.0	13.3	12.6	12.6	12.6	12.9	14.4	12.9	12.1	12.6	12.8
100	12.8	14.0	14.2	14.8	13.3	13.1	12.5	12.7	12.9	13.0	14.9	12.7	12.2	12.4	13.3

[1] Radiosonde data only.

7.3.a. Summary of heat budget constituents (mcal cm^{-2} min^{-1}) of the earth-air interface according to the theoretical models by Suomi, Halstead, and Lettau. Net radiation flux R, heat transfer to the soil S, sensible heat transfer to the air Q and latent heat transfer to the air (heat equivalent of evaporation) E. Values are hourly means centered at indicated CST.

	31 August 0435	0635	0835	1035	1235	1435	1635	1835	2035	2235	1 September 1953 0035	0235	0435	0635	0835
Suomi[1]															
R_0	81	56	−319	−650	−767	−636	−252	88	110	107	103	100	100	39	−304
S_0	−52	−31	50	107	127	98	8	−40	−52	−61	−52	−50	−50	−32	36
Q_0	—	—	183	310	542	445	113	—	—	—	—	—	—	—	142
E_0	—	—	86	233	98	93	131	—	—	—	—	—	—	—	126
Halstead															
R_0	70	30	−320	−660	−800	−690	−330	60	90	80	—	—	—	—	—
S_0	−20	−13	1	67	103	90	50	3	−18	−22	—	—	—	—	—
Q_0	−53	−5	278	462	622	588	307	−65	−75	−73	—	—	—	—	—
E_0	58	20	0[2]	40[2]	0[2]	78	87[2]	20	10	30	—	—	—	—	—
Lettau															
R_0	79	36	−335	−685	−814	−675	−286	82	105	100	98	77	88	28	−320
S_0	−36	−25	51	150	174	122	30	−32	−32	−32	−52	−51	−46	−28	76
Q_0	−23	1	221	612	789	534	269	−10	−27	−33	−31	−24	−32	−4	299
E_0	20	59	47	136	39	45	80	50	31	34	19	21	11	49	26

[1] UW temperature and vapor differences produce Bowen ratios which yield $Q_0 > 0$ and $E_0 < 0$ before 0835 and after 1635. Suomi considers this an unrealistic result and has not computed Q_0 and E_0.
[2] Interpolated value.

7.3.b. Representative logarithmic height derivatives of wind speed (zV' mm sec^{-1}, from UCLA and JH data), potential temperature ($z\theta'$, 10^{-3} °C, from JH and UW data), and water vapor pressure (ze', 10^{-3} mb, from JH and UW data); representative values of Karman number k (from zV' and UCLA, JH, and MIT stress data), interpolated ground drag τ_0 (dynes cm^{-2}, from zV' and representative k values), and ratio of heat and momentum diffusivities N_Q; representative ground-flux ratio F_0 and inverse Bowen ratio B. Values refer to indicated CST and are employed in the computation of the heat budget constituents Q_0 and E_0 (Lettau model; see Table 7.3.a).

	31 August										1 September 1953				
	0435	0635	0835	1035	1235	1435	1635	1835	2035	2235	0035	0235	0435	0635	0835
zV'	942	1008	1239	1192	1243	1470	1418	1112	881	975	980	857	998	998	1272
$z\theta'$	123	−3	−490	−930	−1165	−830	−593	39	165	177	167	154	163	19	−594
ze'	−58	−160	−101	−292	−82	−81	−156	−131	−101	−98	−55	−71	−31	−134	−53
k	0.37	0.38	0.39	0.40	0.40	0.39	0.39	0.38	0.37	0.37	0.37	0.37	0.37	0.38	0.39
τ_0	1.37	1.60	2.51	2.42	2.60	3.53	3.18	1.86	1.16	1.44	1.45	1.11	1.53	1.56	2.68
N_Q	0.90	0.96	1.53	2.25	2.25	1.86	1.40	0.94	0.86	0.88	0.86	0.84	0.90	0.94	1.66
F_0	1.7[1]	−16[1]	1.99	1.96	1.83	1.9[1]	1.34	5.3[1]	2.3[1]	1.8[1]	1.29	0.90	1.16	0.0[1]	1.35
B	−0.8[1]	1[1]	−0.33	−0.50	0.11	0.2[1]	0.42	−5.4[1]	−1.0[1]	−0.9[1]	−0.53	−0.74	−0.31	−1.1[1]	0.14

[1] Value disregarded for evaluation of N_Q.

7.4. Richardson number (Ri; units of 10^{-3}) from Mass. Inst. Tech. and Johns Hopkins University data on simultaneous temperature and wind velocity differences, centered at indicated CST and mean height z_m (meters). (Ri') = average height derivative of Richardson number (10^{-3} m^{-1}).

Inst. Set	Height (m)	31 August										1 September 1953				
		0435	0635	0835	1035	1235	1435	1635	1835	2035	2235	0035	0235	0435	0635	0835
MIT	8.0	35	20	−46	−122	−116	−60	−33	21	46	33	51	50	37	29	−48
MIT	4.0	22	8	−40	−102	−95	−52	−31	8	29	31	31	33	20	14	−43
JH	3.2	23	6	—	—	—	−75	−27	10	31	26	25	34	21	8	−44
JH	1.6	11	3	−22	−34	−43	−24	−13	4	17	15	11	16	11	3	−22
JH	0.8	4	1	−8	−17	−22	−9	−8	2	3	7	5	7	6	2	−10
(Ri')		5	2	−8	−19	−19	−13	−6	3	7	6	7	8	5	3	−10

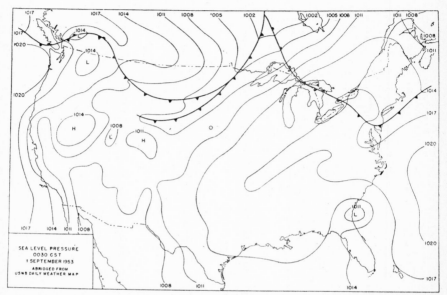

Fig. B.6.1. Continental scale synoptic chart. Sea level pressure distribution for the sixth general observation period.

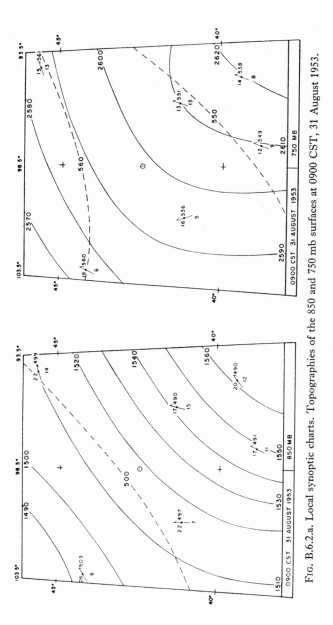

Fig. B.6.2.a. Local synoptic charts. Topographies of the 850 and 750 mb surfaces at 0900 CST, 31 August 1953.

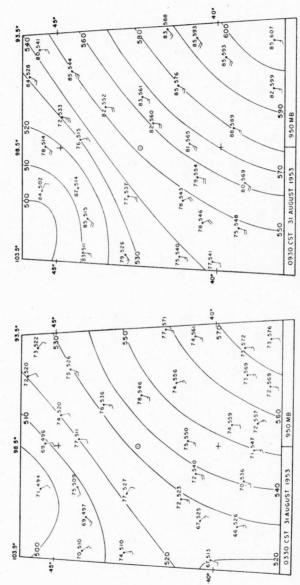

FIG. B.6.3.a. Local synoptic charts. Topography of the 950 mb surface at 0330 and 0930 CST, 31 August 1953.

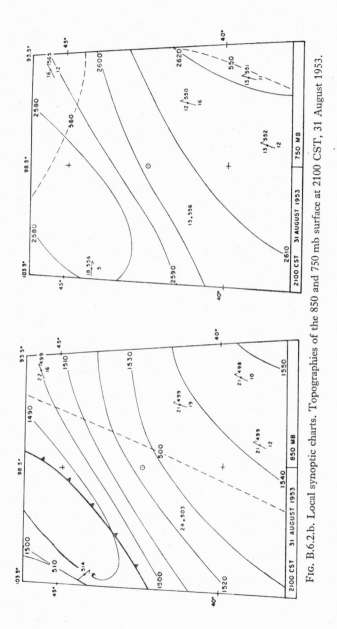

Fig. B.6.2.b. Local synoptic charts. Topographies of the 850 and 750 mb surface at 2100 CST, 31 August 1953.

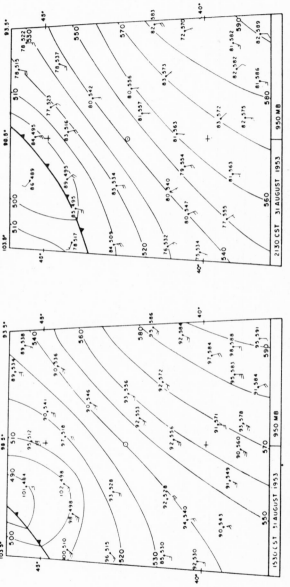

Fig. B.6.3.b. Local synoptic charts. Topography of the 950 mb surface at 1530 and 2130 CST, 31 August 1953.

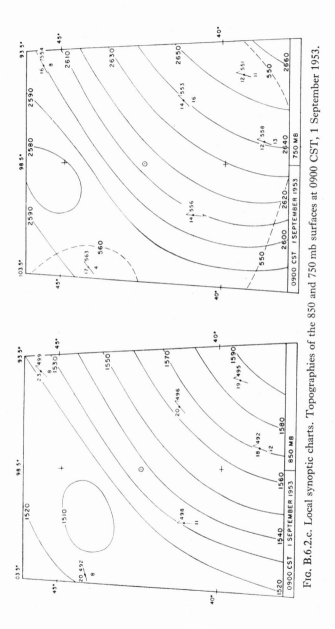

Fig. B.6.2.c. Local synoptic charts. Topographies of the 850 and 750 mb surfaces at 0900 CST, 1 September 1953.

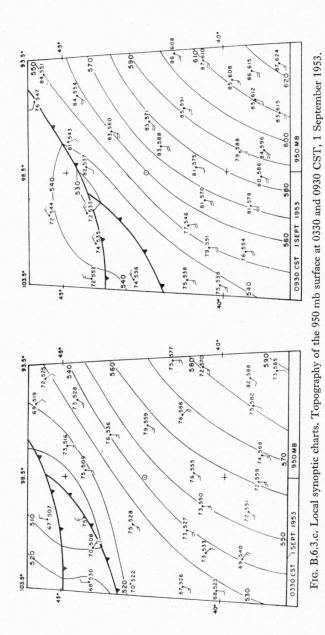

Fig. B.6.3.c. Local synoptic charts. Topography of the 950 mb surface at 0330 and 0930 CST, 1 September 1953.

SEVENTH GENERAL OBSERVATION PERIOD

0405 CST 7 September through 1305 CST 8 September 1953

Solar Data for the Field Site near O'Neill, Nebraska

	Sun's elevation angle at apparent noon	Sunrise CST	Apparent noon CST	Sunset CST
7 September	53° 30′	0605	1232	1859
8 September	53° 07′	0607	1232	1857

Summary of Synoptic Conditions

On 3 and 4 September, a ridge of high pressure pushed southeastward through Western Nebraska. The winds were northwest at 10 to 20 mph, backing to west on the 4th at 5 to 10 mph. The skies were broken to overcast during the morning of the 3rd, then cleared. On 5 and 6 September, a high-pressure area with two centers dominated the western part of the United States. The southern center at Wichita, Kansas, moved eastward on the 6th and started to weaken. The northern center, located at Casper, Wyoming, on the 5th, moved eastward to Iowa on the 6th. There was some very light rain with broken clouds during the morning of the 6th, preceded by scattered clouds and followed by clear skies. The winds were southwest and west on the 5th, shifting to north on the 6th.

On 7 September, the high-pressure area east of Nebraska moved eastward while a trough of low pressure approached from the west. The winds were southerly and initially light, becoming 15 to 20 mph during the afternoon of the 7th, then decreasing to 5 to 10 mph. The skies were generally clear over Nebraska with some scattered cirrus during the morning of the 8th. Cumulo-nimbus clouds and lightning were visible to the north of the test site from the afternoon of the 7th, until the early morning of the 8th. The seventh and last general observation period began at 0405 CST on 7 September and continued until 1305 CST on 8 September under relatively favorable conditions.

1.1.a. Mean geopotential H (dynamic m above 601 = geopotential of test site), West and South components of the geostrophic wind u_g, v_g (m/sec) at indicated pressure (mb) levels. Values are estimated for the O'Neill site from local synoptic charts.

mb	H	7 Sept. 0900		7 Sept. 2100		8 Sept. 0900	
		u_g	v_g	u_g	v_g	u_g	v_g
750	2017	8.4	−2.3	5.8	0.2	2.9	6.8
800	1471	6.8	1.2	6.5	0.1	2.2	7.1
850	956	5.4	4.6	5.3	0.5	2.3	8.0
900	467	5.0	6.2	5.3	4.4	3.6	5.4
950	3	4.4	8.0	4.0	6.6	2.3	7.6

1.1.b. Direction (deg from North) and speed (m/sec) of the 950 mb geostrophic wind. Values are estimated for the O'Neill site from local synoptic charts constructed for indicated CST.

7 September							8 September 1953				
0330	0630	0930	1230	1530	1830	2130	0030	0330	0630	0930	1230
196	209	209	216	218	217	211	212	202	196	197	193
3.6	5.7	9.1	13.3	9.1	9.1	7.7	7.7	10.0	11.8	8.0	9.5

1.2. Direction (deg from North) of the mean surface wind from standard vane recordings at 1-min intervals (Mass. Inst. Tech., 16 m level). Hourly and 15-min averages centered at indicated CST.

	7 September										8 September 1953						
	0435	0635	0835	1035	1235	1435	1635	1835	2035	2235	0035	0235	0435	0635	0835	1035	1235
60-min mean:	163	172	180	176	179	185	184[1]	181	173	178[2]	184	180	182	180	175	191	161[3]
15-min mean:	164	175	178	176	181	182	183[1]	182	173	179[2]	184	179	184	180	172	196	164[3]

[1] Period 1608-1705 CST.   [2] Period 2215-2305 CST.   [3] Period 1205-1242 CST.

1.3. Standard shelter temperature (°F), relative humidity (%); station pressure (inches) and air density (mg cm^{-3}); amount (tenths) and types of clouds.

Month	Day	CST	Temp.	RH	Pressure	Density	Clouds	Remarks
Sept.	7	0430	48	94	28.120	1.17	0 —	Some dew. Clear, wind very light
		0630	48	96	.095	1.17	1 Ci	Still some dew on grass. A few high clouds to S
		0830	64	54	.115	1.14	1 Ac	Wind increasing steadily for past 2 hr. Few high clouds to S and W
		1030	72	46	.085	1.11	0 AcCi	Wind gusts to 20 and occasionally to 25 mph
		1230	78	42	.035	1.10	0 Cu	Few Cu on horizon
		1430	82	33	.000	1.09	0 CuAc	Cu to S has been building during past hour
		1630	83	34	27.985	1.09	0 Cu	Cb far to S, moving E
		1830	77	39	.975	1.10	0 Cb	
		2030	68	56	.975	1.12	0 —	Lightning beyond horizon SE
		2230	63	69	.990	1.13	0 —	Lightning toward horizon N
	8	0030	61	73	.970	1.13	0 Cb	
		0230	57	82	.990	1.14	0 Cb	
		0430	55	84	28.000	1.15	0 Cb	Cloud bank visible to E
		0630	54	90	.015	1.15	0 —	No noticeable dew on grass. Cloud bank still E
		0830	65	66	.010	1.13	0 Ci	Scattered clouds to N
		1030	75	47	.010	1.10	4 AcCi	Ci to N
		1230	82	41	27.995	1.09	2 As	Ci moving up from N and W

2.1.b. Change of soil temperature (°C hr^{-1}) averaged over indicated layers from soil temperature integrators (University of Wisconsin). Values are differences between readings at the end and beginning of 1-hr intervals centered at indicated CST.

Depth (cm)	7 September										8 September 1953				
	0435	0635	0835	1035	1235	1435	1635	1835	2035	2235	0035	0235	0435	0635	0835
0–5	−0.53	0.32	2.03	2.56	1.99	0.33	−1.16	−1.71	−0.88	−0.75	−0.53	−0.51	−0.48	0.21	1.41
5–15	−0.37	−0.21	0.38	0.96	1.15	0.84	0.22	−0.45	−0.52	−0.46	−0.40	−0.41	−0.36	−0.19	0.16
15–50	−0.10	−0.13	−0.13	−0.04	0.05	0.14	0.17	0.13	0.06	0.01	−0.03	−0.05	−0.09	−0.08	−0.08

2.1.a. Soil temperature (°C) from thermistors (University of Texas) and soil thermocouples (University of California and Johns Hopkins University). Values are readings at indicated CST.

Inst. Set	Depth (cm)	7 September										8 September 1953						
		0435	0635	0835	1035	1235	1435	1635	1835	2035	2235	0035	0235	0435	0635	0835	1035	1235
UT	0.5	11.85	11.60	18.36	30.11	37.78	37.28	31.45	24.83	20.76	18.51	16.93	15.63	14.62	14.15	20.45	33.87	43.82
UCLA	1.3	13.72	13.06	16.83	24.06	30.50	32.56	30.11	25.28	22.06	20.11	18.56	17.06	16.17	15.28	18.94	26.39	34.28
UT	1.5	13.21	12.78	16.92	25.48	31.98	33.71	30.75	25.63	21.80	19.76	18.19	16.92	15.88	15.16	18.99	28.31	36.72
UT	2.5	14.13	13.55	16.42	23.42	29.40	31.79	30.01	25.90	22.41	20.40	18.90	17.62	16.67	15.90	18.45	25.86	33.38
JH	2.5	15.44	14.80	15.96	19.54	23.76	26.14	26.34	24.54	22.22	20.69	19.44	18.42	17.48	16.75	17.72	21.30	26.00
UT	3.5	14.72	14.11	16.16	22.08	27.69	30.30	29.47	26.11	22.90	20.95	19.43	18.20	17.25	16.41	18.15	24.29	30.90
UT	4.5	15.20	14.53	16.16	21.31	26.45	29.28	28.91	26.21	23.17	21.31	19.79	18.61	17.55	16.80	18.04	23.15	29.28
JH	5.0	16.50	15.80	16.14	18.48	21.88	24.50	25.35	24.48	22.68	21.31	20.19	19.24	18.34	17.62	17.81	19.93	23.56
UT	5.5	15.80	15.20	16.08	20.39	25.08	27.96	28.23	26.14	23.60	21.78	20.44	19.28	17.95	17.20	18.23	22.27	27.54
UCLA	10.0	17.50	16.33	16.39	18.22	21.22	24.17	25.11	24.44	23.06	21.67	20.56	19.56	18.72	17.78	17.78	19.28	22.61
JH	10.0	18.18	17.46	17.11	17.91	19.89	22.02	23.45	23.68	22.90	21.92	21.04	20.26	19.48	18.83	18.43	19.14	20.77
JH	20.0	20.18	19.68	19.18	18.93	19.08	19.70	20.51	21.25	21.57	21.56	21.31	21.01	20.64	20.26	19.86	19.68	19.55
UCLA	25.0	20.56	20.06	19.44	19.17	19.56	19.72	20.11	20.50	20.83	21.11	21.11	20.67	20.56	20.28	19.72	19.44	19.67
JH	40.0	20.62	20.54	20.38	20.26	20.10	20.02	19.96	20.06	20.16	20.34	20.44	20.52	20.52	20.48	20.40	20.36	19.95
JH	80.0	20.26	20.24	20.19	20.18	20.13	20.06	20.03	20.08	20.06	20.07	20.06	20.06	20.04	20.04	20.00	20.04	—

2.2.a. Soil thermal conductivity (mcal cm^{-1} sec^{-1} deg^{-1}) computed from soil thermistor response to defined heating pulses (University of Texas, Albrecht heat flux meter No. 2). Values are derived from 60-sec trials beginning at indicated CST.

Depth (cm)	7 September 0440	0635	0835	1035	1235	1435	1635	1835	2035	2235	8 September 1953 0035	0235	0435	0635	0835	1035	1235
0.5	0.57	0.58	0.60	0.61	0.61	0.61	0.60	0.57	0.54	0.55	0.58	0.58	0.58	0.58	0.61	0.64	0.64
1.5	0.65	0.62	0.62	0.62	0.63	0.63	0.62	0.62	0.59	0.59	0.59	0.59	0.59	0.59	0.62	0.66	0.69
2.5	0.92	0.91	0.90	0.90	0.90	0.87	0.84	0.81	0.80	0.84	0.85	0.84	0.85	0.84	0.88	0.87	0.89
3.5	0.95	0.95	0.95	0.96	0.95	0.95	0.93	0.90	0.89	0.90	0.89	0.90	0.90	0.89	0.91	0.90	0.90
4.5	0.98	1.00	1.01	1.01	1.02	1.00	0.97	0.96	0.94	0.95	0.96	0.99	0.98	0.98	0.98	0.96	0.98
5.5	1.10	1.08	1.08	1.08	1.09	1.10	1.11	1.12	1.11	1.10	1.08	1.08	1.08	1.08	1.10	1.15	1.16

2.2.b. Soil moisture (% wet weight) and density (g cm^{-3}) from soil samples at the Johns Hopkins University site. Indicated CST refers to the approximate time of soil sample extraction.

Depth (cm)	Soil Moisture 7 Sept. 0900	7 Sept. 1930	8 Sept. 1330	Soil Density 7 Sept. xx[1]	8 Sept. xx[1]
0 to 2.5	5.1	3.8	5.5	—	—
2 to 6	5.4	4.4	4.4	1.41	—
5 to 10	3.9	3.8	4.0	—	—
10	—	—	3.4[2]	—	—
10 to 16	3.1	—	—	1.46	—
20	—	—	3.8[2]	—	1.60
20 to 30	2.6	—	—	—	—
30 to 40	2.7	—	—	—	—
40	—	—	2.6[2]	—	1.84
40 to 50	2.9	—	—	—	—
50 to 60	2.8	—	—	—	—
60	—	—	3.1	—	1.92
60 to 70	2.0	—	—	—	—
70 to 80	2.8	—	—	—	—
80	—	—	5.5	—	1.66
90	—	—	7.2	—	—

[1] Not recorded. [2] Average value from two probes.

2.2.c. Soil heat capacity (cal cm^{-3} deg^{-1}) from soil samples at the University of Wisconsin site (calorimetric determination). Indicated CST refers to the approximate time of soil sample extraction (0-10 cm layer).

7 September 1953 1000	1100
0.40	0.33

2.3. Soil moisture tension (mb) from tensiometers (Johns Hopkins University). Values are readings at indicated CST.

Depth (cm)	7 September 0435	0635	0835	1035	1235	1435	1635	1835	2035	2235	8 September 1953 0035	0235	0435	0635	0835
5	488	488	457	446	457	468	494	541	561	560	557	555	554	553	528
10	463	433	434	518	605	653	690	716	715	703	685	668	653	639	625
20	511	467	439	467	544	609	655	692	705	702	690	674	660	645	620
40	235	102	48	66	145	223	424	513	558	572	564	550	520	489	448

2.4. Vertical flux of heat (mcal cm^{-2} min^{-1}) from soil temperature integrators (University of Wisconsin), Albrecht heat flux meter No. 2 (University of Texas-Al), and Gier and Dunkle heat flow meters (University of California; University of Texas-GD; Johns Hopkins University-GD). UW values are 60-min averages, UCLA values are 15-min averages, and UT and JH-GD values are approximately 2-min averages. All averages are centered at indicated CST.

Inst. Set	Depth (cm)	7 September										8 September 1953						
		0435	0635	0835	1035	1235	1435	1635	1835	2035	2235	0035	0235	0435	0635	0835	1035	1235
UW	0.0	−62	−34	50	120	136	94	19	−42	−40	−44	−46	−50	−56	−24	31	—	—
UT-Al	0.0[1]	−84	−141	110	307	313	202	29	−54	−56	−71	−70	−72	−60	−59	109	410	—
UCLA	0.2[2]	−79	−52	83	219	248	197	70	−41	−52	−58	−57	−62	−60	−50	83	220	296
UT-GD	0.2[2]	−63	−44	124	218	224	161	44	−42	−50	−54	−55	−58	−56	−43	120	238	251
UCLA	1.3	−43	−28	42	105	121	94	39	−13	−25	−29	−29	−33	−32	−28	46	115	150
UT-Al	2.0	−43	−35	23	94	118	87	32	−12	−26	−27	−31	−30	−38	−32	24	113	—
JH-GD	2.5	−37	−35	−7	42	72	67	35	−2	−20	−23	−27	−27	−27	−27	−3	48	73
UW	5.0	−47	−44	−10	44	77	84	54	9	−14	−23	−31	−35	−42	−31	−11	—	—
UCLA	10.0	−34	−35	−23	13	48	68	51	23	0	−11	−17	−20	−23	−25	−15	19	57
UW	15.0	−26	−32	−32	−10	12	36	42	34	16	3	−8	−12	−22	−20	−20	—	—

[1] Values are extrapolated to surface.   [2] Approximative depth; the upper plates of the flow meters were "just covered with soil".

M

3.1. Summary of data on radiation (mcal cm^{-2} min^{-1}). Short-wave radiation from two Eppley pyrheliometers (Johns Hopkins University and GRD); net radiation from two Gier and Dunkle radiometers (Johns Hopkins University and University of Texas) and the Suomi net radiometer (University of Wisconsin); total radiation from the Gier and Dunkle radiometer (University of Texas). Values are hourly averages centered at indicated CST.

	Inst. Set	7 September 0435	0635	0835	1035	1235	1435	1635	1835	2035	2235	8 September 1953 0035	0235	0435	0635	0835	1035	1235
(Short-Wave)	JH	0	60	640	1150	1340	1160	680	80	0	0	0	0	0	50	600	1120	1320
	GRD	0	77	632	1085	1247	1052	583	63	0	0	0	0	0	63	607	1057	1237
	GRD[1]	0	70	630	1090	1250	1060	580	50	0	0	0	0	0	60	620	1070	1230
(Net)	JH	−60	−50	260	610	740	620	280	−70	−100	−80	−80	−70	−70	−50	210	480	620
	UT	−67	−25	356	824	915	713	154	−121	−127	−112	−106	−108	−95	−79	373	826	838
	UW	−77	−47	259[2]	577[2]	700	570	221	−99	−110	−99	−95	−89	−80	−45	276	582	—
(Total)	UT	439[3]	493	1128	1752	1940	1694	1108	510	463	459	451	441	445	597	1165	1716	1946

[1] 10-min average centered at indicated CST.
[2] Calibration points of net radiometer against Eppley pyrheliometer; values agree to within 1 per cent.
[3] 10-min average centered at indicated CST.

3.2. Boundary shear-stress (dynes cm^{-2}) from drag recorder (University of California) and Sheppard-type drag plate (Johns Hopkins University); direction of boundary shear-stress (deg from North) from drag recorder (University of California). Values are 10-min means centered at indicated CST.

Inst. Set	7 September										8 September 1953					
	0435	0635	0835	1035	1235	1435	1635	1835	2035	2235	0035	0235	0435	0635	0835	1035
UCLA	0.11	0.38	1.80[1]	—	—	—	—	1.38[2]	1.75	0.97[3]	1.03	0.71	0.69	0.71[4]	1.25	1.51
JH	0.03	0.2	0.7	1.3	1.4	1.4	1.5	0.8	0.8	0.4	0.4	0.25	0.25	0.25	0.5	—
UCLA	171	172	182[1]	—	—	—	—	188[2]	180	190[3]	186	185	189	178[4]	172	196

[1] For time interval 0834-0844.   [3] For time interval 2232-2256.
[2] For time interval 1831-1846.   [4] For time interval 0631-0640.

3.3. Characteristics of low level smoke-puff drift (Johns Hopkins University); direction of drift (deg from North); time t_{25} (sec) required to cross 25 m circle; lateral width S (deg) at 25 m and time t_D (sec) required to reach threshold of visibility. Values are ensemble averages for 10 smoke puffs fired at approximately 1-min intervals beginning at indicated CST.

	7 September									8 September 1953					
	0400	0600	0800	1000	1200	1400	1600	1800	2000	2200	0000	0200	0400	0600	0800	1000
dd	0	355	13	10	6	358	8	11	1	353	8	6	5	6	352	27
t_{25}	11.4	10.3	4.7	3.9	3.4	3.8	4.0	4.9	4.8	5.6	5.4	5.8	6.8	8.3	5.4	4.5
S	13.9	12.4	11.6	12.3	13.5	12.3	14.0	14.9	18.5	12.4	14.2	13.2	15.7	16.0	11.7	10.8
t_D	—	—	17	13	10	13	10	16	—	—	—	—	—	41	22	17

3.4. Characteristics of surface pressure variations from micro-barograms (GRD, Paulin-type aneroid system); trend (WBAN Synoptic Code number); qualitative index of micro-variations ("a" = calm to "d" = very unruly); trace ratio (trace length relative to trend length); trend ratio (trend length relative to chart length); period (min), amplitude (10^{-2} mb) and number of perceptible waves. Values refer to 2-hr intervals centered at indicated CST.

	7 September			8 September 1953			
	1135[1]	1335	1535[1]	0535[3]	0735	0935	1135
Trend	7	7	6	2	8	7	7
Index	c-d	d	d	a	a-b	b-c	c
Trace ratio	1.4	1.3	1.8	1.3	1.6	1.5	1.4
Trend ratio	1.6	1.6	1.6	1.1	1.0	1.05	1.2
Period	—[2]	—[2]	—[2]	30	30	20	50
Ampl.	—	—	—	3.5	5	4	4
Number	—	—	—	2	1	4	1
Period	—	—	—	—	5	15	10
Ampl.	—	—	—	—	4	4	3.5
Number	—	—	—	—	5	1	2

[1] Instrumental failure before 1135 and after 1535.   [2]Analysis unreliable.
[3] Instrumental failure before 0535.

3.5. Dew desposition data (GRD); Taylor dew gauge trace characteristics and Duvdevani dew block scale numbers. Values are readings at indicated CST.

Inst. Set	Height (cm)	7 September				8 September 1953					
		0435	0535	0635	—	2035	2235	0035	0235	0435	0605
Gauge	7	#[1]	#	#[2]	—	O	O	O	O	#[4]	#[5]
Block	100	—[3]	Tr.	1	—	O	O	O	O	O	O
Block	50	—	Tr.	2	—	O	O	O	O	O	Tr.
Block	8	—	Tr.	2	—	O	O	O	O	O	1
Block	2.5	—	1	3	—	O	O	O	Tr.	1	3a

[1] Beginning of trace 2100 CST.   [4] Beginning of trace 0340 CST.
[2] End of trace 0800 CST.   [5] End of trace 0630 CST.
[3] Blocks first exposed at 0435 CST.

4.1.a. Hourly mean wind speed (cm/sec) from standard three-cup anemometers (Mass. Inst. Tech.), modified Sheppard-type anemometers (University of California), ping-pong ball anemometers (Iowa State College), and modified SCS cup anemometers (Johns Hopkins University); centered at indicated CST.

Set	Height (m)	7 September 0435	0635	0835	1035	1235	1435	1635	1835	2035	2235	8 September 1953 0035	0235	0435	0635	0835	1035	1235
MIT	16.0	510	518	786	1048	1161	1086	1078	800	853	728	706	647	600	541	613	682	472
MIT	8.0	359	410	726	971	1072	1005	980	700	742	610	583	521	478	454	575	641	447
UCLA	8.0	382	416	772	1019	1114	1044	1034	—	787	627	600	543	506	476	613	662	—
ISC	7.0	345	396	727	941	1006	993	958	688	734	600	569	511	462	439	580	627	437
JH	6.4	328	346	714	939	1019	997	930	714	710	562	564	489	462	442	562	640	435
UCLA	4.15	270	344	696	920	1005	946	928	637	686	541	520	458	429	414	562	608	—
MIT	4.0	252	338	666	892	985	922	892	622	659	535	508	446	407	400	529	600	417
ISC	4.0	247	328	661	862	974	911	868	611	653	527	495	435	393	386	532	578	402
JH	3.2	225	276	651	852	930	908	847	638	634	493	495	415	—	—	—	—	—
MIT	2.0	193	291	598	801	881	825	800	551	580	472	437	381	353	355	481	546	394
UCLA	2.0	192	284	610	804	875	831	796	546	596	466	447	388	358	354	496	542	—
JH	1.6	176	237	582	767	836	815	757	562	557	435	435	356	340	332	468	537	374
UCLA	1.0	148	242	527	696	758	719	688	468	508	398	383	329	306	304	432	472	—
ISC	1.0	161	234	514	680	765	714	673	464	497	400	368	319	288	293	422	461	335
JH	0.8	138	199	506	672	734	716	662	491	485	376	376	306	292	290	411	471	336
UCLA	0.5	120	208	454	602	660	622	609	424	436	342	330	282	264	262	374	413	—
JH	0.4	116	168	427	566	621	605	559	413	409	316	318	255	243	243	348	399	290

4.1.b. 15-min mean wind speed (cm/sec) from standard three-cup anemometers (Mass. Inst. Tech.), modified Sheppard-type anemometers (University of California), ping-pong ball anemometers (Iowa State College) and semi-cylindrical anemometers (Johns Hopkins University); centered at indicated CST.

Inst. Set	Height (m)	7 September										8 September 1953						
		0435	0635	0835	1035	1235	1435	1635	1835	2035	2235	0035	0235	0435	0635	0835	1035	1235
MIT	16.0	534	540	740	1058	1172	1118	1118	780	878	703	733	645	611	557	622	645	481
MIT	8.0	372	432	682	980	1081	1041	1014	693	774	588	605	524	483	476	584	605	459
UCLA	8.0	391	401	722	1020	1110	1044	995	—	812	606	626	544	517	502	611	676	479
ISC	7.0	359	406	723	942	1078	1024	967	667	742	573	601	517	463	465	611	606	450
UCLA	4.15	277	333	652	924	1002	940	894	652	712	527	545	460	437	434	560	624	442
MIT	4.0	263	338	618	902	993	956	919	622	689	513	527	453	412	415	544	571	430
ISC	4.0	260	338	655	867	992	937	877	590	660	500	519	444	394	409	558	559	417
JH	3.2	—	—	—	736	—	849	767	542	612	435	439	363	349	356	482	—	—
MIT	2.0	203	311	551	807	885	855	821	547	608	453	456	392	355	368	493	527	405
UCLA	2.0	196	277	571	806	868	831	782	561	612	446	466	391	370	374	502	556	402
JH	1.6	—	—	488	647	—	—	—	—	528	366	369	295	284	—	420	—	—
UCLA	1.0	150	237	494	696	752	716	679	477	523	378	400	334	314	324	430	479	358
ISC	1.0	160	245	508	683	784	730	684	441	505	377	390	326	289	314	435	445	350
JH	0.8	—	—	431	551	583	638	—	402	449	319	325	265	253	264	—	—	—
UCLA	0.5	132	202	428	603	655	620	588	412	550	325	342	284	270	279	372	418	320
JH	0.4	—	—	372	481	536	546	482	344	—	258	244	226	215	228	311	—	—
JH	0.2	—	—	297	394	443	442	378	286	—	226	225	188	182	192	260	—	—
JH	0.1	—	—	—	—	—	257	—	225	236	178	182	135	116	143	200	—	—
JH	0.05	—	—	125	228	254	—	225	—	—	—	—	—	—	—	—	—	—

4.2. Mean air temperature (°C) from aspirated thermocouples (Mass. Inst. Tech., 15-min means; University of California, average of six readings taken every 3 min), shielded thermocouples (Johns Hopkins University, average of 20 readings at each level during a 5-min interval) and shielded thermistors (University of Texas, 10-sec means); centered at indicated CST.

Inst. Set	Height (m)	7 September 0435	0635	0835	1035	1235	1435	1635	1835	2035	2235	8 September 1953 0035	0235	0435	0635	0835	1035	1235
MIT	16.0	13.29	10.64	16.60	21.07	24.18	26.47	26.77	24.04	20.64	17.49	16.58	15.14	13.68	13.24	17.55	22.84	26.62
MIT	8.0	11.41	10.26	16.75	21.30	24.52	26.67	26.91	23.95	20.49	17.27	16.33	14.82	13.32	13.10	17.79	23.14	26.84
UCLA	8.0	10.89	9.50	15.67	20.44	25.00	26.39	26.89	23.67	20.22	17.06	16.11	13.94	12.72	12.44	17.00	21.56	26.56
JH	6.4	10.54	10.03	16.66	21.22	24.63	26.40	26.49	23.91	20.13	17.32	16.06	14.24	12.90	12.66	17.40	22.78	26.03
MIT	4.0	10.29	10.05	16.96	21.62	24.90	26.99	27.07	23.87	20.36	17.14	16.16	14.61	13.09	13.00	18.06	23.48	27.35
UCLA	4.0	9.72	9.50	16.06	20.83	25.00	27.17	27.11	23.61	20.00	16.94	15.94	13.72	12.50	12.33	17.44	22.28	26.67
JH	3.2	9.67	9.90	16.90	21.82	25.30	26.88	26.79	23.79	20.03	17.12	15.90	14.09	12.75	12.60	18.02	23.28	26.49
MIT	2.0	9.60	9.90	17.30	22.40	25.80	27.80	27.50	23.70	20.20	17.00	16.00	14.40	12.90	12.90	18.50	24.10	28.00
UCLA	2.0	8.72	9.17	16.56	21.50	25.56	27.50	27.22	23.61	19.83	16.78	15.61	13.33	12.22	12.06	18.33	23.22	27.17
JH	1.6	9.17	9.81	17.10	22.34	25.66	27.30	26.99	23.63	19.91	16.96	15.75	13.92	12.53	12.52	18.39	23.84	27.51
UCLA	1.0	8.44	8.67	16.28	22.06	26.39	28.28	28.28	23.33	19.56	16.61	15.56	13.11	11.94	11.78	17.78	24.00	28.28
JH	0.8	8.79	9.73	17.50	22.66	26.53	28.06	27.28	23.54	19.78	16.82	15.61	13.75	12.41	12.43	18.67	24.56	27.80
UT	0.8	9.35	10.2	17.25	24.35	27.35	28.65	27.7	22.9	19.5	16.75	15.8	14.0	13.1	13.2	19.5	24.6	29.1
UCLA	0.5	8.17	9.00	16.50	22.61	27.61	29.44	28.33	23.17	19.50	16.39	15.39	12.89	12.22	11.94	18.06	24.28	29.50
UT	0.5	9.25	9.95	18.25	24.15	27.05	29.30	28.0	23.0	19.2	16.6	15.6	13.85	13.0	13.0	19.3	25.8	29.55
JH	0.4	8.51	9.66	17.90	23.22	27.31	28.62	27.56	23.41	19.64	16.63	15.43	13.55	12.26	12.32	19.12	25.41	28.96
UT	0.3	9.05	10.1	18.65	24.8	27.25	30.45	28.15	22.85	19.2	16.6	15.5	14.0	13.0	13.2	19.75	26.75	30.0
JH	0.2	8.27	9.54	18.22	23.90	28.16	29.04	27.86	23.26	19.48	16.45	15.27	13.43	12.11	12.28	19.63	26.29	30.05
JH	0.1	8.10	9.49	18.80	24.93	28.72	29.98	28.15	23.12	19.34	16.34	15.15	13.27	11.98	12.20	20.02	26.93	31.09
UT	0.1	8.6	10.25	19.5	25.35	30.25	30.7	28.6	22.8	19.05	16.15	15.3	13.5	12.6	12.95	20.95	27.5	32.95

4.3.a. Mean water vapor pressure (mb) from dew-point apparatus (Johns Hopkins University). Simultaneous air sampling at given intake levels. Values are 5-min averages centered at indicated CST.

Height (m)	7 September 1953 0435	0635[1]
6.4	9.64	11.26
3.2	9.42	11.24
1.6	9.39	11.17
0.8	9.36	11.06
0.4	9.36	11.10
0.2	9.32	11.15
0.1	9.30	11.25

[1] No data after 0635 due to instrumental failure.

4.3.b. Mean vertical difference (between 82 and 39 cm) of dry-bulb temperature $(10^{-3}\,°C)$ and water vapor pressure $(10^{-3}\,mb)$ from double psychrometer lift-apparatus (University of Wisconsin). Values are hourly means (based on one sample every 10 min) centered at indicated CST.

	7 September										8 September 1953					
	0435	0635	0835	1035	1235	1435	1635	1835	2035	2235	0035	0235	0435	0635	0835	1035
$10^{-3}\,°C$	437	61	−502	−737	−765	−661	−370	108	148	119	136	132	134	38	−475	−758
$10^{-3}\,mb$	198	5	−151	−180	−143	−46	−57	22	24	9	−19	−60	−5	−70	−99	−184

4.4. Mean ozone concentration $(10^{-8}\,g\,O_3/g\,air)$ from automatic ozone recorders (University of New Mexico). Values are 60-min means estimated from traces on chart recorders centered at indicated CST.

Height (m)	7 September										8 September 1953					
	0430	0630	0830	1030	1230	1430	1630	1830	2030	2230	0030	0230	0430	0630	0830	1030
12.5	2.2	—	—	4.4	5.5	5.3	5.5	5.2	4.6	4.0	3.7	3.4	—	—	—	5.3
6.25	1.6	1.6	3.2	4.3	5.3	5.2	5.3	5.2	4.5	3.8	3.6	3.1	2.8	2.7	3.7	5.4
1.6	1.6	1.6	3.0	4.4	5.3	5.1	5.2	5.2	4.4	3.8	3.4	3.0	2.8	2.7	3.6	5.3
0.4	1.1	1.5	3.2	4.3	5.2	5.1	5.1	4.9	4.2	3.5	3.2	2.8	2.4	2.5	3.6	5.3

5.1. Standard deviation of temperature fluctuations (10^{-2} °C) from fast-response thermocouples (Mass. Inst. Tech., one sample per sec during 11-min periods) and bead thermistors (Iowa State College, 10 samples per sec during 10-min periods). Periods are centered at indicated CST.

Inst. Set	Height (m)	7 September										8 September 1953						
		0435	0635	0835	1035	1235	1435	1635	1835	2035	2235	0035	0235	0435	0635	0835	1035	1235
MIT	12.0	20	9	42	24	—	—	14	17	7	9	7	13	12	9	24	43	47
ISC	8.0	33	16	—	81	109[1]	97	58	29	59	22	31	27	22	—	43	108	108
MIT	6.0	11	12	48	35	—	—	23	16	8	9	10	11	10	9	31	71	75
ISC	4.0	30	17	67	97	118[1]	118	57	28	55	24	27	—	18	—	58	126	136
MIT	3.0	20	13	56	53	—	—	32	22	17	15	15	15	14	12	45	79	95
ISC	2.0	27	18	64	100	112[1]	116	55	28	46	24	28	25	19	—	79	120	167
MIT	1.5	20	13	46	35	—	—	25	24	14	12	13	12	12	12	47	61	81
ISC	1.0	25	18	69	110	132[1]	136	—	25	47	23	28	25	18	—	83	122	187
ISC	0.5	25	18	63	113	110[1]	119	51	23	41	27	28	23	19	—	84	129	202
ISC	0.25	25	—	—	118	132[1]	120	58	19	41	28	28	17	20	—	86	129	209

[1] From interpolated values in the calibration reduction.

5.2.a. Statistics of fluctuations quantities from 1-sec samplings of fast-response probes (Mass. Inst. Tech.). Total air speed V (cm/sec); standard deviation of horizontal (parallel and perpendicular to 10-min mean wind) and vertical eddy components $S(u)$, $S(v)$, and $S(w)$ (cm/sec); gustiness ratios $G(x)$, $G(y)$, and $G(z)$; mean cross products of eddy components $\overline{uv}$, $\overline{vw}$, and $\overline{uw}$ (cm^2 sec^{-2}); horizontal Reynolds' stress (parallel to 10-min mean wind) τ (dynes cm^{-2}); linear correlation coefficients between eddy components and air temperature (u,v), (v,w), (u,w), $(u;T)$, $(v;T)$, and $(w;T)$; mean cross product of vertical eddy component and air temperature multiplied by density and specific heat of air Q (mcal cm^{-2} min^{-1}). Values are 10-min means or totals centered at indicated CST.

Date	CST	Height	V	$S(u)$	$S(v)$	$S(w)$	$G(x)$	$G(y)$	$G(z)$	$\overline{uv}$	$\overline{vw}$	$\overline{uw}$	τ	(u,v)	$(v;w)$	(u,w)	$(u;T)$	$(v;T)$	$(w;T)$	Q
1953 7 Sept.	0435	12.0	458	22	32	8	.05	.07	.02	−440	0	−30	0.0	−0.63	0.00	−0.17	0.68	−0.31	0.00	0
		6.0	314	26	42	9	.08	.13	.03	−480	−70		0.0	−0.44	−0.19	0.00	0.35	0.22	0.00	0
		3.0	229	19	23	5	.08	.10	.02	50	0	−10	0.0	0.11	0.00	−0.10	0.26	0.65	0.00	0
		1.5	175	21	24	5	.12	.14	.03	40	40	−10	0.0	0.08	0.33	−0.10	0.24	0.63	0.00	0
	0635	12.0	483	42	35	27	.09	.07	.06	−140	20	−170	0.2	−0.10	0.02	−0.15	0.53	0.00	0.00	0
		6.0	399	44	16	29	.11	.04	.07	10	−20	−50	0.1	0.01	−0.04	−0.04	0.19	0.00	0.00	0
		3.0	333	47	41	23	.14	.12	.07	270	−40	−90	0.1	0.14	−0.04	−0.08	0.33	0.19	0.00	0
		1.5	282	46	23	22	.16	.08	.08	0	−20	−40	0.0	0.00	−0.04	−0.04	0.17	0.33	0.00	0
	0835	12.0	709	99	99	63	.14	.14	.09	−780	−490	−2180	2.5	−0.08	−0.08	−0.35	−0.07	0.22	0.19	84
		6.0	651	95	80	52	.15	.12	.08	−810	−150	−1340	1.5	−0.11	−0.04	−0.27	−0.33	0.13	0.20	84
		3.0	573	91	103	45	.16	.18	.08	710	−90	−1240	1.4	0.08	−0.02	−0.30	−0.39	0.10	0.24	96
		1.5	515	93	84	41	.18	.16	.08	−1540	−130	−1130	1.3	−0.20	−0.04	−0.25	−0.26	0.16	0.05	18
	1035	12.0	1009	166	144	74	.16	.13	.07	690	−930	−3400	3.8	0.03	−0.09	−0.28	−0.23	−0.20	0.34	96
		6.0	943	163	117	61	.17	.12	.07	2960	30	−2370	2.7	0.16	0.00	−0.24	−0.26	−0.24	0.19	66
		3.0	854	150	144	61	.18	.17	.07	950	230	−2270	2.5	0.04	0.03	−0.25	−0.39	−0.17	0.19	96
		1.5	743	150	131	58	.20	.18	.08	−560	440	−2990	3.3	−0.03	0.06	−0.34	−0.15	−0.15	0.10	30
	1635	12.0	1044	184	137	78	.17	.13	.07	470	−610	−4660	5.1	0.02	−0.06	−0.32	−0.39	−0.05	0.18	30
		6.0	967	137	119	62	.14	.12	.06	110	630	−2570	2.8	0.01	0.09	−0.30	−0.48	−0.11	0.14	30
		3.0	866	158	108	54	.18	.12	.06	910	180	−2760	3.0	0.05	0.03	−0.32	−0.61	−0.03	0.17	48
		1.5	757	156	135	60	.21	.18	.08	−1400	500	−1840	3.1	−0.07	0.06	−0.30	−0.49	0.00	0.07	18
	1835	12.0	724	101	74	51	.14	.10	.07	900	−130	−1480	1.6	0.12	−0.03	−0.29	0.23	0.16	−0.12	−18
		6.0	651	99	63	38	.15	.10	.06	250	−200	−1000	1.1	0.04	−0.08	−0.27	0.32	0.20	0.00	0
		3.0	583	96	55	42	.16	.09	.07	1050	−200	−1370	1.5	0.20	−0.09	−0.34	0.57	0.17	−0.11	−18
		1.5	490	95	70	36	.19	.14	.07	620	−150	−1120	1.2	0.09	−0.06	−0.33	0.44	0.12	−0.12	−18

Date	CST	Height	V	S(u)	S(v)	S(w)	G(x)	G(y)	G(z)	ūv	v̄w	ūw	τ	(u,v)	(v,w)	(u,w)	(u,T)	(v,T)	(w,T)	Q
	2035	12.0	825	102	84	61	.12	.10	.07	-160	-50	-1050	1.2	-0.02	-0.01	-0.17	0.28	-0.17	-0.23	-18
		6.0	743	108	60	47	.15	.03	.06	900	170	-1050	1.2	0.14	0.06	-0.21	0.46	0.00	-0.27	-18
		3.0	657	106	79	48	.16	.12	.07	940	-210	-1360	1.5	0.11	-0.06	-0.27	0.55	0.00	-0.12	-18
		1.5	556	108	69	45	.19	.12	.08	350	100	-1740	2.0	-0.05	0.03	-0.36	0.40	-0.10	0.00	0
	2235	12.0	652	69	55	42	.11	.08	.06	-10	40	-920	1.0	0.00	0.02	-0.32	0.32	0.00	-0.26	-18
		6.0	554	69	31	31	.12	.06	.06	0	-40	-710	0.8	0.00	-0.04	-0.33	0.48	0.00	-0.36	-18
		3.0	489	73	39	33	.15	.08	.07	380	0	-860	1.0	0.13	0.00	-0.36	0.46	0.17	-0.20	-18
		1.5	413	67	48	29	.16	.12	.07	-80	90	-680	0.8	-0.03	0.07	-0.35	0.37	0.00	-0.29	-18
1953 8 Sept.	0035	12.0	656	72	59	44	.11	.09	.07	-710	-10	-670	0.8	-0.17	0.00	-0.21	0.40	0.00	0.00	0
		6.0	571	75	57	35	.13	.10	.06	510	290	-630	0.7	0.12	0.15	-0.24	0.40	0.00	0.29	-18
		3.0	498	70	38	32	.14	.08	.06	30	40	-560	0.6	0.01	0.03	-0.25	0.57	0.00	-0.21	-18
		1.5	412	69	48	32	.17	.12	.08	-130	70	-600	0.7	-0.04	0.05	-0.27	0.67	-0.16	0.00	0
	0235	12.0	574	56	54	32	.10	.09	.06	20	50	-410	0.5	0.01	0.03	-0.23	0.55	0.14	-0.24	-18
		6.0	481	55	37	28	.11	.08	.06	160	-60	-440	0.5	0.08	-0.06	-0.29	0.50	0.25	-0.32	-18
		3.0	431	57	34	29	.13	.08	.07	160	-10	-400	0.5	0.08	-0.01	-0.24	0.58	0.00	-0.23	-18
		1.5	353	56	42	25	.16	.12	.07	-130	0	-360	0.4	-0.06	0.00	-0.26	0.45	0.00	0.00	0
	0435	12.0	545	55	44	35	.13	.08	.06	110	40	-390	0.4	0.05	0.03	-0.22	0.30	0.00	0.00	0
		6.0	442	54	35	32	.12	.08	.06	150	-10	-370	0.4	0.08	-0.01	-0.25	0.37	0.00	0.00	0
		3.0	394	53	33	26	.13	.08	.07	320	0	-150	0.2	0.18	0.00	-0.11	0.54	0.22	0.00	0
		1.5	322	56	36	24	.17	.11	.08	90	-60	-270	0.3	0.05	-0.07	-0.20	0.45	0.00	0.00	0
	0635	12.0	520	65	66	35	.13	.13	.07	660	-70	-320	0.4	0.15	-0.03	-0.14	0.00	0.00	0.00	0
		6.0	446	55	29	32	.12	.07	.07	140	-90	-310	0.4	0.09	-0.10	-0.18	0.20	0.00	0.00	0
		3.0	397	61	48	28	.15	.12	.07	480	-30	-450	0.5	0.16	-0.02	-0.26	0.27	0.22	0.00	0
		1.5	334	54	41	27	.16	.12	.08	190	50	-360	0.4	0.09	0.05	-0.25	0.15	0.00	0.00	0
	0835	12.0	604	73	74	49	.12	.12	.08	-690	-320	-1120	1.3	-0.13	-0.09	-0.31	0.00	-0.23	0.17	30
		6.0	560	76	69	35	.13	.12	.06	450	-120	-600	0.7	0.09	-0.05	-0.23	-0.34	-0.14	0.28	48
		3.0	525	80	84	36	.15	.16	.07	-280	140	-830	0.9	-0.04	0.05	-0.29	-0.44	-0.05	0.25	66
		1.5	450	80	67	36	.18	.15	.08	-100	-60	-1020	1.1	-0.02	-0.03	-0.35	-0.40	0.00	0.12	30
	1035	12.0	617	103	112	63	.17	.18	.10	-1149	-49	-1960	2.2	-0.10	-0.01	-0.30	0.07	-0.17	0.44	198
		6.0	582	106	115	46	.18	.20	.08	-1180	-190	-1020	2.1	-0.10	-0.04	-0.21	-0.27	-0.05	0.43	228
		3.0	550	100	89	48	.18	.16	.07	-470	10	-1080	1.2	-0.05	0.00	-0.27	-0.32	0.00	0.32	162
		1.5	476	95	90	39	.20	.19	.08	-370	-160	-1360	1.5	-0.04	-0.05	-0.37	-0.21	-0.02	0.17	66
	1235	12.0	459	105	96	43	.23	.21	.09	1350	-270	-680	0.7	0.13	-0.07	-0.15	-0.02	-0.16	0.45	144
		6.0	432	114	92	43	.26	.21	.10	2030	220	-350	0.4	0.19	0.06	-0.07	-0.14	-0.03	0.50	252
		3.0	409	110	93	33	.27	.23	.08	1040	320	-910	1.0	0.10	0.10	-0.25	-0.09	0.16	0.38	186
		1.5	368	94	89	28	.26	.24	.08	1500	50	-610	0.7	0.18	0.02	-0.23	0.11	0.01	0.22	78

5.2.b. Standard deviation $S(u)$, $S(w)$ of eddy components (in the direction of the estimated mean wind, u, and the vertical; cm/sec) and gustiness ratios $G(x)$, $G(z)$, from rotating pressure tube anemometer (Texas A & M College); one sample per sec during 5-min periods centered at indicated CST.

Date (1953)	CST	Height (m)	u	$S(u)$	$S(w)$	$G(x)$	$G(z)$
7 Sept.	0435	3.1	313	33	9	0.11	0.029
	0632	3.1	487	35	9	0.14	0.018
	0832	3.1	589	50	11	0.12	0.019
	1232	3.1	762	110	21	0.14	0.028
	1432	3.1	650	158	24	0.24	0.037
7 Sept.	1632	3.1	545	144	29	0.26	0.053
	1832	3.1	470	107	30	0.23	0.064
	2033	3.1	637	107	20	0.17	0.031
	2232	3.1	649	52	16	0.08	0.025
8 Sept.	0038	3.1	666	57	16	0.09	0.024
	0232	3.1	542	52	16	0.10	0.030
	0432	3.1	509	56	15	0.11	0.030
	0632	3.1	469	56	15	0.12	0.032

6.1.a. Loeser technique of daytime wind profile measurements (GRD). Mean height Z (m); duration t (sec) of evaluated drift; mean West, South, and upward components u, v, w (m/sec) of drift of individual smoke puffs. Values are t-sec averages centered at indicated CST$+t/2$ sec.

7 September 1953

CST	Z	t	u	v	w	CST	Z	t	u	v	w	CST	Z	t	u	v	w
0630	1145	120	5.0	2.7	0.2	0635	1292	84	6.7	3.3	0.5	0640	1226	120	6.0	2.9	0.3
	932	120	5.1	3.2	0.2		1080	120	4.5	2.5	0.3		991	120	4.4	2.7	0.4
	781	120	6.0	5.3	0.2		921	120	4.8	3.2	0.2		801	120	5.7	4.9	0.4
	649	96	4.9	7.8	0.2		790	120	5.8	5.0	0.3		629	96	4.9	8.3	0.4
	531	78	3.8	10.4	0.2		647	78	4.7	7.7	0.1		392	90	3.0	12.9	0.3
	434	78	3.1	12.1	0.2		548	66	3.8	10.8	0.3		287	96	2.4	13.3	0.3
	343	78	1.9	12.3	0.2		387	114	2.6	12.5	0.1		195	42	0.0	13.4	−0.1
	268	72	2.2	13.2	0.2		315	72	2.2	13.3	0.3		126	12	0.6	13.8	0.2
	195	12	1.0	13.0	1.0		269	114	1.5	13.4	0.2						
							223	54	0.5	13.5	0.3						
							181	48	0.4	14.0	0.1						
0830	1052	120	5.4	8.2	0.0	0835	1156	96	5.2	8.0	0.3	0840	1307	120	6.8	6.2	0.2
	874	120	6.4	9.5	0.1		958	90	5.6	9.2	0.2		1095	120	5.4	8.2	0.2
	743	120	7.4	10.5	0.2								916	120	5.8	9.3	0.1
	615	120	6.2	11.6	0.1								757	120	7.2	10.8	0.1
	525	120	5.4	13.5	0.2								648	120	6.1	11.7	0.1
	421	108	5.2	14.0	0.0								539	120	5.7	13.7	0.1
	348	108	4.9	15.0	0.2								433	120	5.4	14.2	0.0
	284	96	2.8	14.8	0.1								327	114	4.1	16.2	−0.2
	213	36	2.0	11.3	0.1								261	24	0.8	12.2	−0.5
	165	36	1.8	10.8	−0.1								239	36	1.1	9.1	0.6
	128	12	3.1	8.8	0.7								185	30	1.3	8.9	0.4
													147	12	1.5	9.9	0.9

CST	Z	t	u	v	w
1030	1229	72	10.1	6.3	0.3
	1021	66	8.6	8.8	0.5
1230	1279	120	7.4	5.7	−0.1
	1065	114	10.8	10.8	0.0
	747	108	7.1	15.0	−0.2
	642	108	4.6	14.3	−0.2
	551	102	3.1	13.9	0.6
	478	60	1.6	15.0	0.4
	400	90	0.3	14.4	0.4
1430	1254	120	9.3	9.5	−0.4
	1094	72	1.0	12.0	1.4
	1043	84	0.1	11.2	1.5
	855	84	0.6	13.3	1.5
	704	90	0.7	12.9	1.3
	576	90	−0.7	13.3	0.8
	474	102	−0.7	12.3	0.3
	377	42	−0.7	12.0	0.1
	324	42	0.9	12.6	0.3
	293	42	0.0	12.5	0.8
	245	42	−0.4	12.4	0.8
	150	36	−1.4	12.5	−0.9
1630	1509	102	8.3	7.6	0.0
	1294	120	9.1	10.9	−0.1
	1104	120	6.3	12.3	−0.5
	963	120	5.2	12.9	−0.5
	857	120	4.6	12.8	−0.2
	754	120	4.0	13.4	0.0
	672	114	3.8	13.0	0.0
	524	114	3.5	13.7	−1.2
	508	114	2.5	13.9	0.1
	392	90	1.5	14.1	−0.4
	350	96	1.3	13.7	−0.3
1830	1172	120	3.6	9.3	0.0
	947	120	5.1	12.0	0.2
	780	120	3.7	12.7	0.2
	633	90	2.6	13.2	−0.1
	526	90	1.8	13.5	0.4
	389	12	0.5	13.0	0.3

8 September 1953

CST	Z	t	u	v	w
0630	1183	120	0.2	−1.0	0.2
	989	78	4.1	0.5	0.1
	829	108	7.0	4.2	0.0
	685	120	8.9	8.6	0.1

CST	Z	t	u	v	w
1035	1333	48	9.6	3.3	0.6
	1159	78	10.1	7.0	0.5
	1026	108	8.5	8.8	0.7
	773	120	7.1	12.2	0.6
	642	108	7.1	13.5	0.4
	485	36	3.1	12.6	−0.4
	425	48	1.7	11.0	−0.1
	374	96	1.7	11.9	0.4
1235	1341	120	6.6	4.7	0.0
	1108	120	9.5	9.5	0.1
	938	120	10.2	11.8	0.1
	784	120	7.7	13.9	−0.1
	713	72	5.1	12.3	0.2
	600	120	4.7	12.5	0.2
	531	102	4.0	13.2	0.3
	454	120	2.4	13.1	0.5
	377	114	2.4	13.9	0.4
	312	114	1.8	13.7	0.1
	259	60	1.1	13.0	0.3
	202	84	0.2	12.3	0.0
1435	1392	114	7.0	7.2	−0.8
	1136	120	8.4	10.2	−1.5
	1076	96	3.5	12.4	0.0
	942	114	2.9	12.4	0.3
	815	120	2.8	12.0	0.4
	693	120	2.6	11.4	0.0
	581	114	2.1	11.4	0.2
	458	84	3.0	12.0	−0.3
1635	1677	120	8.6	6.3	0.5
	1462	120	10.5	9.2	0.3
	1241	120	5.6	13.0	0.1
	1078	120	5.4	13.7	0.2
	855	102	4.6	14.5	1.1
	692	78	2.4	12.7	1.6
1835	1281	120	10.9	6.0	0.4
	1046	120	8.4	10.9	0.4
	730	120	4.1	13.2	0.2
	596	90	2.5	13.4	0.0
	488	90	2.3	14.0	−0.3
	394	24	1.8	14.8	0.0
0635	1436	120	0.7	−1.1	0.3
	1219	120	−0.1	−1.2	0.3
	896	96	5.4	0.2	0.2
	776	114	7.8	5.2	0.2

CST	Z	t	u	v	w
1240	1376	120	6.5	5.4	−0.1
	925	114	10.5	11.9	0.0
	748	114	6.2	12.9	−0.5
	567	72	3.5	13.1	−1.2
	616	102	3.5	11.2	1.5
	459	72	3.0	12.2	0.6
	343	54	1.4	12.2	−0.2
	250	78	0.1	12.4	0.0
	224	78	−0.1	13.5	0.6
	130	12	0.4	13.2	−1.0
	98	36	0.9	12.9	−0.3
1440	1578	120	6.2	6.9	−0.2
	1305	120	8.3	9.1	−0.9
	1165	78	6.2	11.3	−0.7
	980	120	2.7	12.9	−0.6
	853	120	3.2	13.3	−0.3
	667	120	3.3	13.6	−1.0
	553	108	2.5	13.3	−0.6
	425	96	2.4	13.0	−1.2
	413	54	2.4	13.0	−1.0
	329	66	2.0	13.4	−1.2
	291	66	1.1	13.2	−1.1
	239	66	1.1	13.7	−1.2
1640	1684	108	7.8	7.3	0.7
	1436	120	9.5	8.9	0.7
	1197	120	6.7	12.6	0.2
	1020	114	3.6	13.2	0.1
	806	120	3.2	12.5	−0.9
	696	120	2.7	12.6	−0.6
	538	30	1.0	13.2	−1.2
	505	30	0.2	12.4	−0.3
1840	1607	120	10.4	8.4	0.5
	1375	120	10.4	5.6	0.4
	1196	102	11.4	6.3	0.4
	1024	96	9.0	10.7	0.3
	780	60	4.8	12.8	0.3
	677	60	3.3	13.0	0.2
	598	54	3.0	13.4	0.3
0640	1467	114	0.5	−1.1	0.3
	1193	114	0.2	−1.1	0.2
	1002	108	3.4	−0.2	0.2
	834	108	7.0	4.2	0.1

CST	Z	t	u	v	w	CST	Z	t	u	v	w	CST	Z	t	u	v	w
	549	120	11.7	11.2	0.0		660	114	8.8	8.2	0.4		692	102	8.7	7.6	0.0
	443	120	10.3	12.3	0.2		569	114	11.3	10.1	0.4		453	102	10.8	12.0	0.2
	342	120	8.4	11.6	0.1		484	108	10.9	12.3	0.4		360	84	8.9	11.5	0.1
							428	108	10.0	12.3	0.3		285	84	7.3	10.3	0.2
							361	108	9.2	11.9	0.3		220	12	7.2	9.4	−0.1
							317	108	7.9	10.9	0.4		163	6	−0.7	7.8	0.7
							278	96	7.4	10.4	0.3						
0830	1245	120	−0.1	2.5	0.0	0835	1461	120	−0.8	3.3	0.3	0840	1572	102	0.3	3.7	0.0
	1082	120	1.7	1.3	0.2		1193	120	0.8	1.9	0.3		1325	96	−1.7	3.4	0.0
	919	120	4.1	0.4	0.1		986	114	3.1	0.2	0.3		806	84	4.9	1.3	0.4
	565	114	9.1	6.2	0.2		824	120	5.5	1.2	0.2		683	84	6.5	2.3	0.6
	462	96	10.3	10.0	0.2		670	120	7.4	2.9	−0.1		558	78	8.3	5.5	0.4
	388	102	8.8	9.4	0.1		551	120	8.6	6.0	−0.2		442	78	9.7	10.4	0.3
	323	84	8.4	8.7	0.2		436	114	9.4	10.6	0.1		358	78	7.9	9.2	0.3
	203	108	4.5	7.1	0.0		347	114	7.7	9.0	0.0		228	72	4.8	7.6	0.0
	159	36	1.8	6.8	0.0		282	114	7.0	8.1	0.0		192	48	2.2	7.9	0.2
							218	102	4.1	7.0	0.0						
							171	24	1.4	7.7	−0.7						
							129	18	0.6	7.1	0.0						
1030	1275	120	1.4	6.4	0.2	1035	1282	120	1.6	6.0	0.4	1040	1406	120	2.9	5.2	0.3
	1111	120	−0.4	6.6	0.2		1066	120	−0.4	7.0	0.3		1189	120	0.7	7.0	0.3
	976	120	−1.8	6.4	0.2		885	120	−1.7	6.5	0.3		1008	120	−0.9	7.1	0.3
	851	120	−0.7	5.2	0.2		735	120	0.0	6.1	0.4		870	120	−0.7	6.3	0.3
	752	120	0.4	5.9	0.3		503	114	4.6	5.1	0.6		737	120	0.3	6.3	0.3
	671	114	1.5	5.5	0.3		345	54	4.8	6.0	0.6		627	120	1.0	5.4	0.3
	461	114	6.0	5.0	−0.1		279	60	3.6	6.8	0.2		564	120	2.8	5.2	0.6
	377	102	4.4	6.0	−0.8		224	54	3.5	6.3	0.3						
	378	72	3.4	6.0	−0.4		117	24	1.4	7.0	0.6						
	333	72	3.3	6.2	−0.2		91	18	0.9	6.1	0.4						
1230	1309	120	5.2	8.4	0.0	1235	1432	66	6.2	7.0	0.2	1240	1544	30	7.5	5.2	0.0
	1129	72	3.0	9.8	0.1		1226	114	4.5	9.2	0.1		1312	66	6.1	8.1	−0.2
	985	66	1.5	9.6	0.1		1045	48	1.4	10.0	0.0		1112	60	3.1	9.7	0.2
	849	60	2.7	8.9	0.0		890	54	2.1	8.8	0.4		973	84	1.8	9.6	0.1
	745	66	3.1	8.2	0.4		777	66	2.6	8.4	0.3		470	30	0.4	4.7	−0.5
	387	42	0.8	5.6	−0.3		397	48	0.8	4.3	−0.2		408	66	0.0	5.1	−0.4
	315	60	0.4	5.3	−0.8		314	84	0.0	3.7	−0.4		365	60	0.3	5.2	−0.4
	286	60	0.3	5.4	−0.3		287	42	0.0	3.9	−0.6		324	36	0.3	5.0	−0.3
	258	18	−0.8	5.6	−0.2		246	30	0.3	4.8	−0.8						

6.1.b. Loeser technique of night-time wind profile measurements (GRD). Median values of West and South components u, v (m/sec) of drift; number N of balloons of a pibal swarm which cross the indicated levels. Basic data are overlapping 24-sec mean displacements toward the east and north of each of the N balloons at 12-sec intervals during a 4-min period centered at indicated CST.

Height (m)	7 September 2035			2235			8 September 1953 0035			0235			0435		
	u	v	N	u	v	N	u	v	N	u	v	N	u	v	N
1600	—	—	—	—	—	—	—	—	—	1.3	−0.4	2	−0.1	0.5	1
1400	11.3	1.1	1	7.6	−1.4	1	5.9	−1.5	2	0.8	−0.8	2	0.2	−0.2	1
1200	11.3	6.0	3	9.7	1.3	2	10.5	0.9	3	2.1	−1.2	4	4.4	−0.3	1
1000	11.1	9.7	5	11.6	5.8	3	12.1	4.7	4	6.9	2.0	5	6.3	0.3	1
800	9.5	14.1	6	11.9	13.8	3	14.3	12.5	5	11.6	6.7	5	11.3	4.9	5
700	9.4	16.3	6	9.4	16.9	4	14.0	16.0	5	13.5	10.7	5	11.9	8.8	6
600	8.3	18.5	6	8.5	18.8	4	11.8	19.2	5	11.8	14.8	4	11.7	12.3	7
500	7.2	19.4	7	8.2	20.0	4	8.8	22.0	4	10.1	21.2	4	11.3	15.4	6
400	5.0	19.2	6	7.7	21.5	5	7.9	21.9	6	8.4	21.8	6	10.1	17.5	7
300	2.5	18.7	5	6.6	21.0	5	9.0	22.2	5	8.5	20.2	5	8.0	17.1	7
200	1.2	17.8	4	3.0	18.7	5	6.8	16.5	5	7.5	14.8	4	7.3	13.1	5
100	−0.7	13.5	2	0.1	14.3	2	2.5	12.5	2	3.1	11.9	3	5.3	10.8	4

6.2. Rawinsonde (GMD-1A) wind speed (m/sec) and direction (deg from North) from 1-min mean drift at 30-sec intervals, for first 7 min of ascent started at indicated CST.

7 September 1953

0509			0635			0900			1043			1235		
m	m/sec	deg	m	m/sec	deg	m	m/sec	deg	m	m/sec	deg	m	m/sec	deg
2193	9.8	290	2434	10.7	287	2308	9.2	271	2075	8.8	258	2318	11.7	254
1895	9.1	253	2094	11.3	264	1980	8.5	280	1838	7.1	263	2042	8.5	252
1747	8.2	189	1922	12.1	265	1812	8.4	282	1721	6.8	262	1904	6.6	249
1590	8.1	265	1752	11.7	257	1645	9.2	276	1585	6.9	263	1765	7.3	239
1434	8.1	270	1581	10.9	254	1480	9.6	258	1444	7.1	260	1627	8.1	229
1282	7.7	255	1413	9.3	248	1315	10.3	235	1303	9.2	249	1448	9.1	232
1128	7.4	233	1246	7.5	244	1153	10.7	222	1163	11.2	238	1270	11.6	229
970	8.9	224	1070	5.8	245	987	11.4	211	1023	13.4	225	1094	13.6	233
795	10.5	216	887	6.6	230	818	12.7	208	857	16.2	214	921	16.0	223
621	11.1	209	698	9.5	218	647	14.1	207	680	15.5	206	742	13.0	205
449	12.3	203	512	12.3	202	477	13.9	204	506	11.1	195	563	10.5	188
277	12.9	192	334	14.7	189	311	13.6	193	333	9.1	181	384	10.2	174
137	10.9	183	166	13.5	183	154	13.8	185	165	9.2	180	198	11.6	176

7 September 1953

1435			1635			1835			2035		
m	m/sec	deg	m	m/sec	deg	m	m/sec	deg	m	m/sec	deg
2203	8.0	253	2051	7.5	235	1957	10.5	232	2163	4.8	266
1962	5.3	259	1814	6.0	241	1708	14.6	226	1873	5.6	264
1843	5.0	250	1696	6.2	236	1562	15.7	228	1724	7.3	286
1709	8.2	231	1562	9.7	233	1419	13.9	231	1566	9.5	267
1574	10.9	224	1417	13.6	226	1275	12.3	217	1412	11.7	282
1439	11.0	218	1270	14.6	217	1131	12.2	229	1257	12.9	244
1303	11.2	221	1127	14.1	207	988	13.2	217	1100	14.4	232
1170	12.0	222	985	14.8	197	850	12.8	206	945	16.4	221
1023	13.0	210	809	14.0	189	715	11.0	201	788	18.2	212
830	12.4	197	627	12.7	184	578	11.3	194	633	21.2	205
643	11.8	187	450	11.9	186	442	13.2	188	479	21.7	197
455	13.5	189	277	12.0	190	304	14.4	186	324	20.6	188
246	13.1	186	137	12.1	189	151	13.8	185	165	18.7	181

7 September			8 September 1953								
2235			0035[1]			0235			0435		
m	m/sec	deg	m	m/sec	deg	m	m/sec	deg	m	m/sec	deg
2155	3.6	301	2256	8.2	255	2425	5.6	263	2392	2.9	335
1856	5.1	292	1957	17.5	273	2120	5.2	238	2074	1.5	12
1708	6.0	294	1808	14.9	264	1956	4.0	242	1914	1.1	22
1559	7.0	294	1643	10.4	243	1813	1.3	282	1757	0.7	174
1405	8.3	285	1476	7.1	226	1657	0.6	303	1574	1.0	184
1244	9.3	267	1305	3.5	215	1471	0.8	281	1390	1.0	277
1084	10.0	258	1137	1.2	319	1282	1.4	301	1208	2.8	286
925	13.3	240	970	1.1	243	1096	3.9	266	1027	4.7	267
763	20.0	225	806	6.6	207	910	10.0	237	862	8.1	249
603	21.0	210	643	15.4	208	722	17.8	222	698	13.3	231
448	22.2	199	479	25.1	204	530	23.0	210	536	19.8	215
288	22.4	200	317	23.6	201	357	24.6	202	372	22.4	207
135	16.2	193	160	17.7	198	176	18.8	199	193	17.3	203

[1] Questionable values.

8 September 1953

0635			0835			1035			1235		
m	m/sec	deg	m	m/sec	deg	m	m/sec	deg	m	m/sec	deg
2083	0.8	276	2153	5.0	242	2346	8.9	283	1920	7.1	274
1839	0.8	284	1835	5.3	213	2020	7.5	269	1637	8.1	250
1717	0.5	237	1682	4.4	206	1857	7.1	254	1500	8.1	234
1560	0.3	3	1528	3.8	191	1688	7.1	251	1360	8.7	222
1401	0.6	332	1379	3.5	175	1523	6.5	238	1227	9.9	212
1242	0.5	214	1225	2.6	164	1355	6.4	206	1090	10.9	197
1083	1.5	250	1075	2.1	206	1190	6.6	187	948	10.9	188
924	4.6	286	917	3.4	244	1027	6.8	170	798	10.3	188
766	8.5	238	760	6.1	253	852	6.9	166	650	9.3	194
607	14.8	221	602	8.6	247	678	6.3	179	503	6.5	190
452	15.5	223	447	11.2	230	505	5.9	206	355	4.7	166
297	14.6	217	297	11.6	220	334	6.0	214	228	4.5	160
148	11.0	207	148	7.6	200	168	6.4	200	118	4.1	167

6.3. Double theodolite pibal wind speed (m/sec) and direction (deg from North) from 1-min mean drift at 30-sec intervals, for first 7 min of ascent started at indicated CST.

7 September 1953

1030			1430			1530			1730			1830		
m	m/sec	deg	m	m/sec	deg	m	m/sec	deg	m	m/sec	deg	m	m/sec	deg
1020	10.1	222	1570	10.5	222	830	11.9	189	1378	12.5	225	1054	13.0	214
937	13.6	216	1484	9.0	220	708	13.3	188	1295	13.5	215	974	13.0	208
864	14.6	210	1431	9.7	226	648	11.3	185	1204	15.6	207	903	12.8	203
776	13.9	206	1326	11.7	218	600	11.3	184	1083	15.6	203	826	12.3	199
729	12.9	209	1216	10.4	214	544	12.2	184	1000	15.0	199	756	12.3	195
688	15.3	207	1143	12.3	217	466	13.4	183	914	14.9	198	688	13.2	194
642	16.6	204	1036	14.9	210	401	13.5	181	830	14.6	196	616	13.1	193
584	14.9	199	933	13.9	203	353	13.2	183	746	15.5	192	548	13.4	191
526	12.9	193	848	13.0	195	326	14.0	184	661	16.0	188	472	15.5	188
449	12.3	190	751	13.4	189	284	14.8	185	544	14.0	187	387	14.1	187
370	11.1	188	594	12.3	188	240	13.5	187	466	13.2	186	331	12.7	187
291	11.5	188	492	12.0	183	186	12.8	186	362	12.9	184	276	14.2	185
198	12.8	184	330	12.3	180	110	13.6	186	226	11.6	182	208	13.0	185
100	11.5	180	144	10.7	184	70	13.9	184	115	11.1	181	112	10.9	187

7 September

8 September 1953

1930			2130			2230			0030			0130		
m	m/sec	deg	m	m/sec	deg	m	m/sec	deg	m	m/sec	deg	m	m/sec	deg
730	14.9	207	613	14.8	211	615	15.5	219	683	20.1	225	845	8.0	260
686	13.8	202	576	15.4	207	579	14.6	213	611	17.0	225	775	10.5	253
642	13.8	199	544	17.4	203	537	15.3	208	585	12.3	229	690	12.0	244
600	16.0	194	508	16.9	202	510	15.5	204	550	15.9	220	624	16.5	227
541	16.8	193	482	17.9	200	475	18.7	202	516	17.7	213	548	21.0	216
490	16.4	190	444	18.7	198	438	18.8	200	476	20.2	205	498	19.3	210
443	16.3	187	422	18.9	198	402	21.1	200	428	21.3	201	455	18.2	204
392	16.3	185	382	19.7	197	352	21.3	198	380	20.2	199	418	23.2	200
346	16.4	183	356	20.6	196	322	20.9	196	347	22.0	197	342	22.5	191
294	16.7	180	306	21.3	196	267	23.4	197	302	22.7	197	308	20.9	200
237	17.3	178	268	19.3	190	220	19.6	181	268	21.2	198	260	21.8	202
190	16.1	177	217	18.4	185	183	17.3	183	204	17.7	198	204	18.8	203
140	14.0	176	154	18.6	180	132	13.6	182	152	14.2	194	132	15.0	199
85	12.0	174	85	15.2	176	98	10.9	183	86	12.2	187	64	11.2	188

8 September 1953

0330

m	m/sec	deg
850	9.2	239
767	10.3	242
720	9.3	246
659	13.4	232
568	14.8	224
538	13.7	219
510	19.8	208
438	22.6	203
392	20.0	200
342	21.6	198
276	19.3	201

0430

m	m/sec	deg
572	13.3	232
570	12.3	226
511	19.9	234
464	17.8	214
429	17.1	210
382	15.4	207
345	18.6	203
265	19.9	203
215	15.8	207
180	14.3	210
122	12.2	206
92	11.1	196

0535

m	m/sec	deg
907	3.0	277
850	4.5	262
774	7.3	244
688	9.3	234
614	10.2	227
544	12.9	218
470	14.3	213
430	15.0	214
370	17.0	212
314	15.9	207
260	14.7	206
202	12.1	208
150	10.4	206
78	9.6	193

1030

m	m/sec	deg
1174	7.3	180
1076	6.0	173
1020	7.9	165
930	7.6	165
881	6.5	161
797	5.9	166
727	6.0	175
644	6.1	182
574	5.2	195
505	6.2	216
443	7.7	226
356	6.9	220
259	6.6	206
120	6.7	197

6.4. Radiosonde pressure (mb), temperature (°C), and relative humidity (%) at significant levels of ascent started at indicated CST. (M = "motorboating", i.e., a humidity value below the minimum value that the radiosonde can measure at that temperature.)

	7 September										8 September 1953						
	0509	0635	0900	1043	1235	1435	1635	1835	2035	2235	0035	0235	0435	0635	0835	1035	1235
mb	951	952	952	950	950	947	947	947	947	947	947	947	948	948	949	948	947
°C	8.3	9.8	19.4	24.0	26.8	28.0	28.0	2.28	19.9	17.0	15.8	13.9	12.6	12.8	20.0	25.0	29.0
%	87	93	51	43	39	33	37	40	67	78	73	81	89	91	63	50	41
mb	934	930	915	890	915	844	918	844	923	914	913	908	922	916	939	914	892
°C	16.5	16.7	16.6	16.0	21.0 ·15.8		24.0	14.6	20.6	21.4	20.9	20.8	18.6	18.7	18.0	21.5	21.5
%	—	77	59	60	47	56	38	—	53	44	45	57	—	58	61	54	53
mb	912	891	907	869	883	816	860	797	828	876	887	887	914	908	922	899	884
°C	16.8	16.1	18.0	16.3	16.6	17.0	18.6	14.4	17.8	19.7	19.6	19.2	19.3	20.4	20.4	23.4	23.5
%	—	62	57	75	58	36	52	—	48	51	50	55	—	58	59	53	41
mb	880	870	856	855	863	781	824	734	790	849	855	859	903	870	908	884	806
°C	15.6	16.6	16.2	16.6	16.6	14.9	15.8	10.1	15.5	20.3	20.6	20.0	20.7	20.0	20.8	22.9	18.4
%	—	52	48	44	49	46	58	—	56	50	—	50	—	58	58	51	39
mb	807	758	813	833	854	742	806	697	727	807	816	810	881	831	899	875	736
°C	11.5	8.3	13.6	16.5	17.9	11.0	17.0	6.1	10.1	11.8	18.3	18.3	20.5	20.4	21.5	24.2	11.9
%	—	60	76	57	40	68	37	—	61	49	42	38	—	38	58	49	49
mb	691	744	782	807	834	718	744	660	703	748	753	754	857	775	888	855	645
°C	1.1	8.1	13.4	16.0	17.4	9.9	12.2	2.8	8.6	11.9	12.3	12.8	21.5	14.7	21.2	23.6	2.7
%	—	60	56	47	32	48	58	—	40	47	50	43	—	45	60	38	47
mb	669	672	719	763	810	682	727	600	648	708	654	731	824	752	838	794	624
°C	0.2	0.7	6.9	12.0	16.1	6.5	11.0	-3.2	2.6	7.8	3.1	11.0	19.3	13.2	21.0	19.9	0.9
%	—	75	60	40	45	39	47	—	43	56	25	33	—	40	44	34	38
mb	658	654	694	726	713	600	708	—	627	694	548	651	740	714	776	788	573
°C	0.8	1.8	4.6	8.6	8.2	-2.0	9.6	—	1.1	6.6	-9.5	2.7	11.4	8.9	15.6	19.4	-5.0
%	—	43	60	46	50	62	68	—	32	44	35	31	—	46	42	25	59
mb	640	630	620	692	681	—	698	—	562	651	—	566	720	658	761	720	555
°C	0.9	0.4	0.4	5.8	6.4	—	8.9	—	-6.4	2.0	—	-7.6	9.5	2.7	15.2	11.6	-6.9
%	—	38	32	38	38	—	50	—	28	46	—	55	—	70	35	51	54
mb	619	609	556	670	620	—	676	—	—	625	—	—	657	601	687	600	—
°C	-1.2	-1.4	-5.9	4.1	-0.2	—	6.6	—	—	0.6	—	—	3.4	-2.1	7.4	-0.3	—
%	—	54	53	50	45	—	67	—	—	25	—	—	38	63	42	—	—
mb	604	578	—	638	—	—	654	—	—	587	—	—	599	—	641	—	—
°C	-1.5	-3.1	—	1.0	—	—	4.4	—	—	-4.0	—	—	-3.5	—	3.5	—	—
%	—	27	—	45	—	—	51	—	—	—	—	—	—	—	26	—	—
mb	—	—	—	—	—	—	613	—	—	—	—	—	—	603	—	—	—
°C	—	—	—	—	—	—	0.3	—	—	—	—	—	—	-0.6	—	—	—
%	—	—	—	—	—	—	43	—	—	—	—	—	—	39	—	—	—

N

6.5. Air temperature T (°C) and mixing ratio W (g water vapor/kg air) at altitude Z (m) from aerograph (L-20) data. CST of start, top level, and end of flight is indicated.

7 September 1953

(0619-0635-0649)			(0820-0837-0847)			(1015-1032-1052)			(1215-1235-1245)		
Z	T	W	Z	T	W	Z	T	W	Z	T	W
85	14.3	7.3	17	19.0	9.4	17	21.6	8.3	17	23.4	8.1
165	16.5	6.5	51	15.9	7.7	51	21.2	8.1	70	24.0	8.6
240	17.1	6.8	85	15.7	7.6	100	20.5	7.8	100	21.5	7.7
480	16.6	7.2	165	15.5	7.6	165	19.8	7.7	240	21.1	8.0
640	17.0	7.3	320	17.4	7.0	240	18.7	7.4	320	20.6	8.5
950	16.3	6.9	640	17.6	7.5	320	17.8	7.3	640	17.7	7.4
1270	13.6	6.5	950	15.8	6.4	640	17.1	6.8	950	18.9	4.7
1590	11.8	6.6	1270	13.8	7.6	950	16.2	5.5	1270	16.9	5.7
1270	14.1	7.1	1590	12.9	8.0	1270	16.2	7.7	1590	15.5	6.2
950	16.4	6.9	1270	14.3	7.8	1590	14.8	6.3	1270	17.3	6.3
320	17.7	7.4	950	15.9	6.3	1270	16.7	7.3	950	18.9	5.4
165	16.2	6.2	640	17.5	7.1	950	17.4	7.2	640	17.8	7.7
51	13.8	7.2	165	16.4	7.0	640	16.7	7.9	320	21.6	8.7
17	12.4	7.8	100	16.8	7.2	320	19.3	8.2	165	22.9	8.9
			17	17.9	6.0	210	20.6	8.3	100	23.7	8.7
						165	20.7	8.3	17	24.8	9.2
						100	21.2	8.5			
						35	21.5	8.2			
						17	22.4	8.7			

7 September   8 September 1953

(1410-1434-1445)			(1615-1633-1645)			(1811-1832-1841)			(0640-0643-0653)		
Z	T	W	Z	T	W	Z	T	W	Z	T	W
26	26.2	8.4	17	27.2	8.7	17	24.7	7.3	1280	20.0	7.8
100	25.1	7.7	85	26.3	8.0	35	24.2	7.1	1600	16.1	6.6
165	23.8	7.2	165	24.8	7.5	130	23.9	7.4	1280	19.6	8.0
260	23.4	7.7	320	23.6	7.3	320	22.7	7.2	960	21.1	8.6
320	22.9	7.5	640	20.8	7.8	640	19.6	7.2	640	20.7	9.5
640	19.9	7.6	950	17.1	7.1	950	16.6	6.6	480	20.7	9.3
950	17.4	6.8	1270	15.4	6.4	1270	16.9	6.9	320	19.5	7.2
1270	17.6	5.7	1590	15.9	6.2	1590	15.5	6.2	160	17.7	7.4
1590	16.0	6.2	1270	16.3	6.1	1270	16.1	6.9	85	15.6	8.1
1270	17.1	5.7	950	17.5	7.7	950	16.6	7.0	51	14.7	8.1
950	17.1	6.9	640	20.8	8.3	640	18.7	7.8	17	14.3	8.6
640	20.5	8.3	320	23.5	8.6	320	21.9	8.2			
320	23.3	8.9	100	25.9	88.3	480	21.0	8.1			
165	24.7	8.9	51	26.7	8.2	130	23.2	8.7			
35	24.7	8.8				35	23.9	8.5			
17	26.7	8.4									

8 September 1953

(0815-0840-0850)			(1015-1039-1049)			(1215-1230-1240)		
Z	T	W	Z	T	W	Z	T	W
17	17.1	8.6	17	22.7	9.3	17	26.2	10.3
65	16.3	8.2	35	22.3	9.0	51	26.2	10.3
130	15.9	7.9	65	22.1	9.2	240	24.6	10.4
240	17.7	6.8	160	21.0	8.6	320	23.2	9.9
320	19.4	8.1	320	19.5	8.3	640	23.6	9.0
640	19.8	8.7	640	20.6	8.6	960	21.2	7.9
790	20.5	9.4	960	21.8	7.6	1280	20.4	7.2
960	20.6	8.5	1280	19.7	6.6	1600	17.4	6.4
1280	18.7	7.1	1600	17.6	5.0	1280	20.1	7.3
1600	18.6	7.0	1280	19.7	7.1	960	21.8	8.2
1280	16.4	5.9	960	22.3	8.2	640	23.3	8.9
960	19.9	7.9	640	23.6	9.5	480	22.8	10.0
640	20.6	8.9	320	20.6	8.9	320	23.7	10.2
320	19.2	8.0	160	21.7	9.5	160	24.7	10.6
65	18.0	8.4	65	22.9	9.6	17	26.7	11.1
			17	23.7	9.8			

7.1. Representative values of West and South components of the wind u, v (m/sec) at standard heights. Values are estimated from the combination of smoke puff or pibal swarm, rawinsonde and double theodolite pibal data at or near the indicated CST.

	Height (m)	7 September									8 September 1953						
		0635	0835	1035	1235	1435	1635	1835	2035	2235	0035	0235	0435	0635	0835	1035	1235
u	2000	12.7	8.3	7.3	6.5	5.1	5.3	8.1	5.1	4.5	3.4	2.6	−0.3	0.3	3.3	6.6	7.5
	1750	11.0	8.8	7.2	6.5	5.7	6.7	9.5	7.0	5.3	3.8	1.3	0.0	0.3	2.1	5.8	7.2
	1500	9.2	9.0	7.6	7.0	6.9	8.9	10.6	9.9	6.9	4.7	0.7	0.4	0.3	0.2	4.0	6.5
	1250	6.6	7.3	9.3	8.4	7.6	7.5	10.0	11.5	9.1	8.3	1.3	2.9	0.2	−0.5	1.2	4.9
	1000	4.9	6.0	9.0	9.5	5.1	4.7	7.3	11.1	11.2	11.7	6.5	6.0	3.2	2.6	−1.2	2.0
	800	5.7	6.5	8.0	7.7	2.9	3.1	5.0	9.6	12.4	12.8	11.2	10.0	7.2	5.4	−0.7	2.0
	700	5.5	6.7	6.9	5.5	2.2	2.5	3.7	8.9	11.6	12.6	12.4	11.5	8.6	7.0	0.3	2.1
	600	5.0	6.2	5.7	3.8	1.7	2.0	2.7	8.0	9.9	11.5	12.2	11.7	10.3	8.0	1.8	2.1
	500	4.1	5.5	3.3	2.4	1.4	1.6	2.1	6.7	8.5	10.2	10.4	11.3	11.0	8.9	4.1	1.1
	400	3.0	4.7	1.6	1.3	1.1	1.3	1.6	4.7	7.8	9.0	9.0	10.1	9.7	8.8	4.3	0.2
	300	1.9	3.0	0.9	0.6	0.9	1.1	1.3	2.6	6.6	8.0	8.2	8.4	8.1	7.2	3.7	−0.3
	200	0.8	1.5	0.4	0.0	0.6	1.0	1.1	1.0	3.8	6.2	7.1	7.0	6.2	2.8	−0.7	
	100	−0.2	0.5	−0.2	−0.4	0.4	0.9	1.0	−0.5	0.7	3.0	3.3	4.9	3.6	1.1	1.5	−1.1
v	2000	1.4	−1.8	1.0	2.5	1.7	4.0	6.7	0.5	−0.9	0.3	1.0	1.5	0.8	4.0	1.0	0.0
	1750	2.3	−1.0	1.0	3.7	4.0	5.5	8.5	−1.3	−2.3	−0.4	0.2	0.6	0.2	4.0	3.0	2.2
	1500	3.1	1.7	1.2	5.3	8.0	8.0	8.0	0.2	−2.4	−0.8	−0.5	0.1	−0.3	3.6	4.8	5.1
	1250	3.1	6.6	5.0	7.4	9.8	11.7	7.5	5.3	0.3	0.2	−1.0	−0.5	−0.5	1.5	6.5	8.5
	1000	2.8	9.1	9.4	10.9	12.0	13.7	10.5	10.2	4.7	4.1	1.7	0.4	−0.1	1.5	7.0	10.2
	800	5.2	10.8	12.7	13.0	12.8	13.5	12.3	14.5	13.3	11.5	8.3	4.5	4.0	1.5	6.5	9.3
	700	7.2	11.6	13.4	12.9	12.9	13.3	12.8	16.6	16.6	15.2	12.0	8.7	8.1	2.6	6.1	8.4
	600	9.0	12.6	13.2	12.9	12.9	13.1	13.1	18.6	18.8	19.2	16.5	13.1	10.7	4.6	5.8	7.4
	500	11.4	13.4	12.4	12.9	12.9	13.0	13.4	19.6	20.4	22.0	21.2	16.7	11.8	7.3	5.5	6.3
	400	13.0	14.0	11.5	12.9	12.8	12.8	13.5	19.6	21.5	23.5	22.5	18.1	11.6	9.2	5.5	5.3
	300	13.6	14.4	10.9	12.8	12.5	12.6	13.5	19.0	21.3	22.6	21.0	18.0	11.0	8.6	5.9	4.7
	200	13.5	13.5	10.5	12.8	12.2	12.4	13.0	18.2	18.7	16.8	17.0	15.1	10.0	7.7	6.3	4.4
	100	13.0	11.0	10.2	12.7	11.7	12.1	12.1	16.2	14.1	13.3	12.3	11.1	8.0	6.9	6.2	4.0

7.2.a. Air temperature (°C) at standard heights. Values are interpolated and averaged from radiosonde and airplane (L-20) data at or near the indicated CST.

Height (m)	7 September								8 September 1953								
	0435[1]	0635	0835	1035	1235	1435	1635	1835	2035[1]	2235[1]	0035[1]	0235[1]	0435[1]	0635	0835	1035	1235
2000	7.8	8.5	11.1	12.6	12.7	13.3	14.0	12.6	12.7	12.6	13.4	12.9	12.9	12.5	16.5	15.5	13.8
1750	9.4	10.2	12.7	14.2	14.2	14.9	15.1	14.0	14.5	14.8	15.2	15.0	15.0	14.7	17.0	17.5	15.9
1500	11.0	12.1	13.3	15.6	15.7	16.3	16.1	15.3	16.1	17.1	17.0	17.2	17.1	17.2	18.1	18.8	18.0
1250	12.4	13.8	14.3	16.5	17.1	17.2	15.9	15.8	17.5	18.4	18.6	18.7	19.2	19.6	18.6	20.5	20.0
1000	13.8	15.6	15.6	16.7	18.1	16.8	17.3	16.1	18.4	19.2	20.0	19.6	20.8	20.6	20.3	22.3	21.0
800	14.9	16.6	16.7	16.7	17.9	18.6	19.1	17.3	19.0	20.2	20.2	19.7	21.1	20.5	20.6	22.8	22.1
600	15.9	16.7	17.4	16.7	17.8	20.6	21.2	19.0	19.6	20.9	19.6	19.2	20.6	20.5	20.5	22.3	22.9
400	16.7	17.0	17.5	18.2	19.9	22.6	22.9	20.8	20.2	21.3	20.6	20.8	20.0	20.2	20.0	21.1	23.4
200	16.6	16.7	16.7	20.2	22.3	24.5	24.8	22.5	20.4	19.6	18.8	17.3	17.0	17.5	18.3	21.8	25.0
100	13.6	14.6	17.1	21.6	23.2	25.5	26.2	23.3	20.2	18.3	17.3	15.5	14.8	15.5	17.5	22.7	26.2

[1] Radiosonde data only.

7.2.b. Mixing ratio (g water vapor/kg air) at standard heights. Values are interpolated and averaged from radiosonde and airplane (L-20) data at or near the indicated CST.

Height (m)	7 September							8 September 1953								
	0635	0835	1035	1235	1435	1635	1835[2]	2035[1]	2235[1]	0035[1]	0235[1]	0435	0635	0835	1035	1235
2000	5.0	7.3	4.8	5.9	7.1	6.8	5.3	7.1	5.9	6.6	5.3	—	4.0	5.8	4.0	5.7
1750	5.6	7.5	5.6	5.8	6.5	6.3	5.9	7.3	6.7	6.7	5.7	—	5.3	5.9	4.4	6.1
1500	6.2	8.2	6.5	5.7	6.0	6.1	6.4	7.5	7.6	6.8	6.1	—	6.3	6.6	5.9	6.6
1250	6.5	7.9	7.5	5.8	5.8	6.7	6.9	7.5	8.3	7.1	6.9	—	7.5	6.5	7.1	7.2
1000	6.8	6.7	6.3	5.4	6.9	7.8	6.8	7.8	9.0	7.6	8.1	—	8.2	7.6	8.2	7.8
800	7.0	6.9	7.5	6.5	7.5	8.3	7.2	8.1	8.7	8.0	8.7	—	9.4	8.6	9.2	8.4
600	7.5	7.2	7.6	7.8	8.0	8.3	7.6	8.4	8.3	8.2	8.8	—	9.7	9.0	9.4	9.1
400	7.8	7.5	7.7	8.2	8.1	8.2	7.7	8.7	7.9	7.9	9.9	—	9.2	9.7	9.1	10.0
200	7.7	7.4	8.1	8.5	8.3	8.2	7.8	9.3	8.7	8.2	9.3	—	8.1	8.9	9.2	10.5
100	7.5	7.5	8.2	8.5	8.4	8.4	7.9	10.0	9.4	8.5	9.0	—	8.4	8.7	9.5	10.6

[1] Radiosonde data only.   [2] Airplane data only.

7.3.a. Summary of heat budget constituents (mcal cm^{-2} min^{-1}) of the earth-air interface according to the theoretical models by Suomi and Lettau. Net radiation flux R, heat transfer to the soil S, sensible heat transfer to the air Q, and latent heat transfer to the air (heat equivalent of evaporation) E. Values are hourly means centered at indicated CST.

	7 September								8 September 1953							
	0435	0635	0835	1035	1235	1435	1635	1835	2035	2235	0035	0235	0435	0635	0835	1035
Suomi																
R_0	77	47	−259	−577	−700	−570	−221	99	110	99	95	89	80	45	−276	−582
S_0	−62	−34	50	120	136	94	19	−42	−40	−44	−46	−50	−56	−24	31	—
Q_0	−8	−7	140	330	435	425	163	−43	−54	−49	−63	−140	−16	—	184	—
E_0	−6	−1	67	128	129	47	40	−14	−14	−6	14	101	1	—	61	—
Lettau																
R_0	70	44	−276	−629	−749	−610	−230	93	110	95	92	86	79	52	−270	−589
S_0	−70	−61	83	197	211	150	36	−44	−48	−54	−55	−55	−58	−40	75	234
Q_0	−12	−7	265	477	658	508	169	−26	−39	−29	−30	−26	−45	−11	329	993
E_0	−29	−1	86	130	108	34	37	−9	−12	−3	7	21	2	21	45	89

7.3.b. Representative logarithmic height derivatives of wind speed (zV' mm sec^{-1}, from UCLA and JH data), potential temperature ($z\theta'$, 10^{-3} °C, from JH and UW data), and water vapor pressure (ze', 10^{-3} mb, from JH and UW data); representative values of Karman number k (from zV' and UCLA, JH, and MIT stress data), interpolated ground drag τ_0 (dynes cm^{-2}, from zV' and representative k values), and ratio of heat and momentum diffusivities N_Q; representative ground-flux ratio F_0 and inverse Bowen ratio B. Values refer to indicated CST and are employed in the computation of the heat budget constituents Q_0 and E_0 (Lettau model; see Table 7.3.a).

	7 September										8 September 1953					
	0435	0635	0835	1035	1235	1435	1635	1835	2035	2235	0035	0235	0435	0635	0835	1035
zV'	414	485	1074	1389	1474	1446	1305	909	1036	824	801	697	655	617	838	928
$z\theta'$	500	94	−574	−751	−1017	−844	−415	147	189	189	197	210	180	95	−534	−974
ze'	263	7	−200	−239	−189	−61	−76	29	32	12	−25	−80	−7	−92	−131	−196
k	0.31	0.37	0.39	0.39	0.39	0.39	0.38	0.37	0.37	0.37	0.37	0.37	0.37	0.37	0.40	0.44
τ_0	0.19	0.37	2.01	3.30	3.68	3.49	2.75	1.27	1.68	1.06	1.00	0.76	0.67	0.60	1.26	1.84
N_Q	0.36	0.74	1.73	1.86	1.80	1.73	1.33	0.90	0.90	0.84	0.84	0.80	1.73	0.84	2.85	3.57
F_0	0.00	−1.7[1]	1.24	1.68	1.47	1.56	1.54	1.66	1.40	1.17	1.04	0.85	0.79	0.9[1]	1.3[1]	1.3[1]
B	0.85	0.1[1]	0.55	0.50	0.29	0.11	0.29	0.32	0.27	0.10	−0.21	−0.62	−0.06	−1.6[1]	0.4[1]	0.3[1]

[1] Value disregarded for evaluation of N_Q.

7.4. Richardson number (Ri; units of 10^{-3}) from Mass. Inst. Tech. and Johns Hopkins University data on simultaneous temperature and wind velocity differences, centered at indicated CST and mean height z_m (meters). (Ri') = average height derivative of Richardson number (10^{-3} m^{-1}).

Inst. Set	Height (m)	7 September										8 September 1953						
		0435	0635	0835	1035	1235	1435	1635	1835	2035	2235	0035	0235	0435	0635	0835	1035	1235
MIT	8.0	175	90	−62	−73	−74	−61	−20	36	40	49	55	66	68	59	−144	−262	−730
MIT	4.0	130	57	−62	−67	−62	−59	−27	22	24	35	35	46	52	39	−133	−194	−683
JH	3.2	95	35	−34	−53	−43	−37	−22	21	17	38	32	32	43	24	−159	−140	−559
JH	1.6	92	25	−21	−19	−23	−23	−10	9	9	18	16	23	—	—	—	—	—
JH	0.8	72	13	−12	−8	−13	−11	−5	4	5	9	9	14	11	10	−19	−30	−74
(Ri')		32	13	−11	−13	−12	−11	−5	5	5	8	8	10	11	8	−28	−39	−128

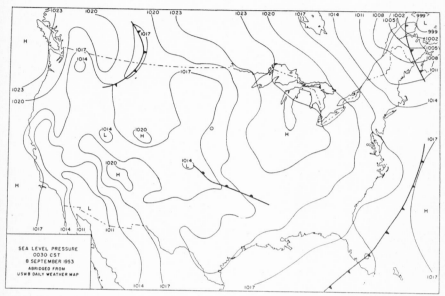

FIG. B.7.1. Continental scale synoptic chart. Sea level pressure distribution for the seventh general observation period.

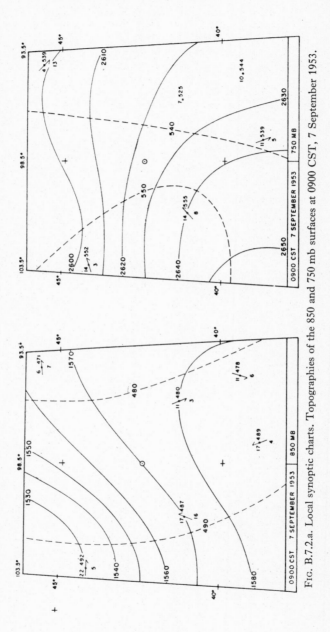

FIG. B.7.2.a. Local synoptic charts. Topographies of the 850 and 750 mb surfaces at 0900 CST, 7 September 1953.

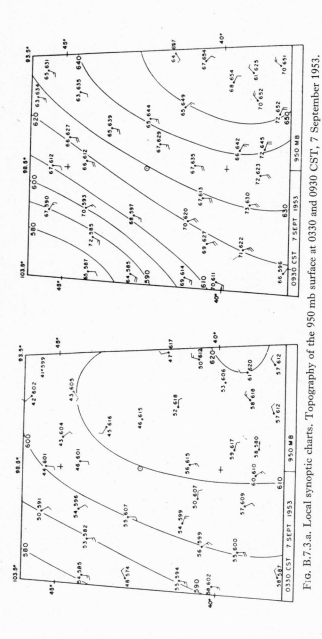

FIG. B.7.3.a. Local synoptic charts. Topography of the 950 mb surface at 0330 and 0930 CST, 7 September 1953.

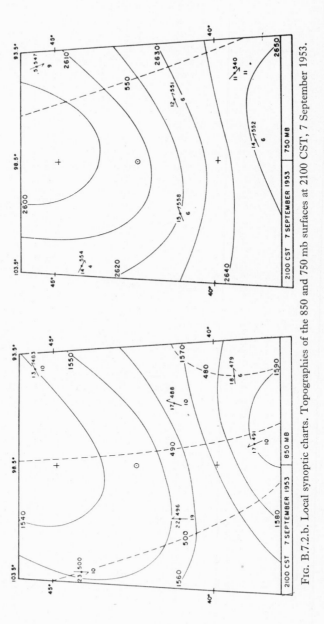

Fig. B.7.2.b. Local synoptic charts. Topographies of the 850 and 750 mb surfaces at 2100 CST, 7 September 1953.

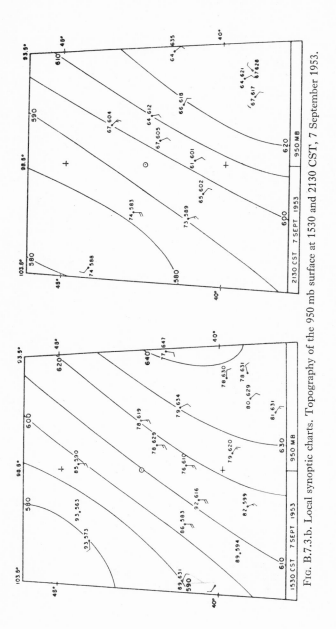

Fig. B.7.3.b. Local synoptic charts. Topography of the 950 mb surface at 1530 and 2130 CST, 7 September 1953.

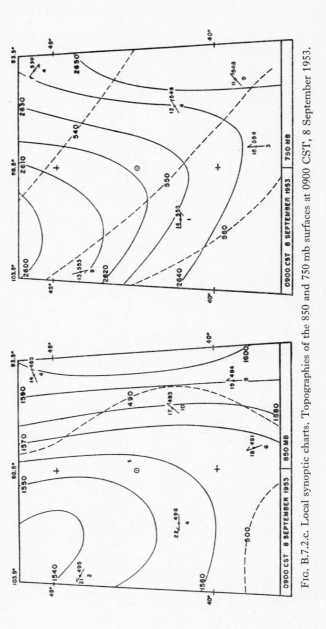

FIG. B.7.2.c. Local synoptic charts. Topographies of the 850 and 750 mb surfaces at 0900 CST, 8 September 1953.

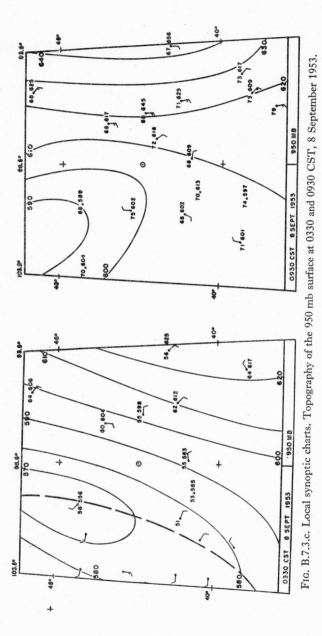

Fig. B.7.3.c. Local synoptic charts. Topography of the 950 mb surface at 0330 and 0930 CST, 8 September 1953.

INDEX

Science